PLANNING DESIGN CRITERIA

PLANNING DESIGN CRITERIA

JOSEPH DE CHIARA
LEE KOPPELMAN

IN COOPERATION WITH THE
SCHOOL OF ARCHITECTURE—PRATT INSTITUTE

VAN NOSTRAND REINHOLD COMPANY

NEW YORK   TORONTO   LONDON   MELBOURNE

FOREWORD

The dynamic growth of contemporary society makes great demands on the evolving field of urban design and planning. Guides, controls and study of this development have matured in the past several decades into an essential and integral element of our methodology of resolving urban problems. However, no single source existed for basic reference material that is needed by the planner and urban designer.

This book gathers into one source vast and important factual references which are necessary to these professionals interested in physical aspects of current urbanization. The need for such a body of technical information has long been felt in this area of broad scope. The detailed information in this publication will assist us greatly to cope with the scale and rationale of the ever-expanding horizons of urban planning. It must be noted, however, that such a book is never complete and the information it contains cannot be all-inclusive or final. Its usefulness rests on its approach in giving the planner, designer and architect the basic pattern of information required to aid in solving the many varied and complex problems of our cities.

Also, the material which is comprehensive in scope, will be highly valuable to all disciplines related to urban planning. This results from the fact that the book, in addition to being a basic reference manual, also offers a wide range of data related to current practices which could be obtained only after extensive research.

This volume may be characterized as being unique literature because it presents maximum useful information with concise graphic explanation. In short, this book will be warmly welcomed by all interested professionals and students who seek to make our environment a more functional and more attractive place to live.

January, 1969

OLINDO GROSSI, Dean
School of Architecture, Pratt Institute
Brooklyn, New York

PREFACE

The general aim of this book is to afford those interested in urban planning—whether they be students, teachers or practitioners—a graphic reference of current urban design standards.

One of the major problems in the preparation of such an effort is the selection of the most appropriate standards in an emerging field of study, from among the vast wealth of data available. In order to maintain a manageable form, it was therefore, necessary to select material that would represent a balanced presentation rather than to attempt the inclusion of redundant or secondary information.

We wish to acknowledge the generous support and courtesy of the many agencies and publications in allowing the use of their material.

January, 1969

JOSEPH DE CHIARA
LEE KOPPELMAN

CONTENTS

CONTENTS

MASTER PLAN STUDIES AND SPECIAL STUDIES

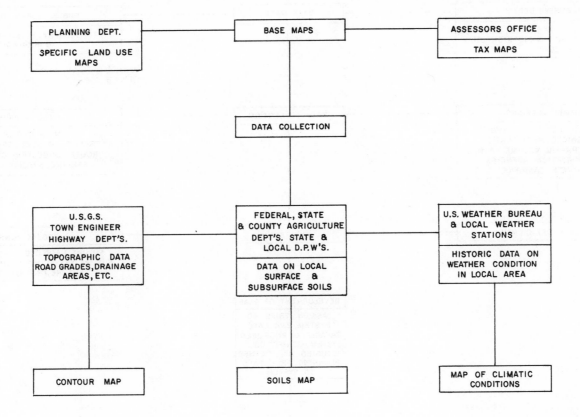

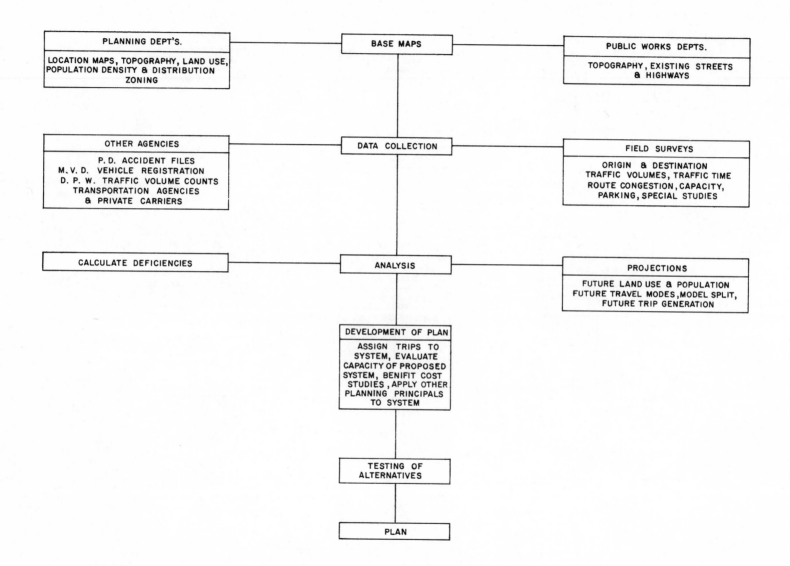

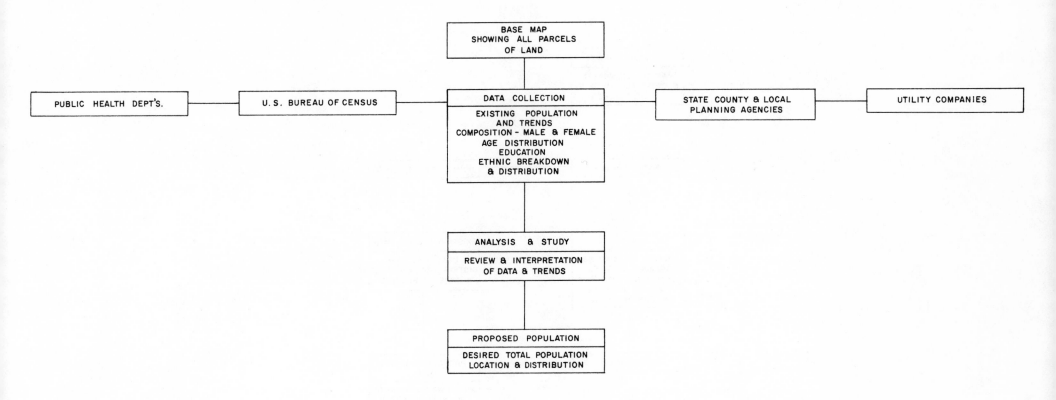

BASE MAP
SHOWING ALL PARCELS
OF LAND

PUBLIC HEALTH DEPT'S.　　U.S. BUREAU OF CENSUS　　DATA COLLECTION　　STATE COUNTY & LOCAL PLANNING AGENCIES　　UTILITY COMPANIES

EXISTING POPULATION
AND TRENDS
COMPOSITION - MALE & FEMALE
AGE DISTRIBUTION
EDUCATION
ETHNIC BREAKDOWN
& DISTRIBUTION

ANALYSIS & STUDY

REVIEW & INTERPRETATION
OF DATA & TRENDS

PROPOSED POPULATION

DESIRED TOTAL POPULATION
LOCATION & DISTRIBUTION

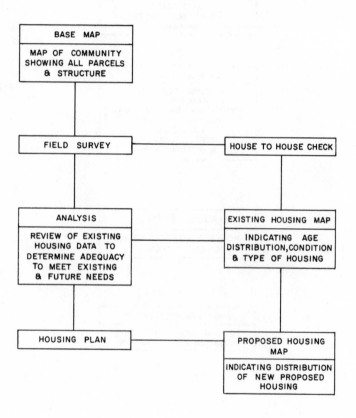

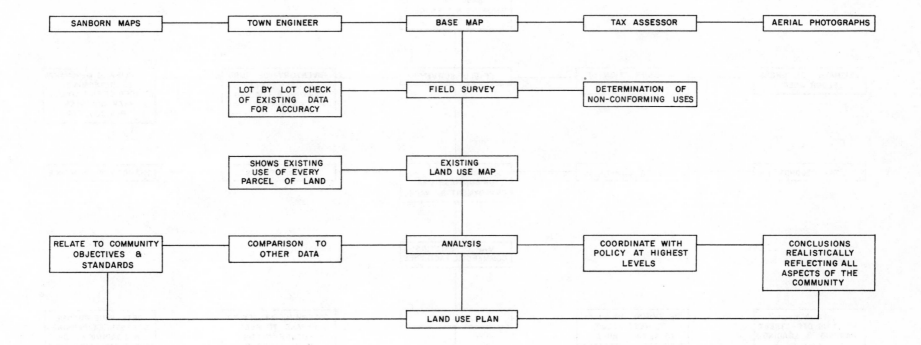

| SANBORN MAPS | | TOWN ENGINEER | | BASE MAP | | TAX ASSESSOR | | AERIAL PHOTOGRAPHS |

LOT BY LOT CHECK OF EXISTING DATA FOR ACCURACY — FIELD SURVEY — DETERMINATION OF NON-CONFORMING USES

SHOWS EXISTING USE OF EVERY PARCEL OF LAND — EXISTING LAND USE MAP

RELATE TO COMMUNITY OBJECTIVES & STANDARDS — COMPARISON TO OTHER DATA — ANALYSIS — COORDINATE WITH POLICY AT HIGHEST LEVELS — CONCLUSIONS REALISTICALLY REFLECTING ALL ASPECTS OF THE COMMUNITY

LAND USE PLAN

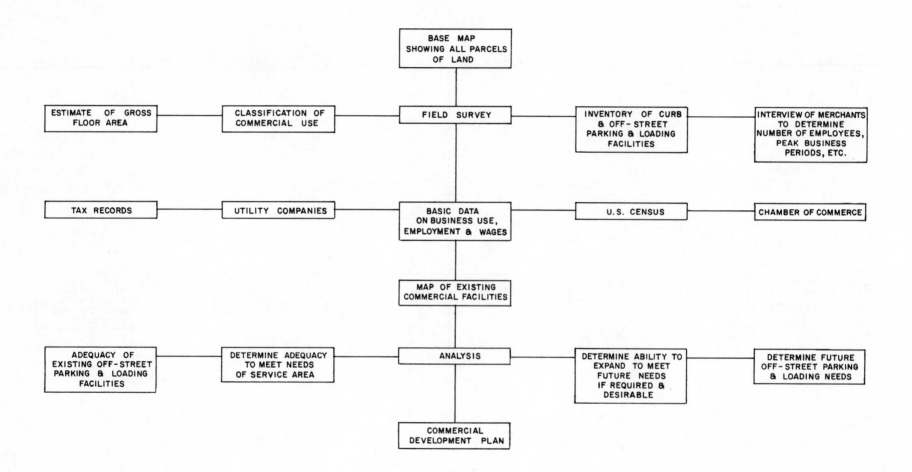

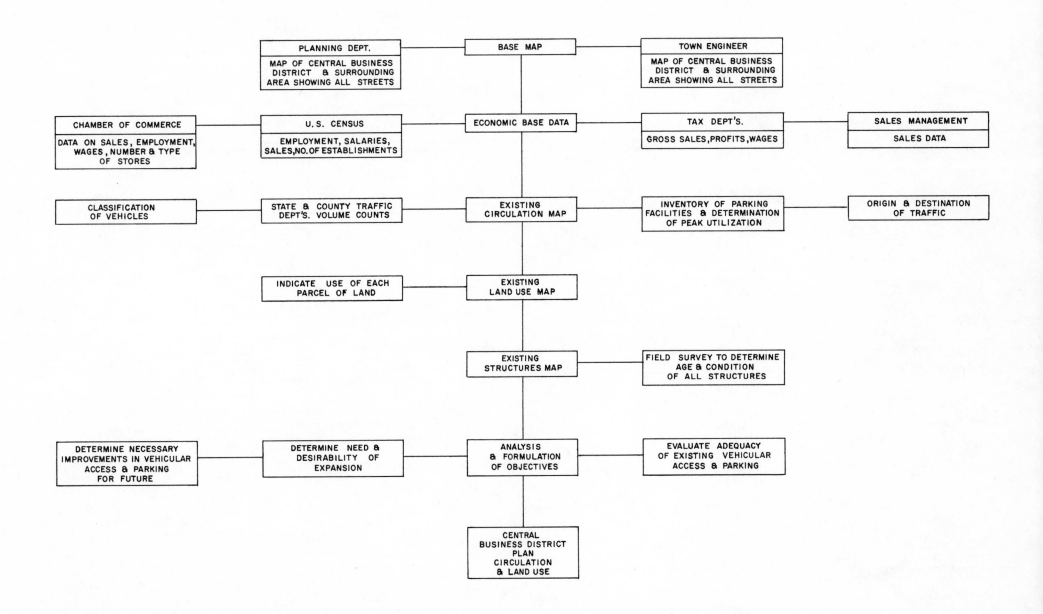

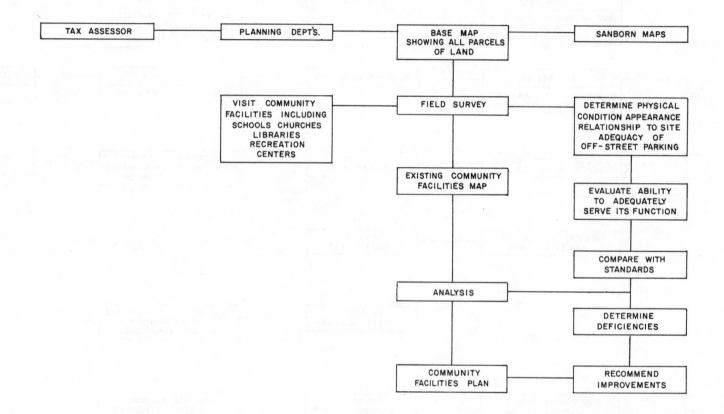

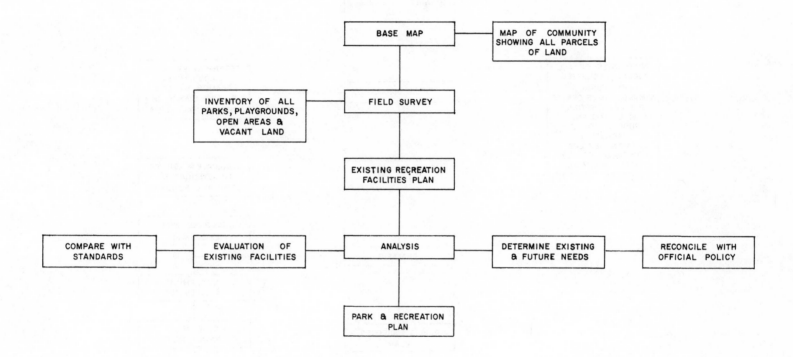

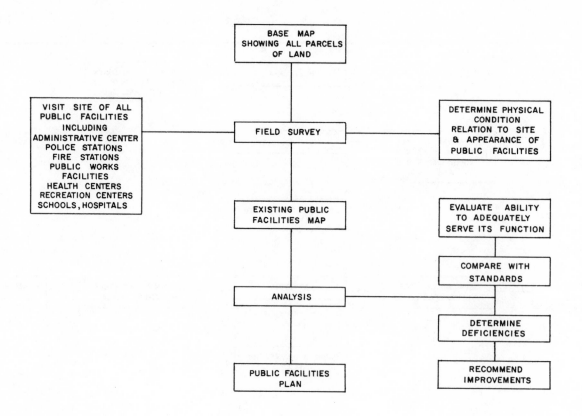

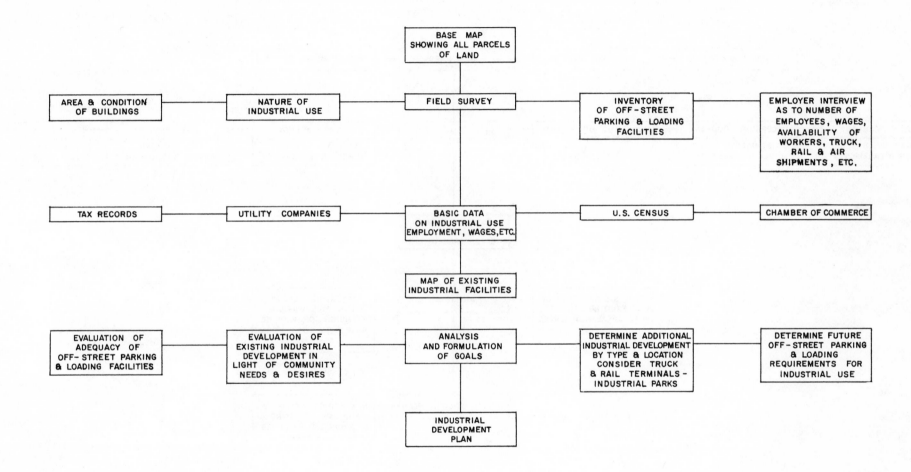

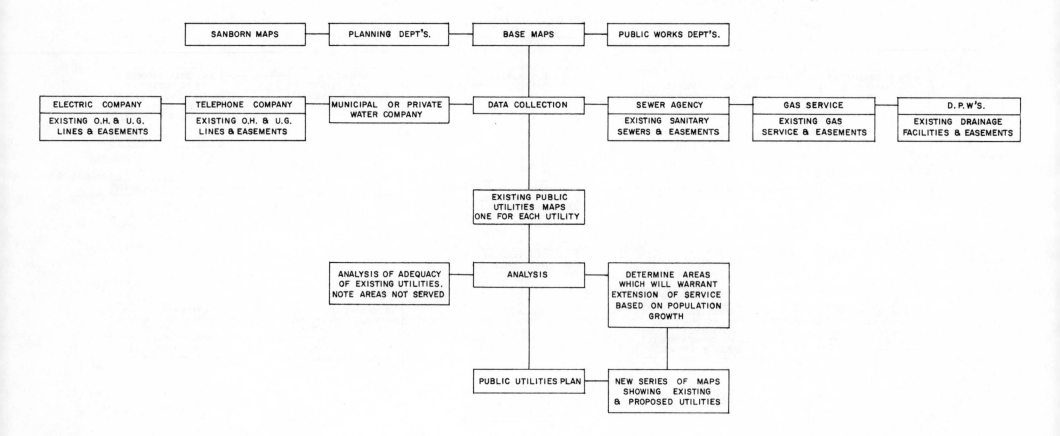

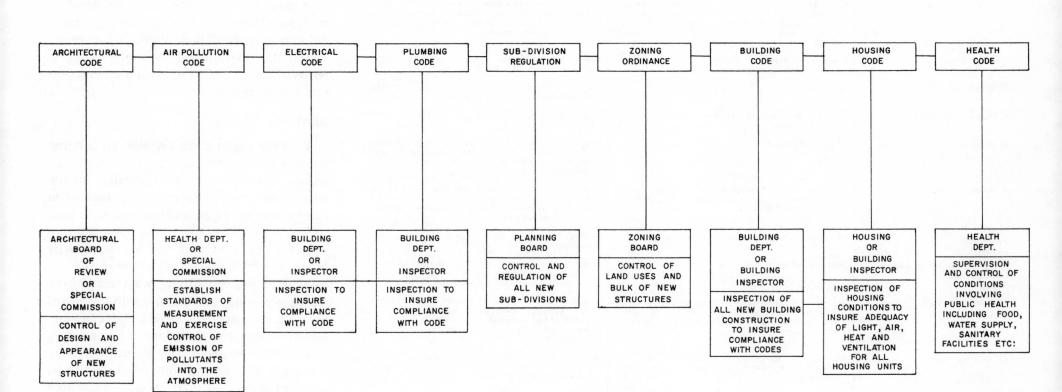

ARCHITECTURAL CODE	AIR POLLUTION CODE	ELECTRICAL CODE	PLUMBING CODE	SUB-DIVISION REGULATION	ZONING ORDINANCE	BUILDING CODE	HOUSING CODE	HEALTH CODE
ARCHITECTURAL BOARD OF REVIEW OR SPECIAL COMMISSION CONTROL OF DESIGN AND APPEARANCE OF NEW STRUCTURES	HEALTH DEPT. OR SPECIAL COMMISSION ESTABLISH STANDARDS OF MEASUREMENT AND EXERCISE CONTROL OF EMISSION OF POLLUTANTS INTO THE ATMOSPHERE	BUILDING DEPT. OR INSPECTOR INSPECTION TO INSURE COMPLIANCE WITH CODE	BUILDING DEPT. OR INSPECTOR INSPECTION TO INSURE COMPLIANCE WITH CODE	PLANNING BOARD CONTROL AND REGULATION OF ALL NEW SUB-DIVISIONS	ZONING BOARD CONTROL OF LAND USES AND BULK OF NEW STRUCTURES	BUILDING DEPT. OR BUILDING INSPECTOR INSPECTION OF ALL NEW BUILDING CONSTRUCTION TO INSURE COMPLIANCE WITH CODES	HOUSING OR BUILDING INSPECTOR INSPECTION OF HOUSING CONDITIONS TO INSURE ADEQUACY OF LIGHT, AIR, HEAT AND VENTILATION FOR ALL HOUSING UNITS	HEALTH DEPT. SUPERVISION AND CONTROL OF CONDITIONS INVOLVING PUBLIC HEALTH INCLUDING FOOD, WATER SUPPLY, SANITARY FACILITIES ETC:

Element	Purpose	Type of works and measures
1. Watershed management	Conservation and improvement of the soil, sediment abatement, runoff retardation, forest and grassland maintenance and improvement, water storage, and improvement of water supply.	Soil conservation practices, forest and range management practices, headwaters control structures, debris detention dams, and farm ponds.
2. Flood management	Conservation storage, river regulation, recharging ground water, water supply, development of power, protection of life, reduction of flood damage, and protection of economic developments.	Dams, storage reservoirs, levees, flood walls, channel improvements, floodways, pumping stations, watershed treatment practices, flood-plain zoning. (See 8 below.)
3. Water supply	Provision of water for domestic, industrial, commercial, municipal, and other uses.	Dams, reservoirs, wells, conduits, pumping plants, treatment plants, distribution systems.
4. Navigation	Transportation	Dams, reservoirs, canals, locks, open channel improvements, harbor improvements.
5. Hydroelectric power	Provision of power for economic development and improved farm and living standards.	Dams, reservoirs, penstocks, power plants, transmission lines.
6. Irrigation	Agricultural production	Dams, reservoirs, wells, canals, pumps or pumping plants, weed control and desilting works, distribution systems, drainage facilities, farm land grading, farmsteads.
7. Pollution abatement	Protection of water supplies for municipal, domestic, industrial and agricultural use, and for aquatic life and recreation.	Treatment facilities, private and public. Reservoir storage for augmenting low flows and for water purification, sewage collection systems. Legal control measures.
8. Drainage	Agricultural production and protection of the public health	Ditches, tile drains, levees, pumping stations, soil treatment.
9. Recreational use of water resources	Increased well-being of the people	Reservoirs, lakes, facilities for recreational use, works for pollution control, scenic park and monument reservations, and wilderness areas.
10. Fish and wildlife	Reduction or prevention of fish or wildlife losses due to man's works, enhancement of sports opportunities, provision for expansion in commercial fishing.	Wildlife refuges, fish hatcheries, fish ladders and screens, reservoir storage regulation of stream flows, stocking of streams and reservoirs with fish, pollution control, and land management.
11. Sediment control	Reduction of silt load in streams, protection of reservoirs, improvement of water supply, fostering of fish.	Soil conservation, sound forest practices, proper highway construction, desilting works, channel and revetment works.
12. Salinity control	Abatement or prevention of salt water contamination of agricultural, industrial, and municipal water supplies.	Reservoirs for augmenting low stream flow, barriers.
13. Insect control	Public health. Protection of recreational values. Protection of forests and crops.	Proper design and operation of reservoirs and associated works, drainage and extermination measures.

SOURCE: *The Report of the President's Water Resources Policy Commission—1950*
A water policy for the American people

THE MAIN ELEMENTS

The main elements in a water resources plan, with their relationship to a comprehensive regional program may be summarized as shown.

In any comprehensive resources development plan these elements must be considered not only in terms of their physical, economic, and social relation one to another, but in terms of their relation to the underlying purposes to be served.

GENERAL PRINCIPLES

1. **Each regional plan should be comprehensive and coordinated,** covering the conservation, development, and utilization of the natural resources of the region and seeking to meet the needs of agriculture, industry, public health, welfare, and all the other fields in which needs exist that can be satisfied by proper use of the resources of the region.

2. **Planning should be approached with the multiple-purpose concept** and with the aim of maximum net benefits based on full consideration of alternative plans for meeting existing and anticipated needs. This means that, from the start of planning, full weight must be given to watershed management, municipal and industrial water supply, hydroelectric power, pollution abatement, fish and wildlife, and recreation, as well as to flood control, irrigation, and navigation, to the extent of their importance in the particular region. It should assure joint coordinated action of all interested Federal, State, and local agencies on an effective cooperative basis.

3. **Planning should proceed from actual or potential needs to projects and programs** in order that basin programs may not become ends in themselves.

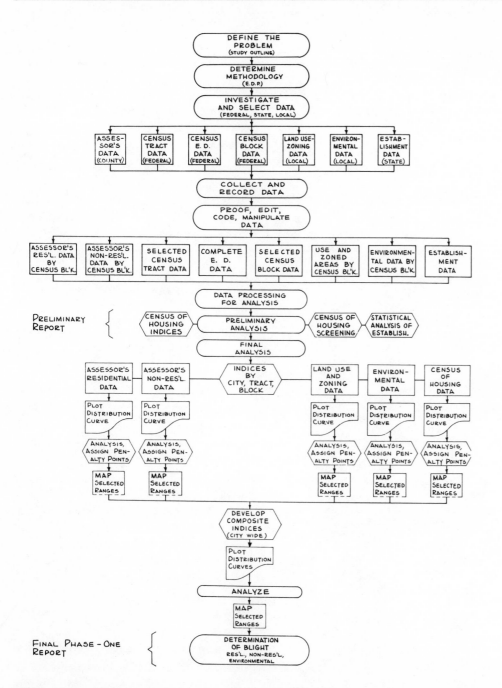

THE SYSTEM'S FRAMEWORK

The total system was designed to:

1. Take full advantage of electronic data processing and computer applications.

2. Provide data for the Community Renewal Project first, and for other users secondly.

3. Utilize secondary data with a minimum amount of field work and none if possible.

4. Provide for future updating but not on an immediate day-to-day basis.

5. Diversify the data bank and provide cross checks by using varied data sources to answer the same question.

6. Find a common denominator or base unit of measurement, i.e., some spatial unit common to all the data.

7. Provide a data recall and graphical display system capable of operation by the user without consulting with or hiring an experienced programmer or computer technician.

SOURCE: Urban Renewal Service, Urban Renewal Administration Housing & Home Finance Agency, Wash., D. C.—1962
Spokane C. R. P. Data System Design Using Computer Graphics in Community Renewal

PHYSICAL AND CLIMATIC CHARACTERISTICS

PERIOD 1899-1938

SOURCE: Climate and Man Yearbook of Agriculture—1941 Dept. of Agriculture

PERIOD 1899-1938

SOURCE: Climate and Man Yearbook of Agriculture—1941 Dept. of Agriculture

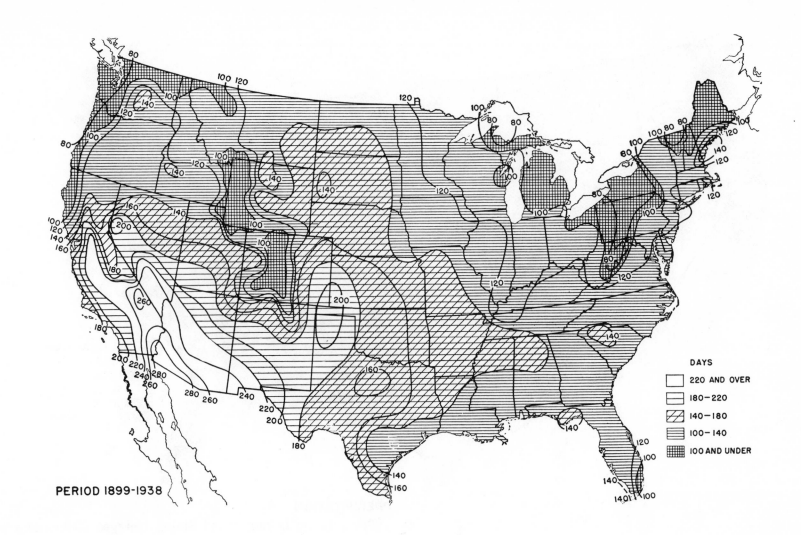

PERIOD 1899-1938

DAYS

	220 AND OVER
	180–220
	140–180
	100–140
	100 AND UNDER

SOURCE: Climate and Man Yearbook of Agriculture—1941 Dept. of Agriculture

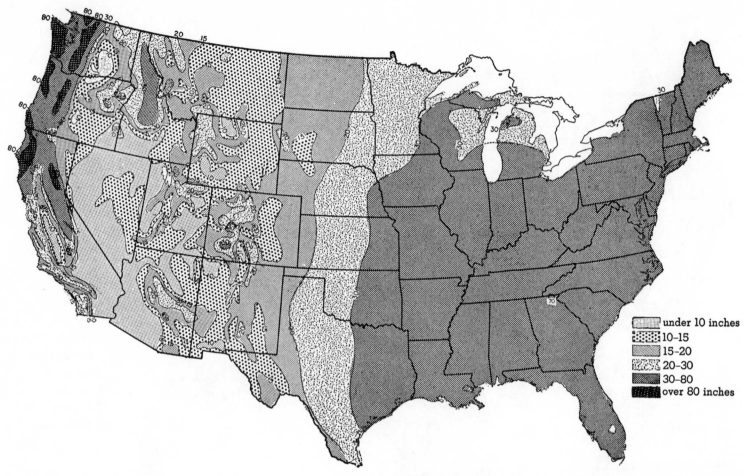

SOURCE: *A Water Policy for the American People. Vol. 1, The Report of the President's Water Resources Policy Commission—1950*

Legend:
- under 10 inches
- 10–15
- 15–20
- 20–30
- 30–80
- over 80 inches

PRECIPITATION

Precipitation in the United States averages 30 inches a year, with a variation of from under 10 to more than 80 inches. The Great Plains receives from 20 to 30 inches. The Great Plains to the Rocky Mountains, from 15 to 20 inches; and in the lowlands of the Intermountain Region, from 10 to 15 inches. In Nevada, southeastern California, and southwestern Arizona, the precipitation is under 10 inches a year, the least in the nation. On the West Coast, precipitation is the highest in the United States, averaging more than 80 inches in places.

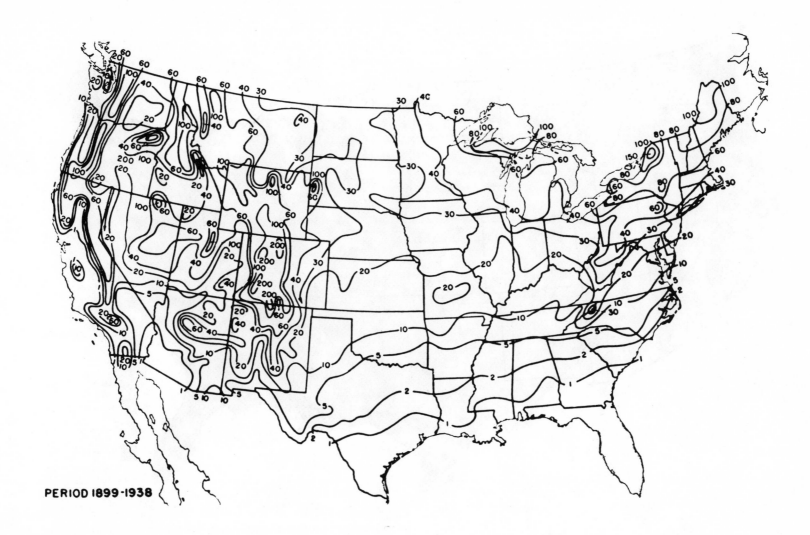

PERIOD 1899-1938

SOURCE: Climate and Man Yearbook of Agriculture—1941 Dept. of Agriculture

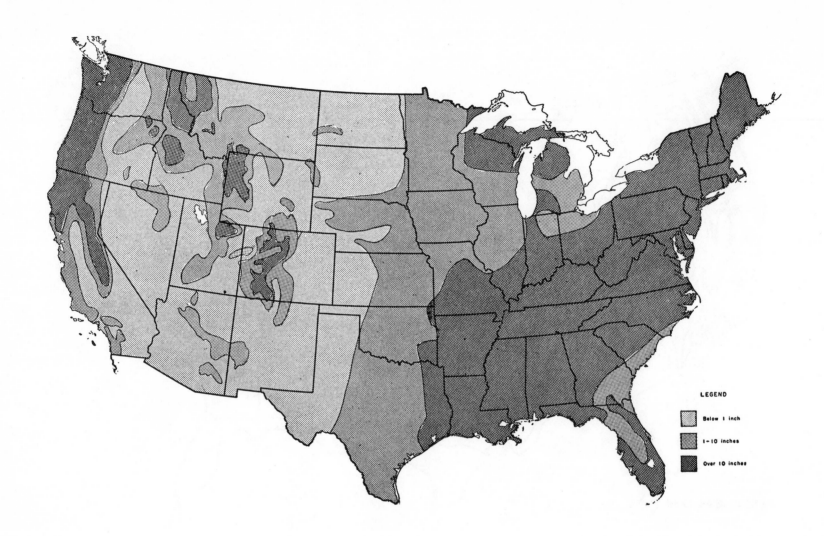

LEGEND

Below 1 inch

1-10 inches

Over 10 inches

SOURCE: The Report of the President's Water Resources Policy Commission—1950
A water policy for the American people

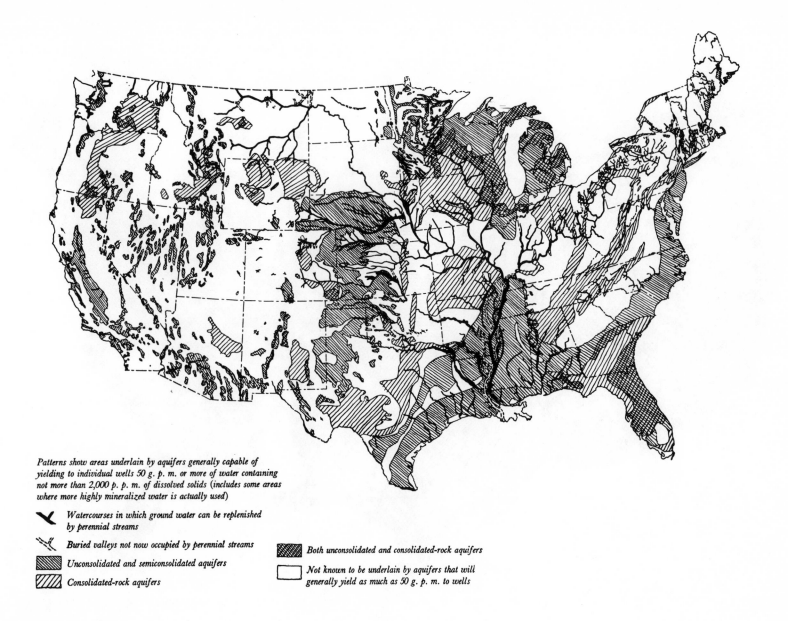

Patterns show areas underlain by aquifers generally capable of
yielding to individual wells 50 g. p. m. or more of water containing
not more than 2,000 p. p. m. of dissolved solids (includes some areas
where more highly mineralized water is actually used)

⟍ Watercourses in which ground water can be replenished
by perennial streams

⟍ Buried valleys not now occupied by perennial streams

▨ Unconsolidated and semiconsolidated aquifers

▧ Consolidated-rock aquifers

▨ Both unconsolidated and consolidated-rock aquifers

☐ Not known to be underlain by aquifers that will
generally yield as much as 50 g. p. m. to wells

SOURCE: *Yearbook of Agriculture U. S. Dept. of Agriculture 1955*

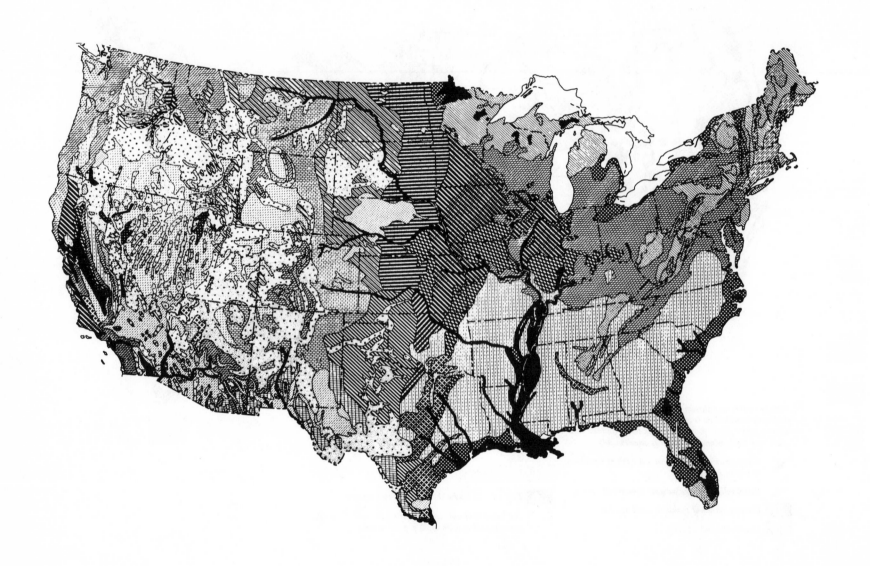

ZONAL

Great groups of soils with well-developed soil characteristics, reflecting the dominating influence of climate and vegetation. (As shown on the map, many small areas of intrazonal and azonal soils are included.)

PODZOL SOILS
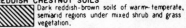
Light-colored leached soils of cool, humid forested regions.

BROWN PODZOLIC SOILS
Brown leached soils of cool-temperate, humid forested regions.

GRAY-BROWN PODZOLIC SOILS
Grayish-brown leached soils of temperate, humid forested regions.

RED AND YELLOW PODZOLIC SOILS
Red or yellow leached soils of warm-temperate, humid forested regions.

PRAIRIE SOILS
Very dark brown soils of cool and temperate, relatively humid grasslands.

REDDISH PRAIRIE SOILS
Dark reddish-brown soils of warm-temperate, relatively humid grasslands.

CHERNOZEM SOILS
Dark-brown to nearly black soils of cool and temperate, subhumid grasslands.

CHESTNUT SOILS
Dark-brown soils of cool and temperate, subhumid to semiarid grasslands.

REDDISH CHESTNUT SOILS
Dark reddish-brown soils of warm-temperate, semiarid regions under mixed shrub and grass vegetation.

BROWN SOILS
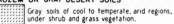
Brown soils of cool and temperate, semiarid grasslands.

REDDISH BROWN SOILS
Reddish-brown soils of warm-temperate to hot, semiarid to arid regions, under mixed shrub and grass vegetation.

NONCALCIC BROWN SOILS
Brown or light reddish-brown soils of warm-temperate, wet-dry, semiarid regions, under mixed forest, shrub, and grass vegetation.

SIEROZEM OR GRAY DESERT SOILS
Gray soils of cool to temperate, arid regions, under shrub and grass vegetation.

RED DESERT SOILS
Light reddish-brown soils of warm-temperate to hot, arid regions, under shrub vegetation.

INTRAZONAL

Great groups of soils with more or less well-developed soil characteristics reflecting the dominating influence of some local factor of relief, parent material, or age over the normal effect of climate and vegetation. (Many areas of these soils are included with zonal groups on the map.)

PLANOSOLS

Soils with strongly leached surface horizons over claypans on nearly flat land in cool to warm, humid to subhumid regions, under grass or forest vegetation.

RENDZINA SOILS

Dark grayish-brown to black soils developed from soft limy materials in cool to warm, humid to subhumid regions, mostly under grass vegetation.

SOLONCHAK (1) AND SOLONETZ (2) SOILS

(1) Light-colored soils with high concentration of soluble salts, in subhumid to arid regions, under salt-loving plants.

(2) Dark-colored soils with hard prismatic subsoils, usually strongly alkaline, in subhumid or semiarid regions under grass or shrub vegetation.

WIESENBÖDEN (1); GROUND WATER PODZOL (2), AND HALF-BOG SOILS (3)

(1) Dark-brown to black soils developed with poor drainage under grasses in humid and subhumid regions.

(2) Gray sandy soils with brown cemented sandy subsoils developed under forests from nearly level imperfectly drained sand in humid regions.

(3) Poorly drained, shallow, dark peaty or mucky soils underlain by gray mineral soil, in humid regions, under swamp-forests.

BOG SOILS
Poorly drained dark peat or muck soils underlain by peat, mostly in humid regions, under swamp or marsh types of vegetation.

The areas of each great soil group shown on the map include areas of other groups too small to be shown separately. Especially are there small areas of the azonal and intrazonal groups included in the areas of zonal groups.

AZONAL

Soils without well-developed soil characteristics. (Many areas of these soils are included with other groups on the map.)

LITHOSOLS AND SHALLOW SOILS (ARID-SUBHUMID)

(HUMID)
Shallow soils consisting largely of an imperfectly weathered mass of rock fragments, largely but not exclusively on steep slopes.

SANDS (DRY)

Very sandy soils.

ALLUVIAL SOILS

Soils developing from recently deposited alluvium that have had little or no modification by processes of soil formation.

SOURCE: Roy L. Donahue, Soils: An Introduction to Soils and Plant Growth, © 1965, 2nd Ed.
(After map, "Soil Associations of the United States," published in Soils and Men, Yearbook of Agriculture for 1938)
General pattern of Great Soil Groups
Courtesy Division of Soil Survey, Bureau of Plant Industry, U. S. D. A.

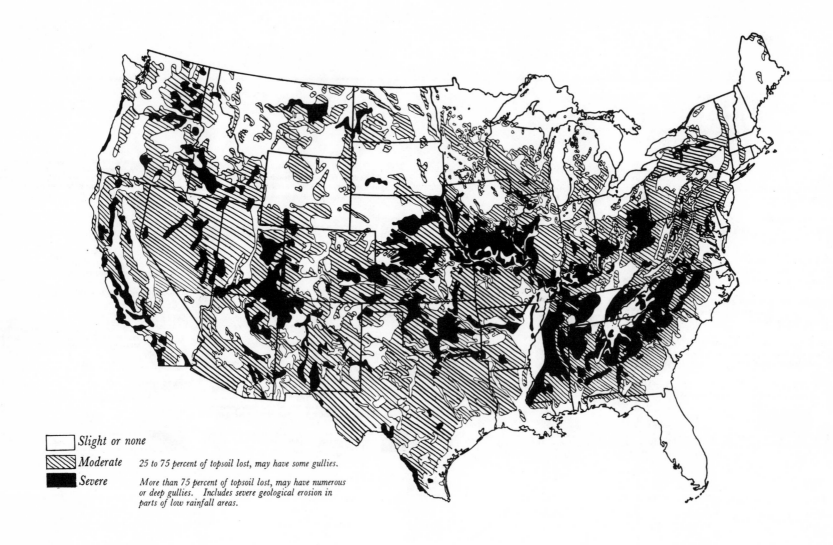

Slight or none

Moderate   25 to 75 percent of topsoil lost, may have some gullies.

Severe   More than 75 percent of topsoil lost, may have numerous
            or deep gullies.   Includes severe geological erosion in
            parts of low rainfall areas.

SOURCE: The Report of the President's Water Resources Policy Commission—1950
A Water Policy for the American People

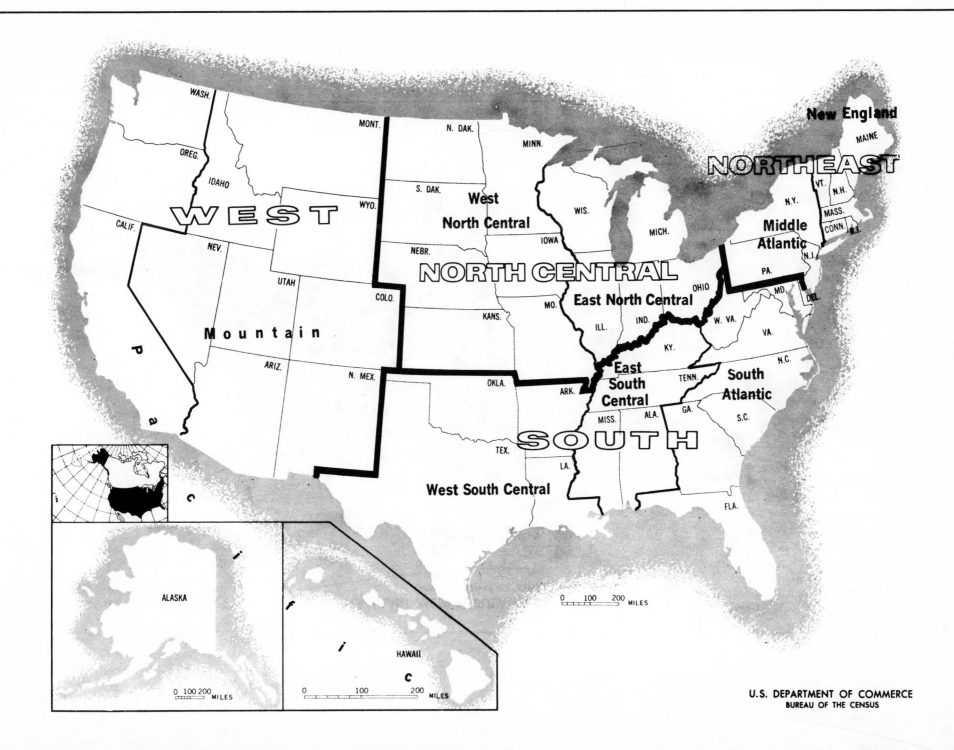

WASH.

OREG.

IDAHO

CALIF.

NEV.

UTAH

ARIZ.

W E S T

M o u n t a i n

P a c i f i c

MONT.

WYO.

COLO.

N. MEX.

N. DAK.

S. DAK.

NEBR.

KANS.

OKLA.

TEX.

MINN.

West North Central

IOWA

MO.

ARK.

LA.

West South Central

WIS.

MICH.

ILL.

IND.

KY.

TENN.

MISS.

ALA.

GA.

FLA.

NORTH CENTRAL

East North Central

OHIO

W. VA.

VA.

N.C.

S.C.

East South Central

SOUTH

South Atlantic

New England

MAINE

VT.

N.H.

MASS.

CONN.

R.I.

N.Y.

PA.

N.J.

MD.

DEL.

NORTHEAST

Middle Atlantic

ALASKA

0 100 200 MILES

HAWAII

0 100 200 MILES

0 100 200 MILES

U.S. DEPARTMENT OF COMMERCE
BUREAU OF THE CENSUS

STANDARD METROPOLITAN STATISTICAL AREAS OF THE U. S.—1964

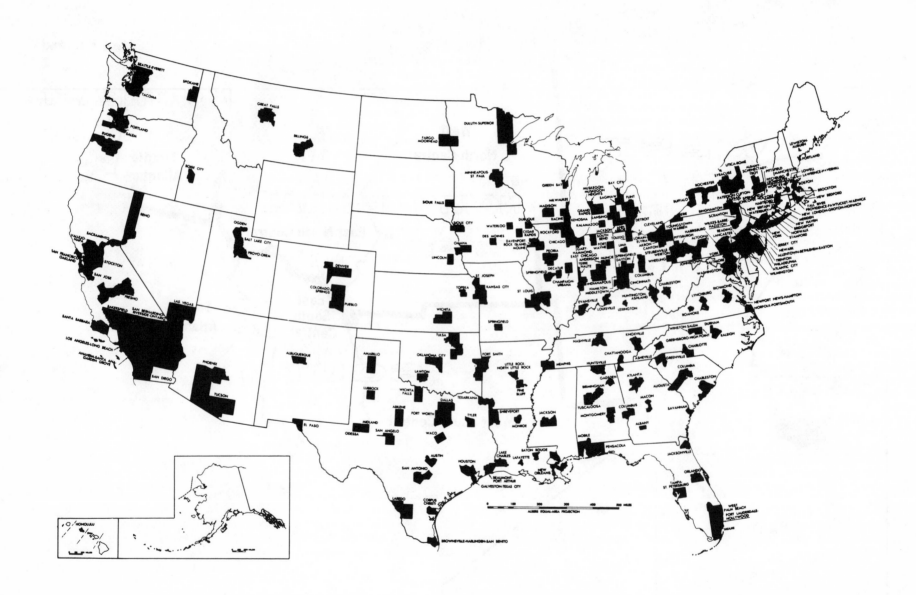

SOURCE: U. S. Dept of Commerce Bureau of the Census

STANDARD METROPOLITAN STATISTICAL AREAS

It has long been recognized that for many types of analysis it is necessary to consider as a unit the entire area, in and around a city, in which the activities form an integrated economic and social system. Prior to the 1950 Census, areas of this type had been defined in somewhat different ways for different purposes and by various agencies. Leading examples were the metropolitan districts of the 1940 Census of Housing, the industrial areas of the Census of Manufactures, and the labor market areas of the Bureau of Employment Security. To permit all Federal statistical agencies to utilize the same areas for the publication of general-purpose statistics, the Bureau of the Budget has established "standard metropolitan statistical areas" (SMSA's). Every city of 50,000 inhabitants or more according to the 1960 Census of Population is included in an SMSA.

The definitions and titles of standard metropolitan statistical areas are established by the Bureau of the Budget with the advice of the Federal Committee on Standard Metropolitan Statistical Areas. This Committee is composed of representatives of the major statistical agencies of the Federal Government. The criteria used by the Bureau of the Budget in establishing the SMSA's are presented below.

Population criteria.—The criteria for population relate to a city or cities of specified size according to the 1960 Census of Population.

1. Each standard metropolitan statistical area must include at least:

    b. Two cities having contiguous boundaries and constituting, for general economic and social purposes, a single community with a combined population of at least 50,000, the smaller of which must have a population of at least 15,000.

2. If each of two or more adjacent counties has a city of 50,000 inhabitants or more (or twin cities under **1b**) and the cities are within 20 miles of each other (city limits to city limits), they will be included in the same area unless there is definite evidence that the two cities are not economically and socially integrated.

Criteria of metropolitan character.—The criteria of metropolitan character relate primarily to the attributes of the contiguous county as a place of work or as a home for a concentration of nonagricultural workers.

3. At least 75 percent of the labor force of the county must be in the nonagricultural labor force.

4. In addition to criterion 3, the county must meet at least one of the following conditions:

    a. It must have 50 percent or more of its population living in contiguous minor civil divisionsâ with a density of at least 150 persons per square mile, in an unbroken chain of minor civil divisions with such density radiating from a central city in the area.

    b. The number of nonagricultural workers employed in the county must equal at least 10 percent of the number of nonagricultural workers employed in the county containing the largest city in the area, or the county must be the place of employment of 10,000 nonagricultural workers.

    c. The nonagricultural labor force living in the county must equal at least 10 percent of the number in the nonagricultural labor force living in the county containing the largest city in the area, or the county must be the place of residence of a nonagricultural labor force of 10,000.

5. In New England, the city and town are administratively more important than the county, and data are compiled locally for such minor civil divisions. Here, towns and cities are the units used in defining standard metropolitan statistical areas. In New England, because smaller units are used and more restricted areas result, a population density criterion of at least 100 persons per square mile is used as the measure of metropolitan character.

Criteria of integration.—The criteria of integration relate primarily to the extent of economic and social communication between the outlying counties and central county.

6. A county is regarded as integrated with the county or counties containing the central cities of the area if either of the following criteria is met:

    a. Fifteen percent of the workers living in the county work in the county or counties containing central cities of the area, or

    b. Twenty-five percent of those working in the county live in the county or counties containing central cities of the area.

Criteria for titles.—The criteria for titles relate primarily to the size and number of central cities.

7. The complete title of an SMSA identifies the central city or cities and the State or States in which the SMSA is located:

    a. The name of the standard metropolitan statistical area includes that of the largest city.

    b. The addition of up to two city names may be made in the area title, on the basis and in the order of the following criteria:

    (1) The additional city has at least 250,000 inhabitants.

    (2) The additional city has a population of one-third or more of that of the largest city and a minimum population of 25,000, except that both city names are used in those instances where cities qualify under criterion **1b**. (A city which qualified as a secondary central city in 1950 but which does not qualify in 1960 has been temporarily retained as a central city.)

    c. In addition to city names, the area titles will contain the name of the State or States in which the area is located.

Relation to earlier censuses.—In 1950, data were presented for standard metropolitan areas (SMA's) which were established in connection with cities of 50,000 inhabitants or more in 1950. In 1940, a somewhat similar type of area called the "metropolitan district" was used. In 1958, the criteria for delineating SMA's were revised by the Bureau of the Budget, and in 1959 the areas were designated as standard metropolitan statistical areas (SMSA's). In some cases, the 1960 SMSA has the same boundaries as the 1950 SMA; in other, parts have been added or deleted. The designation of the central cities also has changed for some areas. The relationship can be readily determined by comparing the 1960 and 1950 boundaries for the particular area.

In 1950, a total of 168 standard metropolitan areas were identified in conterminous United States, and the Honolulu SMA was identified in Hawaii. A few of the 1950 SMA's were split into several SMSA's for 1960. Some entirely new SMSA's were added to the metropolitan territory of the existing SMA's; in terms of the 1950 counts, the net addition resulting from the designation of new metropolitan territory and changes in boundaries amounted to approximately 6 percent of the total units in the 1950 SMA's.

STANDARD CONSOLIDATED AREAS

In view of the special importance of the metropolitan complexes around New York and Chicago, the Nation's largest cities, several contiguous SMSA's and additional counties that do not appear to meet the formal integration criteria but do have strong interrelationships of other kinds have been combined into the New York-Northeastern New Jersey and Cihcago-Northwestern Indiana Standard Consolidated Areas, respectively. The former is identical with the New York-Northeastern New Jersey SMA of 1950, and the latter corresponds roughly to the Chicago SMA of 1950 (two more counties having been added).

The New York-Northeastern New Jersey Standard Consolidated Area comprises four SMSA's and two additional counties; the Chicago-Northwestern Indiana Standard Consolidated Area comprises two SMSA's.

URBAN-RURAL RESIDENCE

According to the definition adopted for use in the 1960 Censuses, the urban population comprises all persons living in:

a. places of 2,500 inhabitants or more incorporated as cities, boroughs, villages and towns (except towns in New England, New York and Wisconsin)

b. the densely settled urban fringe, whether incorporated or unincorporated, of urbanized areas (see "Urbanized Areas" for definition)

c. towns in New England and townships in New Jersey and Pennsylvania which contain no incorporated municipalities as subdivisions and have either 25,000 inhabitants or more, or a population of 2,500 to 25,000 and a density of 1,500 persons or more per square mile

d. counties in States other than the New England States, New Jersey and Pennsylvania that have no incorporated municipalities within their boundaries and have a density of 1,500 persons or more per square mile

e. unincorporated places of 2,500 inhabitants or more outside urbanized areas

The population not classified as urban constitutes the rural population.

PLACES

The term "place" refers to a concentration of population, regardless of the existence of legally prescribed limits, powers, or functions. Most places are incorporated as cities, towns, villages, or boroughs. In addition, the larger unincorporated places outside the urbanized areas (see "Urbanized Areas" for definition) have been delineated and those with a population of 1,000 or more treated in the same manner as incorporated places of equal size. Furthermore, unincorporated places within urbanized areas are treated in the same manner as other places if they have 10,000 inhabitants or more and if there was an expression of local interest in their recognition. The towns in New England and townships in New Jersey and Pennsylvania recognized as urban (see "Urban-rural Residence" for definition) are also treated as places.

Political units which have been recognized as incorporated places by the Bureau of the Census are those which are incorporated as cities, boroughs, towns, and villages except that towns are not recognized as incorporated places in the New England States, New York, and Wisconsin. In New Jersey and Pennsylvania townships are not classified as "incorporated places" even though some townships possess powers and functions similar to those of incorporated places. However, where towns and townships in these States also qualify as thickly settled centers of population (see "Urban-rural Residence" for definition) they are recognized as such and classified by the Census Bureau as urban towns or townships. In addition, the densely settled portions of some towns and townships are also recognized and are classified as unincorporated places.

SOURCE: U. S. Dept of Commerce Bureau of the Census

STATE ECONOMIC AREAS

State economic areas (SEA's) are relatively homogeneous subdivisions of States. They consist of single counties or groups of counties which have similar economic and social characteristics. The boundaries of these areas have been drawn in such a way that each State is subdivided into relatively few parts, with each part having certain significant characteristics which distinguish it from adjoining areas. The result is a group of areas, smaller than States, on the one hand, and larger than counties, on the other, which are relatively homogeneous with respect to a large number of characteristics.

Generally, SEA's are classified as metropolitan or nonmetropolitan on the basis of their relationship to SMSA's. Each SMSA with a total population of a 100,000 or more in 1960 and a central city of 50,000 or more is also recognized as a separate metropolitan SEA. When such an SMSA is located in two or more States, each State part becomes a metropolitan SEA. However, this correspondence does not exist in New England because SMSA's are built up from MCD's. In New England, counties with more than half their population in one or more SMSA's are components of metropolitan SEA's.

URBANIZED AREAS

An urbanized area contains (1) at least one city of 50,000 inhabitants or more in 1960 or two cities having contiguous boundaries and constituting, for general economic and social purposes, a single community with a combined population of at least 50,000, the smaller of which must have a population of at least 15,000, and (2) all the surrounding closely settled incorporated places and unincorporated areas that meet the criteria listed below. All persons residing in an urbanized area are included in the urban population. Since the urbanized area outside of incorporated places was defined in terms of enumeration districts, the boundaries for the most part follow such landmarks as roads, streets, railroads, streams, and other clearly defined lines which may be easily identified by census enumerators in the field and often do not conform to the boundaries of political units.

In addition to its central city or cities, an urbanized area also contains the following types of contiguous areas, which together constitute its urban fringe:

1. Incorporated places with 2,500 inhabitants or more

2. Incorporated places with less than 2,500 inhabitants, provided each has a closely settled area of 100 dwelling units or more

3. Towns in the New England States, townships in New Jersey and Pennsylvania, and counties elsewhere, which are classified as urban

4. Enumeration districts in unincorporated territory with a population density of 1,000 inhabitants or more per square mile (Areas devoted to nonresidential urban land uses such as railroad yards, factories, and cemeteries were excluded in computing the population density of an enumeration district.)

5. Other enumeration districts in unincorporated territory with lower population density, provided that they served one of the following purposes:

a. Elimination of enclaves

b. Closing of indentations in the urbanized area of one mile or less across the open end

c. Linking of outlying enumeration districts of qualifying density that were no more than 1-1/2 miles from the main body of the urbanized area

Urbanized areas are divided into two parts: (1) the central city, or cities, and (2) the remainder of the area, or the urban fringe. Any city in an urbanized area which is a central city of an SMSA is also a central city of the urbanized area. With but two exceptions, the names of the central cities appear in the titles of the areas. The New York-Northeastern New Jersey urbanized area includes the central cities of New York, Newark, Jersey City, Paterson, Clifton, and Passaic. The Chicago-Northwestern Indiana urbanized area includes the central cities of Chicago, Gary, Hammond, and East Chicago.

SOURCE: U. S. Dept of Commerce Bureau of the Census

Census tracts:—Census tracts are small, permanently established geographic areas into which cities and counties have been divided for statistical purposes. Tract boundaries are selected by a local tract committee and approved by the U. S. Bureau of the Census. They remain the same for a long time, so that statistical comparisons can be made from year to year and from census to census.

Tract boundaries usually follow permanent and easily recognized lines. These may be streets, railroads, creeks, and the like. In a few cases, city limits are used when there is little or no likelihood of change.

Enumeration districts:—Enumeration districts are areas of small population which are defined and used by the Census Bureau for the collection and tabulation of data. They are the smallest areas for which data are tabulated with the exception of census blocks. Each enumeration district (ED) represents a discrete statistical unit designed to be covered by one enumerator and should contain not more than 1,000 inhabitants.

The EDs observe the boundaries of all political units and statistical areas to be reported in Census tabulations. Therefore, ED boundaries will follow the city limits as of April 1, 1960 (the date of the Census), the 1950 city limits if they differ from the 1960 city limits, and census tract boundaries. The remaining ED lines were for convenience in setting up areas for each enumerator.

Census blocks:—Census statistics by blocks are published for cities with a population over 50,000 in 1960.

A census block is usually a well-defined rectangular piece of land bounded by streets or roads. However, it may be irregular in shape or bounded by railroad tracks, streams or other features. Each block is consecutively numbered within a census tract. However, where more than one census blocked-city was located in a tract, the blocks in each city in the tract were numbered consecutively, creating a duplication of numbers.

COUNTIES

The primary divisions of the States are, in general, termed counties, but in Louisiana these divisions are known as parishes. Alaska is divided into 24 election districts. There are also a number of cities which are independent of any county organization and thus constitute primary divisions of their States, namely, Baltimore in Maryland, St. Louis in Missouri, and 32 cities in Virginia. The District of Columbia, which is not divided into counties, also is considered the equivalent of a county, as are the three parts of Yellowstone National Park in Idaho, Montana, and Wyoming. There were 3,072 counties and parishes in the United States in 1960 and 62 county equivalents, making a total of 3,134.

The number of countries declined by three between 1950 and 1960. The number of country equivalents in conterminous United States increased by five. Alaska was redistricted after 1950, and its judicial divisions were replaced by 24 election districts. Changes in the number of counties were fairly frequent some decades ago but have become progressively rarer.

SOURCE: U. S. Dept of Commerce Bureau of the Census

LAND USE

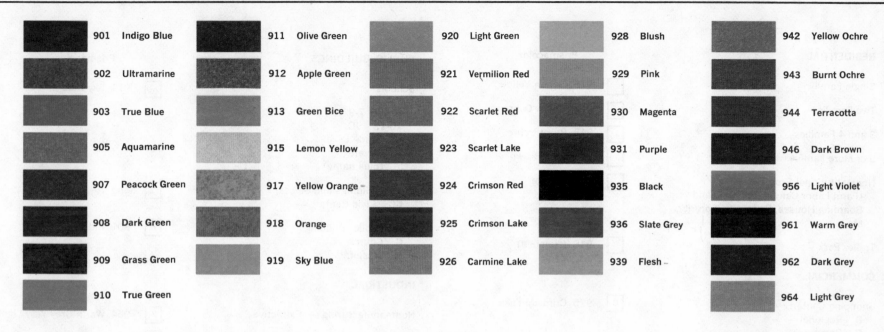

	901	Indigo Blue		911	Olive Green		920	Light Green		928	Blush		942	Yellow Ochre
	902	Ultramarine		912	Apple Green		921	Vermilion Red		929	Pink		943	Burnt Ochre
	903	True Blue		913	Green Bice		922	Scarlet Red		930	Magenta		944	Terracotta
	905	Aquamarine		915	Lemon Yellow		923	Scarlet Lake		931	Purple		946	Dark Brown
	907	Peacock Green		917	Yellow Orange		924	Crimson Red		935	Black		956	Light Violet
	908	Dark Green		918	Orange		925	Crimson Lake		936	Slate Grey		961	Warm Grey
	909	Grass Green		919	Sky Blue		926	Carmine Lake		939	Flesh		962	Dark Grey
	910	True Green											964	Light Grey

RESIDENTIAL   **Prismacolor**

Single-family	SF	☐	915 Lemon Yellow
2-family	2F	☐	939 Flesh (or 942)
3- and 4-family	34F	☐	917 Yellow Orange
Boarding and rooming houses	BH	☐	943 Burnt Ochre
Multiple dwelling (over 4-family)	APT	☐	946 Dark Brown
Tourists and trailer courts	T	☐	930 Magenta
Hotel	H	☐	931 Purple

BUSINESS & COMMERCIAL

Local (neighborhood) business	LB	☐	929 Pink
Offices and banks	OB	☐	921 Vermilion Red
General business	GB	☐	923 Scarlet Lake
Intensive business, theatres, recreation	IB	☐	925 Crimson Lake

INDUSTRIAL

Light industry	LM	☐	964 Light Gray
Railroads and public utilities	PM	☐	962 Dark Gray
Heavy industry	HM	☐	935 Black

PUBLIC   **Prismacolor**

Parks	P	☐	910 True Green
Public schools	P	☐	909 Grass Green
Public buildings	P	☐	903 Dark Green

QUASI-PUBLIC

Quasi-public open uses	QP	☐	903 True Blue (or 904)
Churches	QP	☐	902 Ultramarine
Quasi-public buildings & institutions	QP	☐	901 Indigo Blue
Cemeteries	QP	☐	905 Aquamarine

AGRICULTURAL

| Crop land | AC | ☐ | 912 Apple Green |
| Livestock land | AL | ☐ | 911 Olive Green |

MINING

| | E | ☐ | No color |

VACANT LAND

| | V | ☐ | No color |

Colors and numbers refer to PRISMACOLOR PENCILS as manufactured by EAGLE PENCIL CO. Because of production complexities, colors as shown are approximate; for precise color and variations consult manufacturer's color chart.

SOURCE: Mapping for Planning Publication No. 101 Public Administration Service, Chicago, Ill.

3-2 COLOR LEGEND FOR LAND USE CATEGORIES
SCHEME 2

RESIDENTIAL		Prismacolor
Single Family	☐	915 Lemon Yellow
Two Families	☐	942 Yellow Ochre
3 and 4 Families	☐	943 Burnt Ochre
5 or More Families	☐	946 Dark Brown
Noninstitutional Group Housing (Farm Labor Camps, Rooming and Boarding Houses, Fraternity, Sorority, etc.)	☐	918 Orange
Trailer Park	☐	946 (Hatched)
COMMERCIAL		
Shopping Center: **R** Regional **C** Community **N** Neighborhood	C	925 Crimson Lake
Self-generative, Auto-oriented (Including "Strip Commercial")	☐	929 Pink
Other Retail Commercial (Including Major Business, Streets, CBDs, Small Clusters, Individual Stores)	☐	922 Scarlet Red
Offices, Banks and Clinics (Outside Shopping Districts)	☐	928 Blush

PUBLIC BUILDINGS		Prismacolor
Schools N K-6 7-9 10-12 JC **C** Grade Level **P** Private (plus name)	7-9	919 Sky Blue
Public Buildings and offices **CC** Civic Center	CC	902 Ultramarine
Quasi-Public Buildings **C** Church **H** Hospitals	H	901 Indigo Blue
INDUSTRIAL		
Nonmanufacturing — Extractive	☐	964 Warm Grey-Very Light
Nonmanufacturing (Warehouses, Wholesale, Heavy Commerical)	☐	936 Slate Grey
Manufacturing 1-5 Nuisance Value	3	961 Warm Grey
Transportation	☐	956 Light Violet
Utilities	☐	931 Purple

FOR COLOR REFER TO PRISMACOLOR PENCILS COLOR CHART ON PAGE 39.

SOURCE: Land Use Inventory Manual County of Santa Clara Planning Dept. San Jose, Calif—1964

OPEN SPACE

RECREATION
Prismacolor

Local Parks, Playgrounds and Playfields
   (Serving a Neighborhood or District)
   N Neighborhood Park
   D District Park
   P Playground
   F Playfield
   [D] 913 Green Bice

Urban or Metropolitan Area Parks
   (Serving a Community or
   Metropolitan Area)
   [ ] 910 True Green

Private Open Space
   G Golf
   R Commercial Recreation
   [R] 912 Apple Green

CEMETERY
[C] 912 Apple Green

AGRICULTURE

Agriculture: Orchard   [ ] 911 Olive Green

Agriculture: Nonorchard, Intensive
   Cultivated   [ ] 907 Peacock Green

Grazing, Range Land   [ ] 920 Light Green

Agriculture: Livestock, Dairy Miscellaneous
   Animal   [ ] 907 (Hatched)

NONURBAN

Forest and Brush   [ ] 908 Dark Green

Lakes, Reservoirs and Bay   [ ] 905 Aquamarine

Creeks and Channels   [ ] 905 (Solid Line)

Water Conservation and Flood control   [ ] 905 (Hatched)

Marshlands   [ ] 920 Light Green

VACANT URBAN

SOURCE: *Land Use Inventory Manual County of Santa Clara Planning Dept. San Jose, Calif—1964*

A SIMPLIFIED SET OF LAND USE CATEGORIES

In communities with simpler or less intensive patterns of development or in suburban, peripheral, or rural areas a less detailed system of land use categories is often adequate. The following suggested list follows the principles discussed above and is essentially a combination of similar uses into more general classifications.

RESIDENTIAL
Prismacolor

Single-family   **SF** [ ] 915 Lemon Yellow
Intensive residential
   (combining 2–family—2F, 3– and
   4–family—34F, and boarding
   houses)   **BH** [ ] 943 Burnt Ochre

Multiple dwelling   **APT** [ ] 946 Dark Brown

Hotel (including tourist and
   trailer courts — T)   **HT** [ ] 931 Purple

BUSINESS AND COMMERCIAL

Local (neighborhood) business   **LB** [ ] 929 Pink

General business (including offices and
   banks — OB, and intensive
   business — IB)   **GB** [ ] 923 Scarlet Lake

INDUSTRIAL

Light industry (including public
   utilities — PM)   **LM** [ ] 964 Light Gray

Heavy industry   **HM** [ ] 935 Black

PUBLIC AND QUASI-PUBLIC

Parks   **P** [ ] 910 True Green

Schools and public buildings   **P** [ ] 909 Grass Green

Quasi-public open uses   **QP** [ ] 903 True Blue

Churches and institutional bldgs.   **QP** [ ] 901 Indigo Blue

Cemeteries   **QP** [ ] 905 Aquamarine

AGRICULTURAL

All types — **AC, AL**   **AA** [ ] 912 Apple Green

VACANT LAND
    V [ ] No color

FOR COLOR REFER TO PRISMACOLOR PENCILS COLOR CHART ON PAGE 39.

SOURCE: *Mapping for Planning Publication No. 101 Public Administration Service, Chicago, Ill.*

AGE OF BUILDINGS

For presenting data in mapped form describing the age of structures the following scale will be found to be generally applicable. Where special conditions extent and subdivisions may be varied.

COLOR LEGEND FOR AGE OF BUILDINGS

Building Age Category		Prismacolor
Under 5 years	☐	915 Lemon Yellow
Over 5 to 15 years	☐	918 Orange
Over 15 to 25 years	☐	926 Carmine Lake
Over 25 to 35 years	☐	931 Purple
Over 35 years	☐	901 Indigo Blue

SQUARE FEET OF LOT AREA PER FAMILY

A map indicating the square feet of lot area per family gives a general indication of the density of population as it defines various areas and, in indicating in general the prevailing lot sizes per family, provides a basic study for zoning. The standards and color scale are suggestions only as the prevailing patterns of lot sizes vary from one community to another. It should be noted that a color not in the ascending color scale (pink) is used to indicate types of residential land uses (boarding and rooming houses) which are difficult to measure but where a relatively high density is probable.

COLOR LEGEND — LOT AREA PER FAMILY

Number Square Feet Per Family		Prismacolor
0 — 1,000 Sq. Ft.	☐	935 Black
1,000 — 2,000 Sq. Ft.	☐	946 Dark Brown
2,000 — 3,500 Sq. Ft.	☐	944 Terracotta
3,500 — 5,000 Sq. Ft.	☐	921 Vermilion Red
5,000 — 6,500 Sq. Ft.	☐	918 Orange
6,500 — 8,000 Sq. Ft.	☐	942 Yellow Ochre
8,000 — 12,000 Sq. Ft.	☐	917 Yellow Orange
12,000 — Over Sq. Ft.	☐	915 Lemon Yellow
Occupied by rooming and boarding houses	☐	929 Pink

SOURCE: Mapping for Planning Publication No. 101 Public Administration Service, Chicago, Ill.

TAX DELINQUENCY OF REAL PROPERTY

Knowledge of the length of time real property has been tax delinquent is often an important factor in planning for community development. The following scale, while generally applicable, may require some adjustment to meet local conditions where the effects of existing statutes of limitations or the powers of the governmental agency to foreclose and take title have direct relationship to the length of time the property can remain tax delinquent.

COLOR LEGEND FOR TAX DELINQUENCY OF REAL PROPERTY

Time Delinquent		Prismacolor
Over 0 to 2 years	☐	915 Lemon Yellow
Over 2 to 5 years	☐	939 Flesh
Over 5 to 10 years	☐	943 Burnt Ochre
Over 10 to 15 years	☐	946 Dark Brown

COLOR LEGEND FOR LAND VALUES

Values		Prismacolor
$ 0.00 — 0.04	☐	915 Lemon Yellow
0.05 — 0.08	☐	917 Yellow Orange
0.09 — 0.16	☐	942 Yellow Ochre
0.17 — 0.25	☐	912 Apple Green
0.26 — 0.55	☐	911 Olive Green
0.56 — 1.00	☐	909 Grass Green
1.01 — 2.00	☐	908 Dark Green
2.01 — 4.00	☐	901 Indigo Blue
4.01 — 8.00	☐	931 Purple
8.00 — Over	☐	924 Crimson Red
Not Assessed	☐	964 Light Gray

FOR COLOR REFER TO PRISMACOLOR PENCILS COLOR CHART ON PAGE 39.

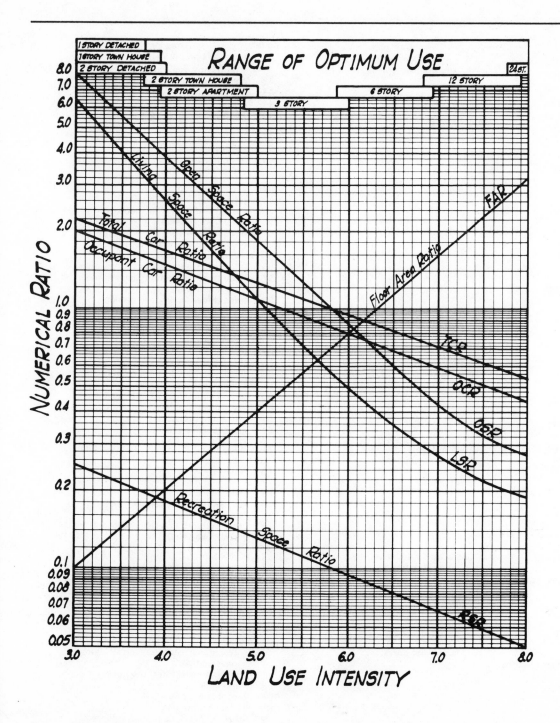

RANGE OF OPTIMUM USE

1 STORY DETACHED
1 STORY TOWN HOUSE
2 STORY DETACHED
2 STORY TOWN HOUSE
2 STORY APARTMENT
3 STORY
6 STORY
12 STORY
24 ST.

NUMERICAL RATIO

Living Space Ratio
Open Space Ratio
Total Car Ratio
Occupant Car Ratio
Floor Area Ratio
FAR
TCR
OCR
OSR
LSR
Recreation Space Ratio
RSR

LAND USE INTENSITY

SOURCE: Federal Housing Administration

The Land-use Intensity Standards show the ratios for Floor Area, Open Space, Livability Space and Car Storage, which apply at various levels of Land-use Intensity

GENERAL

The land-use intensity for a multifamily housing property shall be appropriate to the characteristics of the site and its location in the anticipated community pattern.

LAND-USE INTENSITY RATING FOR THE SITE

Rating Scale. In order to measure the land-use intensity of proposed sites and project plans, the FHA uses a scale of Land-use Intensity Ratings. These ratings correlate the land area, floor area, open space, livability space, recreation space, and car storage capacity of a project. Each full unit on the scale, for example from Land-use Intensity Rating 3.0 to Rating 4.0 (LIR 3.0 to LIR 4.0), equals a 100% increase in floor area as related to land area.

Rating For The Site. After analyzing the characteristics of a proposed site and its relation to the anticipated patterns of the community's land uses, long-term housing needs, and development timing, the FHA determines a Land-use Intensity Rating for the site. The FHA determination of the Land-use Intensity Rating is of utmost importance, as it represents the maximum land-use intensity acceptable to the FHA for the current use of the site for housing development. Information on how FHA makes a Land-use Intensity Rating of a site is issued separately in Land Planning Bulletin No. 7.

If a part of a site has a significantly different intensity from other parts of the site, a different Land-use Intensity Rating is determined by the FHA for each of the several parts. For example, a very large site in a transitional area abutting a community shopping center may have a high intensity portion abutting the shopping center and another portion with medium intensity of land-use more distant from the center. For such cases, the different intensity for each part of the site applies to that part alone, in substantially the same manner as it would if it were a separate site.

Number of Living Units. To determine the number of living units acceptable to FHA on any particular site, (a) obtain the FHA-assigned Land-use Intensity Rating for the site, and then (b) prepare project development programs and project designs properly related to the FHA-assigned rating of the site. The number of living units will depend upon the size of the units and the nature of the project design, as well as upon the Land-use Intensity Rating of the site.

1. GENERAL STRUCTURE

The standard system for coding land use activity is comprised of 9 one-digit categories (2 of which have been assigned to "manufacturing"), 67 two-digit categories, 294 three-digit categories, and 772 four-digit categories. The categories at the four-digit level identify land use activity in the greatest detail, and as the system is aggregated to the three-, two-, and one digit levels the categories become more generalized. The structure of this classification system, therefore, permits an agency to select the level of detail considered most appropriate for analysis and presentation of its data.

THE CATEGORIES AT THE TWO-DIGIT LEVEL OF GENERALIZATION ARE

Code	Category	Code	Category
1	Residential.	7	Cultural, entertainment, and recreational.
2 and 3	Manufacturing.		
4	Transportation, communication, and utilities.	8	Resource production and extraction.
5	Trade.	9	Undeveloped land and water areas.
6	Services.		

THE CATEGORIES AT THE TWO-DIGIT LEVEL OF GENERALIZATION ARE:

Code	Category	Code	Category
1	Residential.	11	Household units.
		12	Group quarters.
		13	Residential hotels.
		14	Mobile home parks or courts.
		15	Transient lodgings.
		19	Other residential.[1]
2	Manufacturing.	21	Food and kindred products—manufacturing.
		22	Textile mill products—manufacturing.
		23	Apparel and other finished products made from fabrics, leather, and similar materials—manufacturing.
		24	Lumber and wood products (except furniture)—manufacturing.
		25	Furniture and fixtures—manufacturing.
		26	Paper and allied products—manufacturing.
		27	Printing, publishing, and allied industries.
		28	Chemicals and allied products—manufacturing.
		29	Petroleum refining and related industries.
3	Manufacturing (continued).	31	Rubber and miscellaneous plastic products—manufacturing.
		32	Stone, clay, and glass products—manufacturing.
		33	Primary metal industries.
		34	Fabricated metal products—manufacturing.
		35	Professional, scientific, and controlling instruments; photographic and optical goods; watches and clocks—manufacturing.
		39	Miscellaneous manufacturing, NEC.
4	Transportation, communication, and utilities.	41	Railroad, rapid rail transit, and street railway transportation.
		42	Motor vehicle transportation.
		43	Aircraft transportation.
		44	Marine craft transportation.
		45	Highway and street right-of-way.
		46	Automobile parking.
		47	Communication.
		48	Utilities.
		49	Other transportation, communication, and utilities, NEC.
5	Trade.	51	Wholesale trade.
		52	Retail trade—building materials, hardware, and farm equipment.
		53	Retail trade—general merchandise.
		54	Retail trade—food.
		55	Retail trade—automotive, marine craft, aircraft, and accessories.
		56	Retail trade—apparel and accessories.
		57	Retail trade—furniture, home furnishings, and equipment.
		58	Retail trade—eating and drinking.
		59	Other retail trade, NEC.
6	Services.	61	Finance, insurance, and real estate services.
		62	Personal services.
		63	Business services.
		64	Repair services.
		65	Professional services.
		66	Contract construction services.
		67	Governmental services.
		68	Educational services.
		69	Miscellaneous services.
7	Cultural, entertainment, and recreational.	71	Cultural activities and nature exhibitions.
		72	Public assembly.
		73	Amusements.
		74	Recreational activities.
		75	Resorts and group camps.
		76	Parks
		79	Other cultural, entertainment, and recreational, NEC.
8	Resource production and extraction.	81	Agriculture.
		82	Agricultural related activities.
		83	Forestry activities and related services.
		84	Fishing activities and related services.
		85	Mining activities and related services.
		89	Other resource production and extraction, NEC.
9	Undeveloped land and water areas.	91	Undeveloped and unused land area (excluding noncommercial forest development).
		92	Noncommercial forest development.
		93	Water areas.
		94	Vacant floor area.
		95	Under construction.
		99	Other undeveloped land and water areas, NEC.

SOURCE: Standard Land USE Coding Manual Urban Renewal Administration, HHFA Bureau of Public Roads, Dept of Commerce Washington, D. C.

2. Purpose and Use of the Auxiliary Codes

There are certain land use activities that are generally found separated from, but are functionally and organizationally linked to other activities. For example:

a. A warehouse operated by a retail concern primarily for its own use and not for public storage;

b. A parking area operated by a manufacturing concern for use by its own employees and not for public parking;

c. An office performing management functions as part of a mining concern which has mines in several States.

These are all important space uses in themselves. However, they are also significant in their relationship to the parent activity they serve.

To provide a link between certain significant auxiliary functions and the parent activities they serve, a series of one-digit "Auxiliary" categories are provided. These should be used with the standard system for coding land use activity. The auxiliary categories are as follows:

Code	Auxiliary categories	Code	Auxiliary categories
0	Not an auxiliary.	5	Automobile parking.[5]
1	Central or administrative office.[4]	6	Motor vehicle garage (maintenance and/or storage of vehicles).
2	Sales office.		
3	Research and development.	7	Steam and power plant.
4	Warehousing and storage.	8–9	(Open codes).[6]

[4] Central or administrative offices are those offices engaged in general administrative, supervisory, purchasing, accounting, or other management functions.

[5] A minimum of 5,000 square feet or approximately 17 parking spaces is necessary before the area can be identified as auxiliary parking area.

[6] Planning agencies desiring to distinguish additional types of auxiliary categories other than those defined (e.g., recreational activities that are subsidiary to or serving another activity) should use open codes 8 and 9.

Codes 1 through 7 should be used when one of the listed activities can be determined to be subsidiary to or serving another activity. For example, if a research and development laboratory of a manufacturer of pharmaceutical preparations is located down the street from the actual manufacturing plant itself, the laboratory would be considered as an auxiliary and would be coded as follows:

Basic activity code	Auxiliary code	Combined activity code
(Pharmaceutical preparations—manufacturing)	(Research and development)	
2834	3	2834–3

An automobile parking area over 5,000 square feet which is an adjunct to an activity, e.g., a grocery store, and which is not used for other purposes in the same sense as a public parking area would be coded as follows:

Basic activity code	Auxiliary code	Combined activity code
(Groceries—retail)	(Automobile parking)	
5410	5	5410–5

The sales office of a manufacturing concern that is separately located from the actual factory, whether it be next door in a separate building, across the street, on the other side of the town, or in another city, is considered as serving the manufacturing process. Similarly, the permanent office of a construction company is considered as serving the construction activity. Therefore, these office activities would be coded as follows:

Basic activity code	Auxiliary code	Combined activity code
(Farm machinery and equipment—manufacturing)	(Sales office)	
3422	2	3422–2
(Building construction—general contractor services)	(Central or administrative office)	
6611	1	6611–1

With respect to wholesaling activity (code 51), those wholesalers without stock (i.e., they do not have a definite storage area set aside to maintain a volume of stock on hand) are also considered to be auxiliary, and they are identified by one of the auxiliary codes, accordingly. For example:

Basic activity code	Auxiliary code	Combined activity code
(Fruits and vegetables, fresh—wholesale)	(With stock)	
5147	0	5147–0
(Fruits and vegetables, fresh—wholesale)	(Sales office, without stock)	
5147	2	5147–2

On the other hand, an independent research, development, and testing laboratory would not be considered as an auxiliary activity, and it would be coded under its respective activity category, code 6391. Parking is coded in a similar way if it is public parking or parking serving more than one concern, such as the parking area of a shopping center. The following examples illustrate this:

Basic activity code	Auxiliary code	Combined activity code
(Research, development, and testing services)	(Not an auxiliary)	
6391	0	6391–0
(Automobile parking)	(Not an auxiliary)	
4600	0	4600–0

The preceding discussion and illustrations of the use of the auxiliary codes are centered primarily on the problem of preserving the linkage between related activities while at the same time identifying important land uses. It is recognized that for some planning studies, such as open space or recreation planning, the two open codes (8 and 9) may not provide sufficient categories for identifying recreational or open space uses which are a part of some larger activity. If it is found necessary or desirable to identify such related uses, a new and separate series of auxiliary codes should be developed to accommodate the needs of the special study, thereby preserving the original auxiliary codes for comparability over a period of time and between cities.

SOURCE: *Standard Land Use Coding Manual Urban Renewal Administration, HHFA Bureau of Public Roads, Dept of Commerce Washington, d. c.*

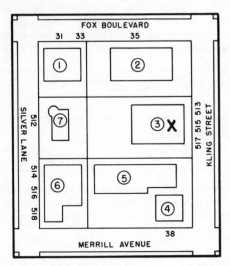

Block Plan

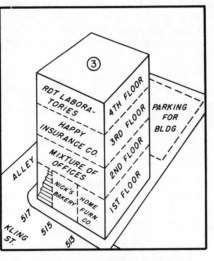

Parcel Schematic

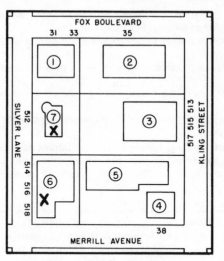

Block Plan

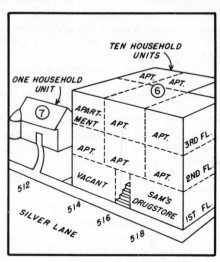

Parcel Schematic

Street No.	Street Name	Building No.	Floor	FIELD OPERATION — Description of Activity	Auxiliary?	Activity Ownership	Residential Structure Type	No. of Household Units	OFFICE OPERATION — Activity Code	Auxiliary Code	Ownership Code	Structure Code	No. of Household Units
1	2	3	4	5	6	7	8	9	5'	6'	7'	8'	9'
513	KLING ST.	3	1	HOME FURNITURE CO. (RETAIL)	—	PRIVATE	—	—	5711	0	20	—	—
515	KLING ST.	3	1	NICK'S BAKERY (WITH OVENS IN REAR)	—	PRIVATE	—	—	5461	0	20	—	—
517	KLING ST.	3	2	BIG TOWN REAL ESTATE CO. (REAL ESTATE AGENTS + BROKERS-OFFICES)	—	PRIVATE	—	—	6152	0	20	—	—
517	KLING ST.	3	2	PHYSICIAN'S OFFICE	—	PRIVATE	—	—	6511	0	20	—	—
517	KLING ST.	3	2	JONES CHEMICAL CORP. (SALES OFF. OF AGRICULTURAL FERTILIZER MFG.)	X	PRIVATE	—	—	2870	2	20	—	—
517	KLING ST.	3	2	AJAX CONSTRUCTION CO. (GENERAL OFFICES - HOME BUILDERS)	X	PRIVATE	—	—	6611	1	20	—	—
517	KLING ST.	3	2	LAW FIRM (OFFICES)	—	PRIVATE	—	—	6520	0	20	—	—
517	KLING ST.	3	3	HAPPY INSURANCE CO. (REGIONAL OFFICE OF COMPANY)	X	PRIVATE	—	—	6141	1	20	—	—
517	KLING ST.	3	4	RDT LABORATORIES (DEVELOPMENT LABORATORIES FOR RDT INDUSTRIES - RADIO TRANSMITTING EQUIPMENT MFG.)	X	PRIVATE	—	—	3436	3	20	—	—
513-517	KLING ST.	—	—	PARKING FOR VISITORS + EMPLOYEES IN THE REAR (20 SPACES)	—	PRIVATE	—	—	4600	0	20	—	—

Example of Land Use Entries on a Field Listing Form

Street No.	Street Name	Building No.	Floor	FIELD OPERATION — Description of Activity	Auxiliary?	Activity Ownership	Residential Structure Type	No. of Household Units	OFFICE OPERATION — Activity Code	Auxiliary Code	Ownership Code	Structure Code	No. of Household Units
1	2	3	4	5	6	7	8	9	5'	6'	7'	8'	9'
518	SILVER LANE	6	1	SAM'S DRUG STORE	—	PRIVATE	—	—	5910	0	20	—	—
516	SILVER LANE	6	2+3	HOUSEHOLD UNITS	—	PRIVATE	WALK-UP APART.	10	1100	0	20	31	10
514	SILVER LANE	6	1	VACANT FLOOR AREA	—	—	—	—	9400	0	—	—	—
512	SILVER LANE	7	1	HOUSEHOLD UNITS	—	PRIVATE	SINGLE UNIT - DETACHED	1	1100	0	20	11	01

Example of Land Use Entries on a Field Listing Form

SOURCE: Standard Land Use Coding Manual Urban Renewal Administration, HHFA Bureau of Public Roads, Dept. of Commerce Washington, D. C.

LAND USE AND ZONING SYMBOLS

Color	Black and white	
White		Vacant Land
Lemon yellow		Single Family Dwelling
Golden yellow		Two Family Dwelling
Brown		Multiple-Dwelling, Apartments, Rooming and BOARDING Houses
Light red		Commerical Building—Local Retail
Dark red		Commerical Building—Central
Yellow Red		Commerical Building—First Floor With Residence Above
Brown Red		Commerical Building—First Floor With Apartments Above
Purple Red		Commerical Building—First Floor With Industry Above
Light purple		Industry—Light
Dark purple		Industry—Heavy
Black		Railroad Property

SYMBOLS FOR TYPES OF STRUCTURE

	Frame Construction
	Brick Veneer Solid Brick
	Concrete Block Solid Concrete
	Stone Veneer Solid Stone
	Stucco
	Miscellaneous— Metal, Panels, etc.

POPULATION

MATHEMATICAL PROJECTIONS

1. The simplest mathematical procedure is to compute the average numerical population change per decade in the past, and then to project this numerical increase into the future. This is called an "arithmetical projection," and it should produce the same result as a straight-line graphic projection on plain coordinate paper.

To illustrate, from 1900 to 1950 the population of California increased an average of 1,823,000 per decade; assuming the same numerical increase, the population, which was 10,586,000 in 1950, would be 12,409,000 in 1960, and 14,232,000 in 1970.

2. Another simple method is to compute the average rate of population change for the area per decade in the past, and then project this average rate, or percent change, into the future. This is called a "geometric projection," and corresponds to a graphic projection on semi-logarithmic paper.

For example, the average rate of increase per decade of the population of California during 1900–50 was approximately 49 percent. Projecting this average rate gives a population of 15,773,000 in 1960, and 23,502,000 in 1970.

3. A more refined procedure is to plot the curve of past population growth on a semi-logarithmic scale and then to develop by the method of least squares an exponential equation that best fits the past curve. From this equation the size of the population in future years can readily be compute

4. Another technique is to fit some other mathematical curve, such as the "logistic" curve, to the curve of past population growth of the area, and then to determine the size of the future population therefrom.

The logistic curve is based on a "law of growth in a limited area" propounded and mathematically developed by P. F. Verhulst in 1838. It is shaped like an elongated and flattened letter S.

The logistic curve implies a constantly decreasing rate of increase per amount of population per unit of time after the initial increment of increase. Its validity for area subject to net in-migration that might accelerate for a time the rate of increase relative to the size of the population, is questionable.

The advantage of graphic or mathematical projections is that they are the easiest to make. They generally are better suited to areas which have had

SOURCE: Van Beuren Stanbery, Better Population
Forecasting for Areas and Communities,
U.S. Dept of Commerce, Wash. D. C.

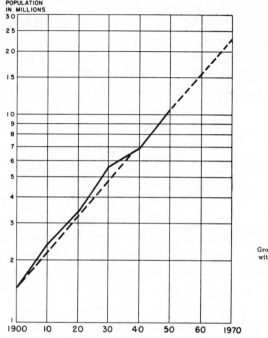

Growth of California population, 1900–1950, with geometrical projection to 1970.

relatively constant changes per decade in the size of their populations, and for which no marked changes from past trends appear likely, than for areas subject to rapid or erratic fluctuations in population. Obviously, they should be more dependable for short-term projections of 5 to 10 years, than for longer projections.

The weakness of such projections is that they are founded on the assumption that the factors and conditions which produced population growth or decline in the area in the past will continue unchanged and will have the same effects in the future, or that they are derived from an assumed curve of population growth. In view of the changes that have recently taken place in fertility, mortality, and migration trends, projections of this kind are becoming less reliable.

As indicated before, graphic and mathematical projections are useful, however, as rough checks on those obtained by other methods. In the absence of other data and analyses, an arithmetical projection might be used as a probable minimum forecast, and a geometrical projection as a maximum figure.

PROJECTIONS OF NET MIGRATION AND OF NATURAL INCREASE

Population forecasts are frequently obtained by making separate but related projections of net migration and of natural increase and adding the figures. Because migration affects the number of births and deaths in an area, projections of net migration are made before those for natural increase.

MIGRATION PROJECTIONS

Logically founded projections of net migration can be developed from study of net migration in the area in the past and the conditions causing people to more into or out of it.

The direction and approximate volume and composition of net migration into or out of the area during recent decades are first determined.

Changes that have occurred, or appear likely to occur, in the conditions and relationships affecting migration in the area are considered. Finally, the probable effects of such changes on net migration during the forecast period are reviewed and appraised.

With these analyses and appraisals, it is usually possible to develop reasonable high and low projections for net migration. At least, they provide some indication whether net migration during the next decade may be expected to be about the same as, or larger or smaller than, that of the preceding decade.

NATURAL INCREASE PROJECTIONS

Projections of natural increase are made by a variety of techniques. Some of them produce approximate figures while others give more precise results. Principal factors to be considered are the racial, sex, and age composition of the area population, and its future birth and death rates.

The most precise, but also the most laborious, procedure is the "cohort-survival" technique. Briefly, this is as follows:

The survivors of the resident population of each sex on the forecast date are first computed for each 5-year or 10-year age group from age-specific mortality tables and trends.

The total net migration projected for the area to the forecast date is then distributed by sex and by age, and added to, or subtracted from, the figures for the surviving residents in the corresponding age groups. It should be noted that the sex and age characteristics of the migrant population are usually quite different from those of the resident populations of the areas from which they move or in which they settle. The sex and age distribution of net migrations into or out of the particular area or its State during recent decades therefore should be carefully analyzed and used as guides in estimating the sex and age distribution of the projected net migration.

Birth rates by age of mother during the forecast period are then projected or assumed. The expected number of births is then obtained by multiplying the assumed age-specific birth rates by the average number of women in each 5-year age group within the child-bearing ages during the forecast period. This average figure is usually obtained by adding the number of women at the beginning and end of the forecast period in each 5-year age group, and dividing by two. The survivors of those births on the forecast date are then computed by using death rates of young children. As the number of male births usually exceeds the number of female births in the ratio of about 105 or 106 to 100, this should be taken into account in precise calculations.

The cohort-survival procedure does not directly measure natural increase itself. Instead, the population projection is obtained by adding the survivors of the resident population, the expected net migration, and the survivors of babies born to former residents and to newcomers during the period. If the net migration is outward, the estimate of births is reduced because of the smaller average number of women in the child bearing ages. Since most of the migrants are between ages 20 45 years, when they move, net out-migration tends to reduce the crude birth rate also. Further refinements, such as allowances for births to in-migrant women who die during the period, are sometimes included in the calculations.

This is being relied on more and more for population projections. For most areas and communities, it should yield better forecasts than other methods, particularly for projections not exceeding two decades.

This method takes into account the size of the area's population at the beginning of the forecast period, and the effects of a population of that size on future births, deaths, and migration. Other methods do not provide as accurate measures of the effects of changes in the size of the population from decade to decade.

SOURCE: Van Beuren Stanbery, *Better Population Forecasting for Areas and Communities*, U.S. Dept of Commerce, Wash. D. C.

PROJECTIONS BASED ON RELATIONSHIPS OF POPULATION GROWTH IN AN AREA TO GROWTH IN OTHER AREAS

Population growth in an area or community is usually more closely related to, or affected by, economic and population changes in the economic region or State in which it lies. Future population changes in those larger areas may have an important influence on growth or decline in the smaller area. Hence, past relationships between population growth in an area or community and that of its economic region or State are valuable guides for projection of the local population. If logically-founded population projections for the Nation, State or economic region are available, projections for the area or community can be derived directly therefrom.

STATISTICAL PROJECTIONS BASED ON RELATIVE RATES OF PAST GROWTH

Statistical projections of the relationships of population growth in a particular area to growth in other areas can be made in various ways. The simplest procedure is to compute the percentages that the population of the particular area represented of the population of its economic region, its State, and the Nation in past census years, and plot them on graph paper. The line or curve of these percentages can then be projected to the forecast date by techniques similar to those for projections of population growth curves described for mathematical methods.

Applying the projected percentages to population projection figures for the Nation, the State, or the economic region will produce numerical projections of the population of the area for applicable forecast dates. If projections for the larger areas are not available, or are considered unreliable, the forecaster can make his own projections for them.

Purely statistical projections made by this method should be used with caution. Former relationships between population growth in the area under consideration and that in other areas may suddenly change. Moreover, the economic and social forces that cause births and migration to increase, or decline, nationally exert differing effects at different times on particular areas. Some areas have shown fairly consistent trends between their population growth and that of their region, State, or the Nation. Others have shown divergent or erratic relationships to population changes in the larger areas. For these, this method appears less valid than for areas exhibiting more consistent trends. A recent evaluation of this method finds it of limited value for forecasting the populations of isolated cities.

SOURCE: Van Beuren Stanbery, Better Population
Forecasting for Areas and Communities.
U.S. Dept of Commerce, Wash. D. C.

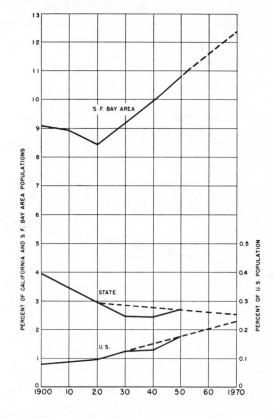

Santa Clara county population as a percent of population of San Francisco Bay area, of California, and of the United States, 1900-1950, with illustrative projections to 1970.

On the other hand, these procedures have several advantages over method I. The factors affecting population growth in the area or community may be more clearly visualized and appraised with a knowledge of its past relationships to growth in its economic region, State, and the Nation than if these relationships have not been studied. It may be easier to foresee and evaluate the effects of new conditions that may change past relationships than it would be to appraise the prospects for future growth in the area irrespective of the rate of growth in other areas. Population projections for the Nation and for States have generally been closer to the mark than those for smaller areas or communities. By trying in their projections with those for the larger area, the range for error may be lessened.

Projections made by this method are also valuable as guides and checks in establishing projections developed by other procedures.

POPULATION BY AGE GROUPS: 1900 1980

By 1980, the population of the United States may reach 245 million, with the age group under 5 increasing as a proportion of the total, and a somewhat smaller increase in the percentage of persons aged 65 and over.

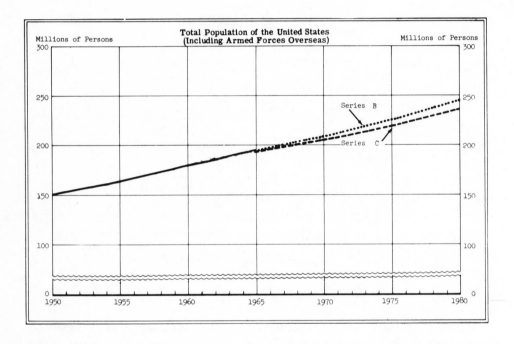

SOURCE: *Trends—1965 U. S. Dept. of Health, Education, and Welfare, Washington, D. C.*

Year[1] (as of July 1)	Population of the United States including armed forces overseas by age group											Population (millions)	
	Millions						Percent					Total excluding armed forces overseas[2]	Total civilian
	All ages	0-4	5-19	20-44	45-64	65+	0-4	5-19	20-44	45-64	65+		
1900	76.1	9.2	24.5	28.8	10.5	3.1	12.1	32.1	37.9	13.8	4.1	-	-
1910	92.4	10.7	28.0	36.2	13.6	4.0	11.5	30.3	39.1	14.7	4.3	-	-
1920	106.5	11.6	31.7	41.0	17.1	4.9	10.9	29.8	38.5	16.1	4.6	-	-
1930	123.1	11.4	36.2	47.2	21.6	6.7	9.2	29.4	38.4	17.5	5.4	-	-
1935	127.3	10.2	36.0	49.3	23.9	7.8	8.0	28.3	38.7	18.8	6.1	-	-
1940	132.1	10.6	34.7	51.6	26.2	9.0	8.0	26.3	39.0	19.9	6.8	132.0	131.7
1945	139.9	13.0	33.3	54.6	28.6	10.5	9.3	23.8	39.0	20.5	7.5	-	-
1950	151.7	16.3	35.1	57.1	30.8	12.3	10.7	23.1	37.6	20.3	8.1	151.2	150.2
1951	154.3	17.2	35.6	57.4	31.3	12.8	11.1	23.1	37.2	20.3	8.3	153.3	151.0
1952	156.9	17.7	37.2	57.6	31.8	13.2	11.0	23.7	36.7	20.3	8.4	155.7	153.3
1953	159.6	17.5	38.5	57.6	32.2	13.6	11.0	24.1	36.1	20.2	8.5	158.2	156.0
1954	162.4	17.9	40.0	57.7	32.8	14.1	11.0	24.6	35.5	20.2	8.7	161.2	159.1
1955	165.3	18.4	41.3	57.7	33.3	14.6	11.1	25.0	34.9	20.1	8.8	164.3	162.3
1956	168.2	18.9	42.7	57.8	33.9	15.0	11.2	25.4	34.4	20.2	8.9	167.3	165.4
1957	171.3	19.4	44.3	57.8	34.4	15.4	11.3	25.9	33.7	20.1	9.0	170.4	168.4
1958	174.2	19.7	45.8	57.8	35.0	15.8	11.3	26.3	33.2	20.1	9.1	173.3	171.5
1959	177.3	20.1	47.3	58.0	35.7	16.2	11.3	26.7	32.7	20.1	9.1	176.5	174.7
1960	180.7	20.3	49.2	58.3	36.2	16.7	11.3	27.2	32.3	20.0	9.2	180.0	178.2
1960[3]	180.0	20.3	48.8	58.2	36.1	16.6	11.3	27.1	32.4	20.0	9.2	179.3	177.5
1961	183.8	20.7	50.8	58.5	36.8	17.1	11.3	27.7	31.8	20.0	9.3	183.0	181.1
1962	186.7	20.7	52.4	58.9	37.2	17.4	11.1	28.1	31.6	19.9	9.3	185.8	183.7
1963	189.4	20.8	53.7	59.6	37.8	17.5	11.0	28.4	31.5	20.0	9.3	188.5	186.5
1964	192.1	20.7	55.1	60.1	38.5	17.9	10.8	28.7	31.3	20.0	9.3	191.3	189.3
1965	194.6	20.4	56.5	60.5	39.0	18.2	10.5	29.0	31.1	20.0	9.4	193.8	191.9
PROJECTIONS[4]													
1970: B	209.0	22.0	60.2	65.3	41.9	19.6	10.5	28.8	31.3	20.0	9.4		
1970: C	206.1	19.7	59.7	65.3	41.9	19.6	9.5	29.0	31.7	20.3	9.5		
1975: B	225.9	25.2	63.4	72.7	43.2	21.2	11.2	28.1	32.2	19.2	9.4		
1975: C	220.1	22.3	60.6	72.7	43.2	21.2	10.1	27.5	33.0	19.7	9.6		
1980: B	245.3	28.3	68.2	82.4	43.0	23.1	11.6	27.8	33.6	17.6	9.4		
1980: C	236.5	25.2	62.5	82.4	43.0	23.1	10.7	26.4	34.8	18.3	9.8		

SOURCE: *U. S. Department of Commerce, Bureau of the Census: Current Population Reports, Population Estimates, eries P-25. 1. Includes Alaska beginning with 1959 (total population only in that year) and Hawaii with 1960. 2. Armed forces overseas are excluded for the years 1900 1946 but are included thereafter. 3. Census of April 1, 1960. 4. Series P-25, No. 279, "Projections of the Population of the United States by Age and Sex to 1985" dated Feb. 4, 1964, contains first major Census Bureau revision of projections, since 1958 and is the first project fertility on the basis of cumulative age-specific fertility rates for birth cohorts of women (born in the same year). The component method used also takes into account a) slight declines in age-sex specific death rates and b) a small constant volume of net immigration (300,000 annually) consistent with recent experience. The series A, B, C and D Census Bureau projections relating to the 50 States and the District of Columbia and including Armed Forces abroad are based on current estimates of the population by age and sex for July 1, 1963 (P-25 No. 275) and take into account the 1960 census.*

POPULATION: BY SEX AND COLOR

The total population of the United States in 1964 exceeded 192 million, an increase of 2.7 million over 1963.

Since 1947, women have represented a steadily larger proportion of the population than men, mainly due to their lower death rate. The nonwhite population—nearly 12 percent of the total in 1964—increased 9 percent between 1960 and 1964, as compared with 6 percent for the white population.

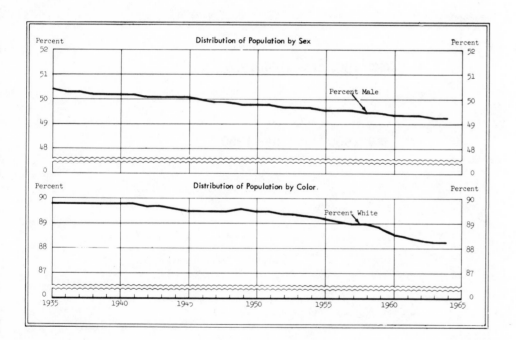

(In millions)

Year [1] (as of July 1)	Total population			Total population by sex and color [2]					
	Including Armed Forces overseas	Residing in United States	Civilian population	Male	Female	Percent male	White	Nonwhite	Percent white
1900	-	76.1	-	38.9	37.2	51.1	66.9	9.2	87.9
1910	-	92.4	-	47.6	44.9	51.5	82.1	10.3	88.9
1920	-	106.5	-	54.3	52.2	51.0	95.5	11.0	89.7
1930	123.2	123.1	122.9	62.3	60.8	50.6	110.6	12.5	89.8
1935	127.4	127.3	127.1	64.1	63.1	50.4	114.3	12.9	89.8
1940	132.1	132.0	131.7	66.4	65.8	50.2	118.6	13.5	89.8
1942	134.9	133.9	130.9	67.6	67.3	50.1	121.0	13.9	89.7
1943	136.7	134.2	127.5	68.5	68.2	50.1	122.6	14.1	89.7
1944	138.4	132.9	126.7	69.4	69.0	50.1	124.0	14.4	89.6
1945	139.9	132.5	127.6	70.0	69.9	50.1	125.3	14.7	89.5
1946	141.4	140.1	138.4	70.6	70.8	50.0	126.6	14.8	89.5
1947	144.1	143.4	142.6	71.9	72.2	49.9	129.1	15.1	89.5
1948	146.6	146.1	145.2	73.1	73.5	49.9	131.3	15.3	89.5
1949	149.2	148.7	147.6	74.3	74.9	49.8	133.6	15.6	89.6
1950	151.7	151.2	150.2	75.5	76.2	49.8	135.8	15.9	89.5
1951	154.4	153.3	151.0	76.8	77.5	49.8	138.1	16.2	89.5
1952	156.9	155.7	153.3	78.1	78.9	49.7	140.4	16.6	89.4
1953	159.6	158.2	156.6	79.3	80.3	49.7	142.6	17.0	89.4
1954	162.4	161.2	159.1	80.6	81.8	49.7	145.0	17.4	89.3
1955	165.3	164.3	162.3	82.0	83.3	49.6	147.4	17.8	89.2
1956	168.2	167.3	165.4	83.4	84.8	49.6	149.9	18.3	89.1
1957	171.3	170.4	168.4	84.9	86.4	49.6	152.5	18.8	89.0
1958	174.2	173.3	171.5	86.2	87.9	49.5	154.9	19.2	89.0
1959	177.3	176.5	174.7	87.6	89.5	49.5	157.5	19.8	88.9
1960	180.7	180.0	178.2	89.3	91.4	49.4	160.0	20.7	88.6
1961	183.8	183.0	181.1	90.8	93.0	49.4	162.6	21.2	88.5
1962	186.7	186.8	183.7	92.2	94.5	49.4	165.0	21.7	88.4
1963	189.4	186.5	186.5	93.5	96.0	49.4	167.2	22.2	88.3
1964	192.1	191.3	189.3	94.7	97.4	49.3	169.4	22.7	88.2

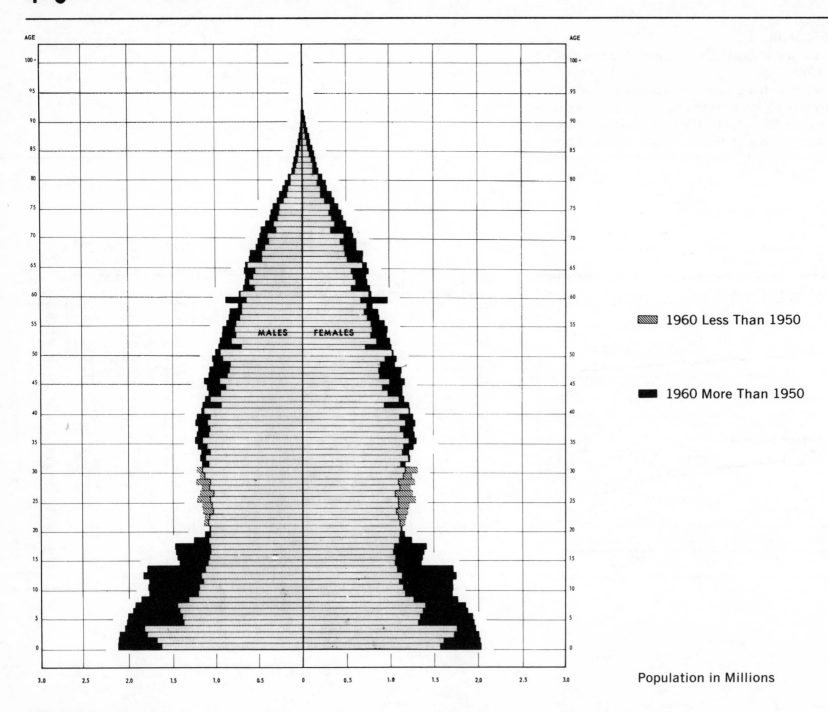

AGE

AGE

MALES   FEMALES

▨ 1960 Less Than 1950

■ 1960 More Than 1950

Population in Millions

3.0   2.5   2.0   1.5   1.0   0.5   0   0.5   1.0   1.5   2.0   2.5   3.0

SOURCE: U.S. Dept of Commerce
Bureau of the Census

56

POPULATION BY EDUCATIONAL AGE GROUPS: 1900 1985

The elementary and secondary school-age population (5 17) totaled 50.1 million as of July 1, 1965, an increase of almost 36 percent since 1955. Bureau of the Census projections indicate that the school age population will increase less rapidly over the next 20 years than during the previous two decades. The proportion of the population in the age group 5 17 will decline slightly from the present ratio of one in four. Nevertheless, by 1985, there will be nearly 60 million children and youth aged 5 17.

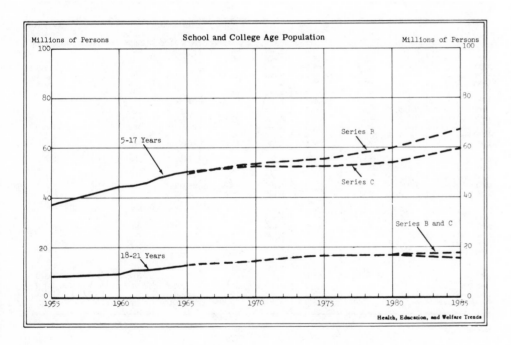

SOURCE: Trends—1965 U. S. Dept of Health, Education, and Welfare, Washington, D. C.

(In millions)

Year (as of July 1)	Total population[1]	Educational age groups[2]					18-21	22-24	5-17 age group as percent of total population
		Under 5		5-17					
		Adjusted[3]	Unadjusted	5-13	14-17	Total			
1900........	76.1	-	9.2	15.4	6.1	21.5	6.0	4.4	28.3
1910........	92.4	-	10.7	17.1	7.3	24.4	7.3	5.4	26.4
1920........	106.5	-	11.6	20.1	7.9	28.0	7.4	5.5	26.3
1930........	123.2	12.1	11.4	22.3	9.4	31.7	9.0	6.4	25.7
1935........	127.4	11.0	10.2	21.7	9.7	31.4	9.2	6.7	24.6
1940........	132.1	11.4	10.6	19.9	9.8	29.7	9.7	6.9	22.5
1945........	139.9	13.8	13.0	19.4	9.1	28.5	9.6	7.2	20.4
1950........	151.7	17.1	16.3	22.3	8.4	30.7	8.9	7.1	20.2
1955........	165.1	19.1	18.4	27.7	9.2	36.9	8.5	6.5	22.6
1960........	180.7	-	20.3	33.0	11.1	44.1	9.6	6.6	24.4
1961........	183.8	-	20.6	33.3	12.0	45.3	10.2	6.7	24.7
1962........	198.7	-	20.7	33.9	12.8	46.7	10.7	6.8	25.0
1963........	189.4	-	20.7	34.5	13.5	48.0	11.1	7.0	25.4
1964........	192.1	-	20.7	35.3	14.2	49.5	11.3		20.5
1965........	194.6		20.4	36.0	14.1	50.1	12.1		25.8
PROJECTIONS[4]									
1970: B	209.0	-	22.0	37.3	15.7	53.0	14.3	10.1	25.3
C	206.1	-	19.7	36.8	15.7	52.4	14.3	10.1	25.4
1975: B	225.9	-	25.2	38.6	16.7	55.3	16.0	11.2	24.5
C	220.1	-	22.3	35.8	16.7	52.4	16.0	11.2	23.8
1980: B	245.3	-	28.3	43.1	16.7	59.7	16.8	12.3	24.4
C	236.5	-	25.2	38.2	15.8	54.0	16.8	12.3	22.8
1985: B	266.3	-	30.5	48.8	18.3	67.2	17.0	12.7	25.2
C	254.0	-	27.0	43.4	16.3	59.2	15.6	12.7	23.5

SOURCE: U. S. Dept. of Commerce, Bureau of the Census: Current Population Reports: Population Estimates; Series P-25 and special tabulations supplied to the Office of Education by the Bureau of the Census. 1. For the years—1900 1920 totals are limited to the population residing in the United States; figures for subsequent years are for the total population including armed forces abroad. 2. The age groups correspond to the preschool (under), elementary school (6 13) high school groups. 3. Adjusted for net census undercount: 4. Series P.25, No. 279 "Projections of the Population of the U. S. by age and sex to 1985" dated Feb. 4, 1964 contains the first major Census Bureau revision of projections since 1958 and is the first to project fertility on the basis of cumulative age-specific fertility rates for birth cohorts of women (born in the same year). The component method used also takes into account: a) slight declines in age-sex specific death rates and b) a small constant volume of net immigration (300,000 annually) consistent with recent experience. The series A, B, C and D Census Bureau projections, relating to the 50 States and the District of Columbia and including Armed Forces abroad, are based on current estimates of t population by age and sex for uly 1, 1963 (P-25, No. 276) and take into account the 1960 census.

BIRTHS

The number of live births in 1965 (3.8 million) fell below four million for the first time since 1953. Both the 1965 fertility rate (at 96.7 births per 1,000 women 15 44 years) and the birth rate (19.4 births per 1,000 population) were more than 8 percent below those of the previous year.

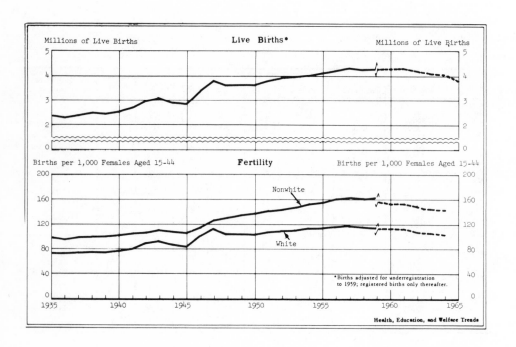

Health, Education, and Welfare Trends

SOURCE: *Trends—1965 U. S. Dept. of Health, Education, and Welfare, Washington, D. C.*

Year [1]	Total live births [2]			White live births [2]			Nonwhite live births [2]		
	Number (000's)	Per 1,000 population	Per 1,000 females aged 15-44	Number (000's)	Per 1,000 population	Per 1,000 females aged 15-44	Number (000's)	Per 1,000 population	Per 1,000 females aged 15-44
1910	2,777	30.1	126.8	2,401	29.2	123.8	-	-	-
1920	2,950	27.7	117.9	2,566	26.9	115.4	383	35.0	137.5
1930	2,618	21.3	89.2	2,274	20.6	87.1	344	27.5	105.9
1935	2,377	18.7	77.2	2,042	17.9	74.5	334	25.8	98.4
1940	2,559	19.4	79.9	2,199	18.6	77.1	360	26.7	102.4
1942	2,989	22.2	91.5	2,605	21.5	89.5	384	27.7	107.6
1944	2,939	21.2	88.8	2,545	20.5	86.3	394	27.4	108.5
1945	2,858	20.4	85.9	2,471	19.7	83.4	388	26.5	106.0
1946	3,411	24.1	101.9	2,990	23.6	100.4	420	28.4	113.9
1947	3,817	26.6	113.3	3,347	26.1	111.8	469	31.2	125.9
1948	3,637	24.9	107.3	3,141	24.0	104.3	495	32.4	131.6
1949	3,649	24.5	107.1	3,136	23.6	103.6	513	33.0	135.1
1950	3,632	24.1	106.2	3,108	23.0	102.3	524	33.3	137.3
1951	3,823	24.9	111.5	3,277	23.9	107.7	546	33.8	142.1
1952	3,913	25.1	113.9	3,358	24.1	110.1	555	33.6	143.3
1953	3,965	25.1	115.2	3,389	24.0	111.0	575	34.1	147.3
1954	4,078	25.3	118.1	3,475	24.2	113.6	603	34.9	153.2
1955	4,104	25.0	118.5	3,488	23.8	113.8	617	34.7	155.3
1956	4,218	25.2	121.2	3,573	24.0	116.0	645	35.4	160.9
1957	4,308	25.3	122.9	3,648	24.0	117.7	660	35.3	163.0
1958	4,255	24.5	120.2	3,598	23.3	114.9	657	34.3	160.5
1959 (Adj.)...	4,295	24.3	120.2	3,622	23.1	114.6	673	34.2	162.2
1959 (Reg.)...	4,245	24.0	118.8	3,597	22.9	113.8	647	32.8	155.9
1960	4,258	23.7	118.0	3,601	22.7	113.2	657	32.1	153.6
1961	4,268	23.3	117.2	3,601	22.2	112.2	667	31.6	153.5
1962 [3]	4,167	22.4	112.1	3,394	21.4	107.5	642	30.5	148.7
1963 [3]	4,098	21.7	108.4	3,326	20.7	103.7	639	29.7	144.8
1964 [3]	4,027	21.0	104.8	3,359	20.0	99.8	658	29.2	141.5
1965	3,767	19.4	96.7						

SOURCE: *U. S. Dept. of Health, Education and Welfare; Public Health Service, National Vital Statistics Division: annual Vital Statistics of the United States and Monthly Vital Statistics Report. 1. Data include Alaska beginning with 1959 and Hawaii beginning with 1960. 2. Adjusted for underregistration through 1958: both adjusted and registered for 1959; registered only beginning with 1960. For years prior to 1933 included adjustments for States not in the birth-registration area. Rates are based on population residing in area, enumerated as of April 1 for the census years 1940, 1950 and 1960 and estimated as of July 1 for other years. Beginning with 1951, data are based on a 50 percent sample of births. 3. White non-white data exclude New Jersey, which did not require reporting of the item.*

DEATHS BY AGE GROUPS

The overall death rate (9.4 per 1,000 population) was the same in 1965 as in 1964. There was a slight decrease in death rates in 1965 for persons under age 24 and for those in the 45 to 64 age group.

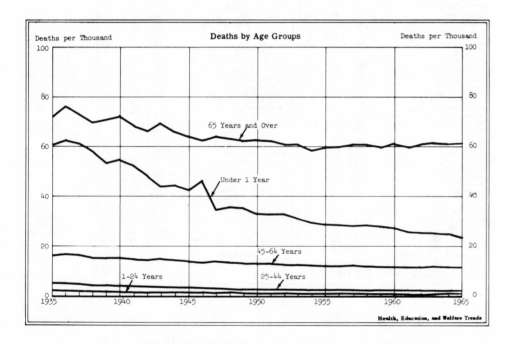

Year	Number of deaths (000's)[1]	Deaths per 1,000 population in age group[2]						
		All ages		Age group in years				
		Unadjusted	Age adjusted[3]	Under 1	1-24	25-44	45-64	65+
1910	697[4]	14.7	15.8	131.8	5.6	7.6	18.4	80.6
1920	1,118[4]	13.0	14.2	92.3	4.8	7.4	16.6	77.5
1930	1,327[4]	11.3	12.5	69.0	3.0	5.7	16.8	73.7
1940	1,417	10.8	10.8	54.9	1.8	4.0	15.3	72.2
1943	1,460	10.9	10.2	44.0	1.7	3.7	14.9	69.5
1944	1,411	10.6	9.7	44.2	1.6	3.6	14.3	65.9
1945	1,402	10.6	9.5	42.5	1.5	3.6	14.1	64.0
1946	1,396	10.0	9.1	46.3	1.4	3.2	13.7	62.4
1947	1,445	10.1	9.0	34.5	1.2	3.0	13.9	64.1
1948	1,444	9.9	8.8	35.7	1.2	2.9	13.6	63.2
1949	1,444	9.7	8.5	35.2	1.1	2.7	13.3	62.2
1950	1,452	9.6	8.4	33.0	1.0	2.6	13.1	62.7
1951	1,482	9.7	8.3	32.3	1.0	2.6	13.0	61.7
1952	1,497	9.6	8.1	32.1	1.0	2.5	12.8	60.7
1953	1,518	9.6	8.0	30.8	.9	2.4	12.6	61.0
1954	1,481	9.2	7.6	29.3	.9	2.3	12.0	58.3
1955	1,529	9.3	7.7	28.5	.8	2.3	11.8	59.7
1956	1,564	9.4	7.6	28.2	.8	2.2	11.8	59.9
1957	1,633	9.6	7.8	28.0	.8	2.3	12.1	61.1
1958	1,648	9.5	7.7	28.1	.8	2.2	11.8	60.8
1959	1,657	9.4	7.5	27.5	.8	2.2	11.6	59.7
1960	1,712	9.5	7.6	27.0	.8	2.2	11.8	61.0
1961	1,702	9.3	7.3	25.3	.7	2.2	11.4	59.5
1962	1,757	9.5	7.5	25.3	.7	2.3	11.5	61.0
1963	1,813	9.6	7.6	25.4	.8	2.3	11.7	62.4
1964	1,801	9.4		24.3	.8	2.3	11.5	60.4
1965(p)	1,825	9.4	–	23.5	.7	2.3	11.5	61.1

SOURCE: U. S. Department of Health, Education and Welfare: Public Health Service, National Vital Statistics Division, annual Vital Statistics of the United States and Monthly Vital Statistics Report. 1. Includes only deaths occurring within the death registration area which by 1933 embraced the entire continental United States. Includes Alaska beginning with 1959, and Hawaii 1960. Excludes fetal deaths. 2. Rates are bas d on population residing in area, enumerated as of April 1, for 1940, 1950, and 1960 and estimated as of July 1 for other years. 3. The age-adjusted death rate takes into account changes in the age composition of the population. For a given year the age-adjusted death rate is that rate which would have resulted if the mortality of each age group during the given year had been experienced by a population with a standard age distribution—in this case the age distribution that prevailed on April 1, 1940. 4. Number of deaths too low because of incompleteness of the registration area and underregistration of deaths in existing area. Correcting for these factors, Thompson and Whelpton in Population Trends in the United States estimated the number of deaths (exclusive of deaths among armed forces overseas) to be 1,424,000 in 1910; 1,433,000 in 1920; and 1,439,000 in 1930.

POPULATION—STANDARD METROPOLITAN STATISTICAL AREAS: 1960

[Areas as defined November 15, 1965. Minus sign (−) denotes decrease. For definition of standard metropolitan statistical area, see text, p. 1. This list of areas is based on *Standard Metropolitan Statistical Areas, 1964* (as amended up to November 15, 1965), issued by the Executive Office of the President, Bureau of the Budget. For area components, see source. Rank based on unrounded figures]

STANDARD METROPOLITAN STATISTICAL AREA	1960 (1,000)	Rank	Percent change, 1950 to 1960
United States (224 areas)	116,969	(X)	26.5
In central cities	58,843	(X)	11.1
Outside central cities	58,126	(X)	47.2
Abilene, Tex	120	183	40.8
Akron, Ohio	605	47	27.7
Albany, Ga	76	217	73.5
Albany-Schenectady-Troy, N.Y.	658	41	11.6
Albuquerque, N. Mex	262	102	80.0
Allentown-Bethlehem-Easton, Pa.-N.J.	492	57	12.4
Altoona, Pa	137	168	−1.6
Amarillo, Tex	149	155	71.6
Anaheim-Santa Ana-Garden Grove, Calif	704	38	225.6
Anderson, Ind	126	180	21.1
Ann Arbor, Mich	172	138	28.1
Asheville, N.C.	130	175	4.6
Atlanta, Ga	1,017	24	39.9
Atlantic City, N.J.	161	147	21.5
Augusta, Ga.-S.C.	217	123	33.7
Austin, Tex	212	124	31.8
Bakersfield, Calif	292	87	27.9
Baltimore, Md	1,727	12	22.9
Baton Rouge, La.	230	115	45.4
Bay City, Mich	107	192	21.0
Beaumont-Port Arthur, Tex.	306	85	29.9
Billings, Mont	79	215	41.4
Binghamton, N.Y.-Pa.	284	89	14.9
Birmingham, Ala.	635	43	13.6
Bloomington-Normal, Ill.	84	212	9.5
Boise City, Idaho	93	201	32.3
Boston, Mass.	2,595	7	7.5
Bridgeport, Conn.	338	74	22.5
Brockton, Mass.	149	156	24.8
Brownsville-Harlingen-San Benito, Tex.	151	152	20.7
Buffalo, N.Y.	1,307	16	20.0
Canton, Ohio	340	73	20.2
Cedar Rapids, Iowa	137	169	31.3
Champaign-Urbana, Ill	132	171	24.8
Charleston, S.C.	255	106	30.5
Charleston, W. Va.	253	107	5.5
Charlotte, N.C.	317	82	32.5
Chattanooga, Tenn.-Ga	283	90	14.9
Chicago, Ill.	6,221	2	20.1
Cincinnati, Ohio-Ky.-Ind.	1,268	17	24.0
Cleveland, Ohio	1,909	11	24.6
Colorado Springs, Colo	144	161	92.9
Columbia, S.C.	261	103	39.6
Columbus, Ga.-Ala.	218	121	27.8
Columbus, Ohio	755	33	34.1
Corpus Christi, Tex.	267	98	32.4
Dallas, Tex.	1,084	22	45.7
Davenport-Rock Island-Moline, Iowa-Ill.	319	80	13.8
Dayton, Ohio	727	35	33.2
Decatur, Ill.	118	186	19.6
Denver, Colo	929	26	51.8
Des Moines, Iowa	266	100	17.8
Detroit, Mich.	3,762	5	24.7
Dubuque, Iowa	80	214	12.2
Duluth-Superior, Minn.-Wis.	277	95	9.4
Durham, N.C.	112	187	10.2
El Paso, Tex.	314	83	61.1
Erie, Pa.	251	108	14.3
Eugene, Oreg.	163	146	29.5
Evansville, Ind.-Ky.	223	118	4.8
Fall River, Mass.-R.I.	138	167	0.6
Fargo-Moorhead, N. Dak.-Minn.	106	194	18.8
Fayetteville, N.C.	148	157	54.6
Fitchburg-Leominster, Mass.	90	207	12.0
Flint, Mich.	416	65	35.7
Fort Lauderdale-Hollywood, Fla.	334	75	297.9
Fort Smith, Ark.-Okla.	135	170	−4.8
Fort Wayne, Ind	232	113	26.4
Fort Worth, Tex.	573	50	46.0
Fresno, Calif.	366	70	32.3
Gadsden, Ala.	97	199	3.3
Galveston-Texas City, Tex.	140	165	24.1
Gary-Hammond-East Chicago, Ind.	574	49	40.5
Grand Rapids, Mich.	462	59	27.6
Great Falls, Mont.	73	219	38.5
Green Bay, Wis.	125	181	27.2
Greensboro-High Point, N.C.	247	110	29.0
Greenville, S.C	256	104	22.9
Hamilton-Middletown, Ohio	199	130	35.2
Harrisburg, Pa.	372	68	17.2
Hartford, Conn.	549	52	30.8
Honolulu, Hawaii	500	55	41.8
Houston, Tex.	1,418	15	51.6
Huntington-Ashland, W. Va.-Ky.-Ohio.	255	105	3.7
Huntsville, Ala.	154	151	41.6
Indianapolis, Ind	917	27	30.4
Jackson, Mich.	132	172	22.3
Jackson, Miss.	221	120	29.4
Jacksonville, Fla	455	61	49.8
Jersey City, N.J.	611	46	−5.7
Johnstown, Pa.	281	92	−3.6
Kalamazoo, Mich.	170	141	33.9
Kansas City, Mo.-Kans.	1,093	21	28.7
Kenosha, Wis.	101	198	33.7
Knoxville, Tenn.	368	69	9.2
Lafayette, La.	85	211	46.6
Lake Charles, La.	145	160	62.3
Lancaster, Pa	278	93	18.6
Lansing, Mich.	299	86	22.4
Laredo, Tex.	65	222	15.4
Las Vegas, Nev.	127	178	163.0
Lawrence-Haverhill, Mass.-N.H.	199	129	4.6
Lawton, Okla.	91	205	64.6
Lewiston-Auburn, Maine	70	220	2.7
Lexington, Ky.	132	173	30.9
Lima, Ohio	104	195	17.6
Lincoln, Nebr.	155	150	29.7
Little Rock-North Little Rock, Ark.	243	111	23.5
Lorain-Elyria, Ohio	218	122	46.8
Los Angeles-Long Beach, Calif.	6,039	3	45.5
Louisville, Ky.-Ind.	725	36	25.7
Lowell, Mass.	164	145	17.1
Lubbock, Tex.	156	149	54.7
Lynchburg, Va.	111	190	14.2
Macon, Ga.	180	136	33.6
Madison, Wis.	222	119	31.1
Manchester, N.H.	103	196	10.2
Memphis, Tenn.-Ark.	675	39	27.4
Meriden, Conn.	52	224	17.6
Miami, Fla.	935	25	88.9
Midland, Tex.	68	221	162.6
Milwaukee, Wis.	1,233	18	25.7
Minneapolis-St. Paul, Minn.	1,482	14	28.8
Mobile, Ala.	363	71	33.5
Monroe, La.	102	197	36.1
Montgomery, Ala.	200	127	17.1
Muncie, Ind.	111	188	22.9
Muskegon-Muskegon Heights, Mich.	150	154	23.4
Nashville, Tenn	464	58	21.5
New Bedford, Mass.	143	162	0.8
New Britain, Conn.	129	177	24.1
New Haven, Conn.	321	79	17.5
New London-Groton-Norwich, Conn.	171	140	27.0
New Orleans, La.	907	28	27.3
New York, N.Y	10,695	1	11.9
Newark, N.J.	1,689	13	15.0
Newport News-Hampton, Va.	225	117	44.9
Norfolk-Portsmouth, Va.	579	48	29.7
Norwalk, Conn.	97	200	47.3
Odessa, Tex.	91	204	116.1
Ogden, Utah	111	189	32.9
Oklahoma City, Okla.	512	53	30.4
Omaha, Nebr.-Iowa.	458	60	25.0
Orlando, Fla.	318	81	124.6
Oxnard-Ventura, Calif.	199	128	73.7
Paterson-Clifton-Passaic, N.J.	1,187	19	35.5
Pensacola, Fla.	203	125	54.9
Peoria, Ill.	313	84	15.3
Philadelphia, Pa.-N.J.	4,343	4	18.3
Phoenix, Ariz.	664	40	100.0
Pine Bluff, Ark.	81	213	7.0
Pittsburgh, Pa.	2,405	8	8.7
Pittsfield, Mass.	77	216	11.9
Portland, Maine	139	166	3.8
Portland, Oreg.-Wash.	822	29	16.6
Providence-Pawtucket-Warwick, R.I.-Mass.	821	30	7.5
Provo-Orem, Utah	107	193	30.6
Pueblo, Colo.	119	185	31.6
Racine, Wis.	142	163	29.4
Raleigh, N.C.	169	142	23.9
Reading, Pa.	275	96	7.7
Reno, Nev.	85	210	68.8
Richmond, Va.	436	63	24.6
Roanoke, Va.	159	148	19.0
Rochester, N.Y.	733	34	19.1
Rockford, Ill.	230	114	35.8
Sacramento, Calif.	626	45	74.0
Saginaw, Mich.	191	131	24.3
St. Joseph, Mo.	91	206	−6.4
St. Louis, Mo.-Ill.	2,105	9	19.9
Salem, Oreg.	147	158	15.4
Salt Lake City, Utah	448	62	46.5
San Angelo, Tex.	65	223	9.7
San Antonio, Tex.	716	37	36.2
San Bernardino-Riverside-Ontario, Calif.	810	31	79.3
San Diego, Calif.	1,033	23	85.5
San Francisco-Oakland, Calif.	2,649	6	24.0
San Jose, Calif.	642	42	121.1
Santa Barbara, Calif.	169	143	72.0
Savannah, Ga.	188	134	24.3
Scranton, Pa.	235	112	−8.9
Seattle-Everett, Wash.	1,107	20	31.1
Shreveport, La.	281	91	29.9
Sioux City, Iowa-Nebr.	120	184	5.0
Sioux Falls, S. Dak.	87	208	22.1
South Bend, Ind.-Mich.	271	97	15.6
Spokane, Wash.	278	94	25.6
Springfield, Ill.	147	159	11.5
Springfield, Mo.	126	179	20.5
Springfield, Ohio	131	174	17.7
Springfield-Chicopee-Holyoke, Mass.-Conn.	494	56	17.0
Stamford, Conn.	178	137	32.3
Steubenville-Weirton, Ohio-W. Va.	168	144	6.3
Stockton, Calif.	250	109	24.5
Syracuse, N.Y.	564	51	21.2
Tacoma, Wash.	322	78	16.6
Tallahassee, Fla.	74	218	43.9
Tampa-St. Petersburg, Fla.	772	32	88.8
Terre Haute, Ind.	172	139	−0.2
Texarkana, Tex.-Ark.	92	203	−3.1
Toledo, Ohio-Mich.	631	44	18.8
Topeka, Kans.	141	164	34.0
Trenton, N.J.	266	99	15.9
Tucson, Ariz.	266	101	88.1
Tulsa, Okla.	419	64	27.8
Tuscaloosa, Ala.	109	191	15.9
Tyler, Tex.	86	209	15.6
Utica-Rome, N.Y.	331	76	16.4
Vallejo-Napa, Calif.	200	126	32.4
Waco, Tex.	150	153	15.3
Washington, D.C.-Md.-Va.	2,002	10	36.7
Waterbury, Conn.	186	135	18.0
Waterloo, Iowa	122	182	21.9
West Palm Beach, Fla.	228	116	98.9
Wheeling, W. Va.-Ohio.	190	132	−3.0
Wichita, Kans.	382	67	50.7
Wichita Falls, Tex.	130	176	23.1
Wilkes-Barre-Hazelton, Pa.	347	72	−11.5
Wilmington, Del.-Md.-N.J.	415	66	37.4
Wilmington, N.C.	92	202	11.5
Winston-Salem, N.C.	189	133	29.6
Worcester, Mass.	329	77	7.4
York, Pa.	290	88	17.5
Youngstown-Warren, Ohio.	509	54	22.2
Puerto Rico			
Mayagüez	84	3	−4.0
Ponce	146	2	14.8
San Juan	589	1	26.4

Source: Dept. of Commerce, Bureau of the Census; *Current Population Reports*, Series P-23, No. 10.

POPULATION—METROPOLITAN AND NONMETROPOLITAN RESIDENCE: 1960 AND 1965

[In thousands, except percent. As of April]

RESIDENCE	1960 [1]	1965	Percent increase, 1960 to 1965 [1]	AVERAGE ANNUAL PERCENT INCREASE 1950 to 1960 [2]	AVERAGE ANNUAL PERCENT INCREASE 1960 to 1965 [1]
Total	178,458	192,185	7.7	1.7	1.5
Standard metropolitan statistical areas [3]	112,323	123,813	10.2	2.3	1.9
Central cities	57,790	59,612	3.2	1.0	0.6
Outside central cities	54,533	64,201	17.7	4.0	3.3
Nonmetropolitan areas	66,135	68,372	3.4	0.8	0.7

[1] For comparability with data from the Current Population Survey, figures from the 1960 Census have been adjusted to exclude members of the Armed Forces living in barracks and similar types of quarters. [2] Based on total population. [3] Covers 212 areas as defined in 1960. See text, p. 1.

Source: Dept. of Commerce, Bureau of the Census; *Current Population Reports*, Series P-20, No. 151.

X Not applicable.

SOURCE: *Statistical Abstracts of the U. S. U. S. Dept. of Commerce, Wash., D. C.*

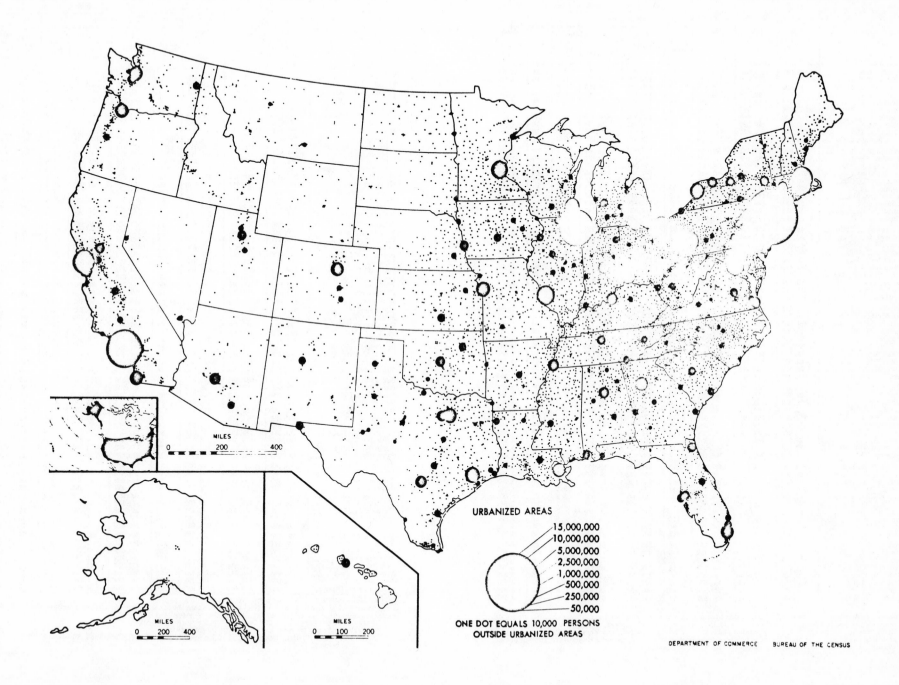

URBANIZED AREAS

15,000,000
10,000,000
5,000,000
2,500,000
1,000,000
500,000
250,000
50,000

ONE DOT EQUALS 10,000 PERSONS
OUTSIDE URBANIZED AREAS

MILES
0 200 400

MILES
0 200 400

MILES
0 100 200

DEPARTMENT OF COMMERCE   BUREAU OF THE CENSUS

4-12 COMPARATIVE POPULATION DENSITIES-1910—1960
MAJOR U. S. CITIES

CITY	1910	1930	1950	1960 Population: Rank order	1960 Population: Total	1960 Nonwhite: Number	1960 Nonwhite: Percent	1960 Land area (sq. mi.)	1960 Population per square mile
Akron, Ohio	69,067	255,040	274,605	45	290,351	37,894	13.1	54	5,387
Albany, N.Y	100,253	127,412	134,995	93	129,726	10,972	8.5	19	6,828
Albuquerque, N. Mex	11,020	26,570	96,815	59	201,189	5,925	2.9	58	3,457
Allentown, Pa	51,913	92,563	106,756	116	108,347	847	0.8	18	6,156
Amarillo, Tex	9,957	43,132	74,246	88	137,969	8,029	5.8	58	2,383
Anaheim, Calif	2,628	10,995	14,556	123	104,184	712	0.7	25	4,118
Atlanta, Ga	154,839	270,366	331,314	24	487,455	186,820	38.3	136	3,587
Austin, Tex	29,860	53,120	132,459	67	186,545	24,739	13.3	45	4,109
Baltimore, Md	558,485	804,874	949,708	6	939,024	328,416	35.0	78	11 993
Baton Rouge, La	14,897	30,729	125,629	80	152,419	45,603	29.9	31	4,917
Beaumont, Tex	20,640	57,732	94,014	102	119,175	35,004	29.4	69	1,720
Berkeley, Calif	40,434	82,109	113,805	114	111,268	29,187	26.2	10	11,354
Birmingham, Ala	132,685	259,678	326,037	36	340,887	135,267	39.7	63	5,420
Boston, Mass	670,585	781,188	801,444	13	697,197	68,493	9.8	48	14,586
Bridgeport, Conn	102,054	146,716	158,709	79	156,748	15,565	9.9	16	9,858
Buffalo, N.Y	423,715	573,076	580,132	20	532,759	73,388	13.8	39	13,522
Cambridge, Mass	104,839	113,643	120,740	119	107,716	6,787	6.3	6	17,098
Camden, N.J	94,538	118,700	124,555	103	117,159	27,892	23.8	9	13,623
Canton, Ohio	50,217	104,906	116,912	109	113,631	11,147	9.8	14	7,946
Charlotte, N.C	34,014	82,675	134,042	58	201,564	56,471	28.0	65	3,111
Chattanooga, Tenn	44,604	119,798	131,041	92	130,009	43,226	33.2	37	3,552
Chicago, Ill	2,185,283	3,376,438	3,620,962	2	3,550,404	837,656	23.6	224	15,836
Cincinnati, Ohio	363,591	451,160	503,998	21	502,550	109,682	21.8	77	6,501
Cleveland, Ohio	560,663	900,429	914,808	8	876,050	253,108	28.9	81	10,789
Columbus, Ga	20,554	43,131	79,611	104	116,779	31,547	27.0	25	4,598
Columbus, Ohio	181,511	290,564	375,901	28	471,316	78,305	16.6	89	5,296
Corpus Christi, Tex	8,222	27,741	108,287	74	167,690	9,327	5.6	37	4,520
Dallas, Tex	92,104	260,475	434,462	14	679,684	131,211	19.3	254	2,676
Dayton, Ohio	116,577	200,982	243,872	49	262,332	57,547	21.9	34	7,808
Dearborn, Mich	911	50,358	94,994	110	112,007	144	0.1	25	4,427
Denver, Colo	213,381	287,861	415,786	23	493,887	35,261	7.1	68	7,295
Des Moines, Iowa	86,368	142,559	177,965	55	208,982	10,558	5.1	63	3,312
Detroit, Mich	465,766	1,568,662	1,849,568	5	1,670,144	487,174	29.2	140	11,964
Duluth, Minn	78,466	101,463	104,511	122	106,884	1,125	1.1	63	1,707
Elizabeth, N.J	73,409	114,589	112,817	120	107,698	11,880	11.0	12	9,205
El Paso, Tex	39,279	102,421	130,485	46	276,687	7,424	2.7	109	2,536
Erie, Pa	66,525	115,967	130,803	87	138,440	6,745	4.9	19	7,364
Evansville, Ind	69,647	102,249	128,636	86	141,543	9,389	6.6	34	4,127
Flint, Mich	38,550	156,492	163,143	61	196,940	34,812	17.7	30	6,587
Fort Wayne, Ind	63,933	114,946	133,607	78	161,776	11,989	7.4	36	4,544
Fort Worth, Tex	73,312	163,447	278,778	34	356,268	56,922	16.0	138	2,578
Fresno, Calif	24,892	52,513	91,669	90	133,929	13,123	9.8	27	4,960
Gary, Ind	16,802	100,426	133,911	70	178,320	69,340	38.9	41	4,403
Glendale, Calif	2,746	62,736	95,702	101	119,442	574	0.5	29	4,105
Grand Rapids, Mich	112,571	168,592	176,515	71	177,313	14,778	8.3	24	7,267
Greensboro, N.C	15,895	53,569	74,389	99	119,574	31,130	26.0	49	2,460
Hammond, Ind	20,925	64,560	87,594	112	111,698	2,586	2.3	23	4,921
Hartford, Conn	98,915	164,072	177,397	77	162,178	25,151	15.5	17	9,429
Honolulu, Hawaii	52,183	137,582	248,034	43	294,194	213,920	72.7	84	3,506
Houston, Tex	78,800	292,352	596,163	7	938,219	217,672	23.2	321	2,923
Indianapolis, Ind	233,650	364,161	427,173	26	476,258	98,684	20.7	70	6,794
Jackson, Miss	21,262	48,282	98,271	84	144,422	51,629	35.7	47	3,106
Jacksonville, Fla	57,699	129,549	204,517	60	201,030	82,744	41.2	30	6,723
Jersey City, N.J	267,779	316,715	299,017	47	276,101	37,274	13.5	15	18,285
Kansas City, Kans	82,331	121,857	129,553	98	121,901	28,327	23.2	20	6,005
Kansas City, Mo	248,381	399,746	456,622	27	475,539	84,191	17.7	130	3,664
Knoxville, Tenn	36,346	105,802	124,769	111	111,827	20,886	18.7	24	4,718
Lansing, Mich	31,229	78,397	92,129	118	107,807	6,993	6.5	21	5,085
Lincoln, Nebr	43,973	75,933	98,884	95	128,521	2,400	1.9	25	5,060
Little Rock, Ark	45,941	81,679	102,213	117	107,813	25,352	23.5	25	4,313
Long Beach, Calif	17,809	142,032	250,767	35	344,168	14,769	4.3	46	7,564
Los Angeles, Calif	319,198	1,238,048	1,970,358	3	2,479,015	417,207	16.8	455	5,447
Louisville, Ky	223,928	307,745	369,129	31	390,639	70,449	18.0	59	6,599
Lubbock, Tex	1,938	20,520	71,747	94	128,691	10,427	8.1	75	1,709
Madison, Wis	25,531	57,899	96,056	[1] 96	126,706	2,388	1.9	36	3,549
Memphis, Tenn	131,105	253,143	396,000	22	497,524	184,725	37.1	129	3,851
Miami, Fla	5,471	110,637	249,276	44	291,688	65,800	22.6	34	8,529
Milwaukee, Wis	373,857	578,249	637,392	11	741,324	65,752	8.9	91	8,137
Minneapolis, Minn	301,408	464,356	521,718	25	482,872	15,594	3.2	57	8,546
Mobile, Ala	51,521	68,202	129,009	62	[2] 194,856	(NA)	(NA)	154	1,321
Montgomery, Ala	38,136	66,079	106,525	89	134,393	47,432	35.3	30	4,421
Nashville, Tenn	110,364	153,866	174,307	73	170,874	64,830	37.9	29	5,933
New Bedford, Mass	96,652	112,597	109,189	125	102,477	3,333	3.3	19	5,365
New Haven, Conn	133,605	162,655	164,443	81	152,048	22,665	14.9	18	8,264
New Orleans, La	339,075	458,762	570,445	15	627,525	234,931	37.4	199	3,157
New York, N.Y.[3]	4,766,883	6,930,446	7,891,957	1	7,781,984	1,141,322	14.7	315	24,697
Bronx Borough	430,980	1,265,258	1,451,277	(X)	1,424,815	168,531	11.8	43	33,135
Brooklyn Borough	1,634,351	2,560,401	2,738,175	(X)	2,627,319	381,460	14.5	76	34,570
Manhattan Borough	2,331,542	1,867,312	1,960,101	(X)	1,698,281	426,459	25.1	22	77,195
Queens Borough	284,041	1,079,129	1,550,849	(X)	1,809,578	154,619	8.5	113	16,014
Richmond Borough	85,969	158,346	191,555	(X)	221,991	10,253	4.6	60	3,700
Newark, N.J	347,469	442,337	438,776	30	405,220	139,331	34.4	24	16,814
Newport News, Va	20,205	34,417	42,358	108	113,662	39,060	34.4	68	1,645
Niagara Falls, N.Y	30,445	75,460	90,872	126	102,394	7,664	7.5	14	7,585
Norfolk, Va	67,452	129,710	213,513	41	[2] 305,872	80,621	26.4	50	5,848
Oakland, Calif	150,174	284,063	384,575	33	367,548	97,025	26.4	52	7,041
Oklahoma City, Okla	64,205	185,389	243,504	37	324,253	42,282	13.0	299	1,086
Omaha, Nebr.[4]	124,096	214,006	251,117	42	301,598	26,268	8.7	51	5,891
Pasadena, Calif	30,291	76,086	104,577	105	116,407	17,967	15.4	22	5,220
Paterson, N.J	125,600	138,513	139,336	85	143,663	21,353	14.9	9	16,705
Peoria, Ill	66,950	104,969	111,856	124	103,162	9,776	9.5	15	6,787
Philadelphia, Pa	1,549,008	1,950,961	2,071,605	4	2,002,512	535,033	26.7	127	15,743
Phoenix, Ariz	11,134	48,118	106,818	29	439,170	25,651	5.8	187	2,344
Pittsburgh, Pa	533,905	669,817	676,806	16	604,332	101,739	16.8	54	11,171
Portland, Oreg	207,214	301,815	373,628	32	372,676	20,919	5.6	66	5,630
Portsmouth, Va	33,190	45,704	80,039	106	114,773	39,681	34.6	20	6,521
Providence, R.I	224,326	252,981	248,674	56	207,498	11,973	5.8	18	11,592
Richmond, Va	127,628	182,929	230,310	52	219,958	92,331	42.0	39	5,834
Rochester, N.Y	218,149	328,132	332,488	38	318,611	24,228	7.6	36	8,753
Rockford, Ill	45,401	85,864	92,927	[1] 96	126,706	5,450	4.3	26	4,873
Sacramento, Calif	44,696	93,750	137,572	63	191,667	24,296	12.7	45	4,278
St. Louis, Mo	687,029	821,960	856,796	10	750,026	216,022	28.8	61	12,296
St. Paul, Minn	214,744	271,606	311,349	40	313,411	9,317	3.0	52	6,004
St. Petersburg, Fla	4,127	40,425	96,738	69	181,298	24,188	13.3	53	3,434
Salt Lake City, Utah	92,777	140,267	182,121	65	189,454	3,975	2.1	56	3,401
San Antonio, Tex	96,614	231,542	408,442	17	587,718	43,221	7.4	148	3,966
San Diego, Calif	39,578	147,995	334,387	18	573,224	44,712	7.8	195	2,944
San Francisco, Calif	416,912	634,394	775,357	12	740,316	135,913	18.4	45	16,307
San Jose, Calif	28,946	57,651	95,280	57	204,196	6,793	3.3	56	3,646
Santa Ana, Calif	8,429	30,322	45,533	130	100,350	2,681	2.7	21	4,801
Savannah, Ga	65,064	85,024	119,638	82	149,245	53,258	35.7	41	3,631
Scranton, Pa	129,867	143,433	125,536	113	111,443	763	0.7	25	4,405
Seattle, Wash	237,194	365,583	467,591	19	557,087	46,528	8.4	82	6,810
Shreveport, La	28,015	76,655	127,206	76	164,372	56,719	34.5	36	4,566
South Bend, Ind	53,684	104,193	115,911	91	132,445	13,169	9.9	24	5,542
Spokane, Wash	104,402	115,514	161,721	68	181,608	4,508	2.5	42	4,293
Springfield, Mass	88,926	149,900	162,399	72	174,463	13,361	7.7	33	5,271
Syracuse, N.Y	137,249	209,326	220,583	53	216,038	12,281	5.7	25	8,642
Tacoma, Wash	83,743	106,817	143,673	83	147,979	7,873	5.3	47	3,135
Tampa, Fla	37,782	101,161	124,681	48	274,970	46,456	16.9	69	3,985
Toledo, Ohio	168,497	290,718	303,616	39	318,003	40,423	12.7	48	6,598
Topeka, Kans	43,684	64,120	78,791	100	119,484	9,797	8.2	35	3,453
Torrance, Calif	([5])	7,271	22,241	128	100,991	1,398	1.4	20	4,951
Trenton, N.J	96,815	123,356	128,009	107	114,167	25,852	22.6	8	15,222
Tucson, Ariz	13,193	32,506	45,454	54	212,892	9,278	4.4	71	3,003
Tulsa, Okla	18,182	141,258	182,740	50	261,685	26,065	10.0	49	5,384
Utica, N.Y	74,419	101,740	101,531	129	100,410	3,193	3.2	17	5,906
Washington, D.C	331,069	486,869	802,178	9	763,956	418,693	54.8	61	12,442
Waterbury, Conn	73,141	99,902	104,477	121	107,130	7,221	6.7	29	3,746
Wichita, Kans	52,450	111,110	168,279	51	254,698	21,159	8.3	51	5,024
Wichita Falls, Tex	8,200	43,690	68,042	127	101,724	8,551	8.4	38	2,677
Winston-Salem, N.C	22,700	75,274	87,811	115	111,135	41,240	37.1	31	3,573
Worcester, Mass	145,986	195,311	203,486	66	186,587	2,307	1.2	37	5,043
Yonkers, N.Y	79,803	134,646	152,798	64	190,634	8,052	4.2	18	10,417
Youngstown, Ohio	79,066	170,002	168,330	75	166,689	31,905	19.1	33	5,021

NA Not available. X Not applicable.

[1] The cities of Madison, Wis., and Rockford, Ill., share the same rank of 96. In order to have the lowest rank equal to the number of cities presented, the number 97 is omitted.

[2] Revised population figure for Mobile is 202,779; for Norfolk, 304,869.

[3] Population shown is for New York City as now constituted.

[4] Omaha and South Omaha cities consolidated between 1910 and 1920. Combined population, 1910: 150,355.

[5] Not incorporated in 1910.

[Increase from census to census includes that due to annexation of territory as well as to direct growth. "Cities" refers to political subdivisions which are incorporated as cities, boroughs, towns, or villages with the exception that towns are not recognized as incorporated places in New England States, New York, and Wisconsin. Land area figures, generally supplied by city engineers, have been revised to agree with those in the Bureau of the Census, *Area Measurement Reports*, Series GE-20, where available]

SOURCE: Dept. of Commerce, Bureau of the Census; U. S. Census of Population: 1960, Vol. I and Area Measurement Reports, Series GE-20.

HOUSING

1 Young couple marries. Their living needs are basic. The five areas used might possibly be contained in one room.

2 Upon the arrival of the first blessed event the areas would have to be expanded. The need for storage is increased, and eventually an additional sleeping area is necessary.

3 The second blessed event requires increased storage and a general increase of the five major areas.

4 The third blessed event requires additional sleeping area with all facilities, plus an additional separate bathing and washing area.

5 At this point the family and house should remain stable, with an increase in living-recreation areas.

6 About this time the first child leaves home, decreasing needs in the house and reducing the family to four persons.

7 The second child leaves, and the house area needed decreases.

8 The third child leaves, bringing the family back to its original state: two persons. The only area that might remain stable is the storage area, for items accumulated are seldom lost or reduced to any great extent.

9 The family may eventually be reduced to one, so that needs are less than at the beginning.

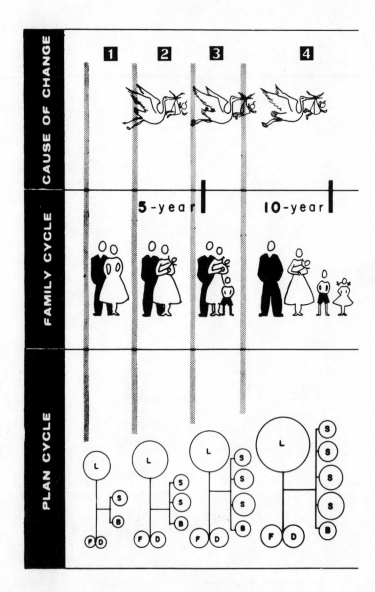

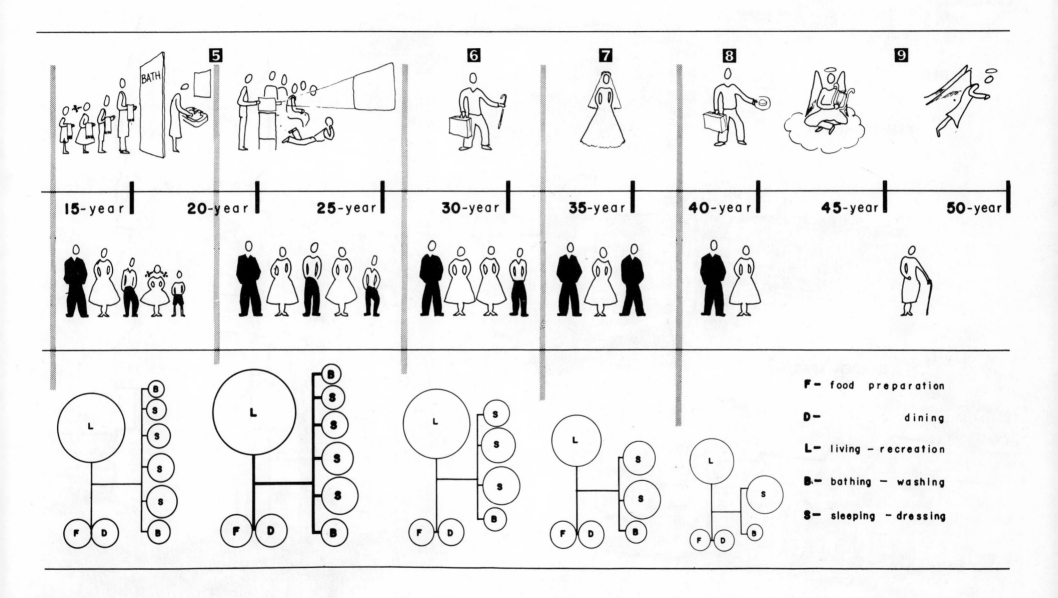

15-year   20-year   25-year   30-year   35-year   40-year   45-year   50-year

F — food preparation
D — dining
L — living – recreation
B — bathing – washing
S — sleeping – dressing

SOURCE: An investigation of the Small House. Pratt Institute School of Architecture

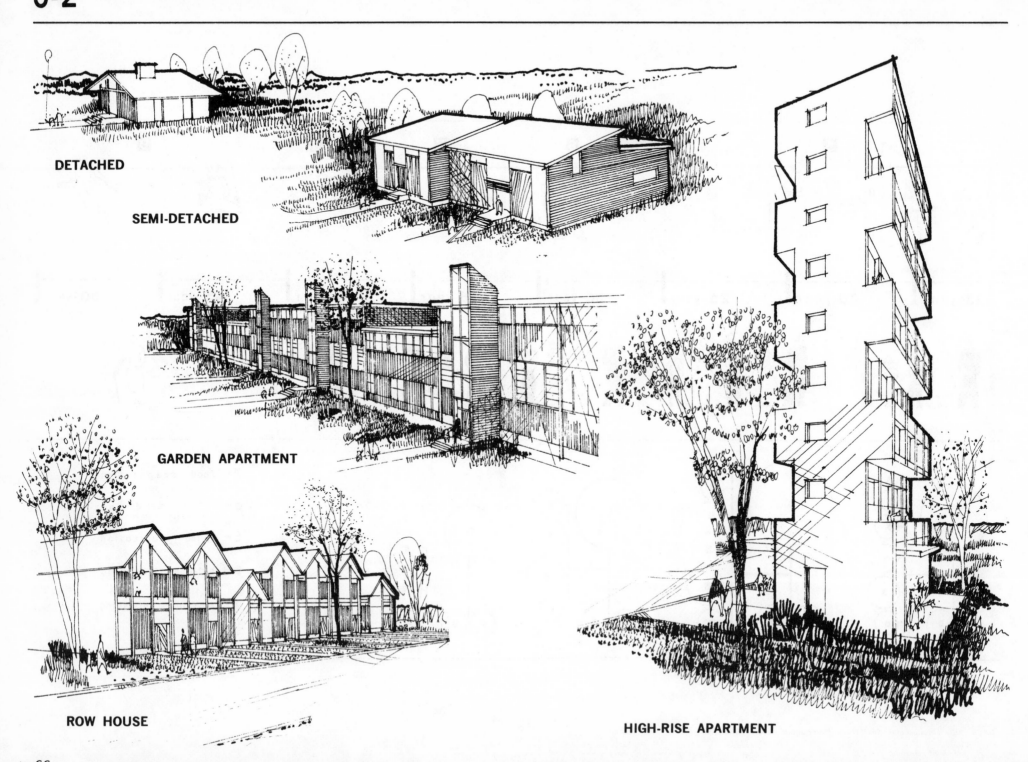

DETACHED

SEMI-DETACHED

GARDEN APARTMENT

ROW HOUSE

HIGH-RISE APARTMENT

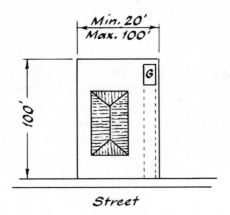

DETACHED HOUSE—One or Two-Family

Probably the most popular type of housing in the U. S. completely independent of any other structure. Garage is located within main building or in separate structure. Generally owner-occupied.

Type of construction includes a wide range, most common are frame and brick veneer. Older houses generally are 2 stories while newer houses are one story.

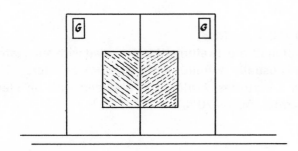

SEMI-ATTACHED (Semi-Detached) One or Two-Family

Utilizes a common wall between houses for economy. Has similar characteristics of detached house except it is usually located on a smaller lot. Separate and independent entrances are maintained. This type of dwelling is usually 2 stories high.

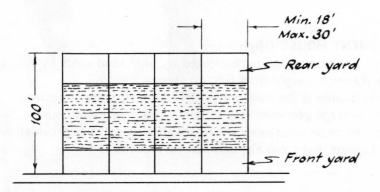

ROW HOUSES (Town Houses)

This type of housing can also be either one-family or two-family. Common walls are used on both sides of the structure for economy. The shape tends to be narrow and deep to maximumize the number of units in a row. Recently in urban areas, the town house has emerged as a popular type of dwelling. This town house is usually one-family and owner-occupied.

The height is most frequently 2 story and construction is brick or brick veneer.

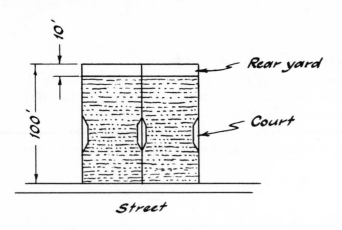

TENEMENT HOUSE

Mostly built during the latter part of the 19th century and early part of the 20th century. Common in most cities. Characterized by high percentage of lot coverage, inadequate light and air, bathroom facilities, and obsolete room layout. Generally of frame and masonry construction. Maximum height 5 or 6 stories often located in older parts of the community.

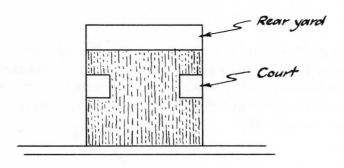

APARTMENT HOUSE (Low Rise)

Common type of multiple dwelling. It is provided with adequate light and air. Construction is usually non-fireproof with brick exterior.

Height is often 5-8 stories; building is provided with an elevator. Lot coverage is moderate. (50%–70%)

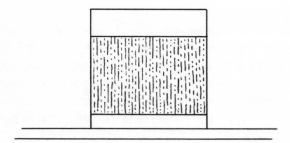

APARTMENT HOUSE (High Rise)

Type of construction necessitated by high land costs in built-up urban areas. Range in height from 6 to 40 stories.

Construction is fireproof with steel frame or poured concrete.

Lot coverage generally less than low-rise apartment house.

Most of these structures are relatively new and are provided with good room layouts, light and air, and several elevators.

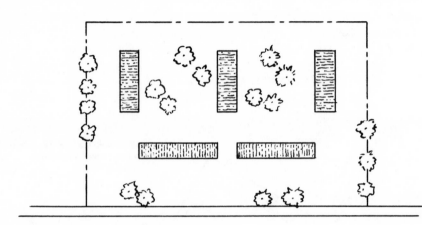

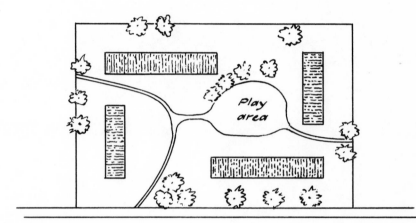

GARDEN APARTMENTS

Most common type of rental housing in suburban or moderately built-up areas; built on a large plot of land under one ownership and provided with some community facilities.

Type of construction is usually frame or brick veneer.

Height of buildings are 1 or 2 stories.

Lot coverage is generally less than apartment houses. Landscaping and open space is moderate.

Garden apartments are usually rental-occupied. In recent years there has been an increase in cooperative and condominium ownership.

PROJECT

A project involves more than one building on a large site, usually a superblock. The type of housing can be either low or high-rise. The site is characterized by low land coverage (20–40%) and provision of basic community facilities, such as play areas and sitting areas. Construction is dependent upon height of building. Because of low lot coverage, the project often has extensive landscaping and open areas.

The project usually is under one ownership and the dwelling units are rented. In recent years there has been an increase in cooperative and condominium ownership.

GENERAL CONSIDERATIONS

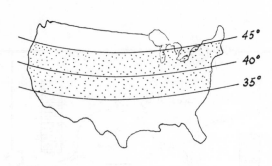

Although the study of orientation is a comprehensive and detailed science, the knowledge and use of a few basic rules will mean comfort and economy for the home owner, and a better house for the developer. The latitude belt between 35° and 45° across our country includes many of the most populated areas. This set of solar conditions thus has a wide application. Below this latitude belt, in most locations, the capturing of summer breezes and protection from intense sun heat is the main consideration. Above the latitude belt shown, the protection from cold winter winds and using the warming rays of the sun in winter is the prime objective. Using the solar conditions of the 35° to 45° belt, except as noted, it is well to remember that the information here becomes more general and less exact as the distance increases from its midpoint of 40°.

LOCATION OF BUILDING ON LOT

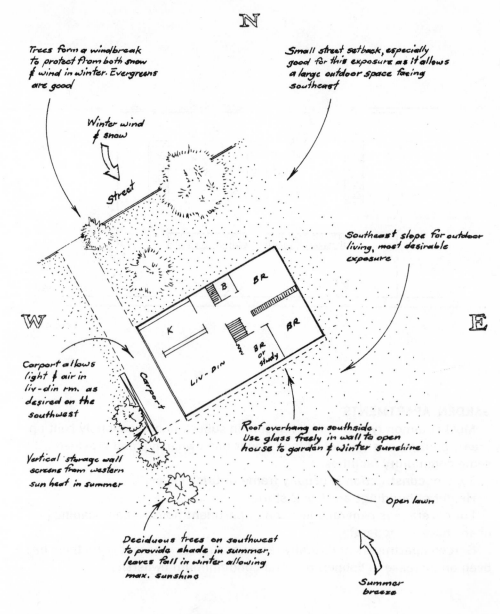

SOURCE: House and Site United. Housing and Home Finance Agency, Wash. D. C. 1952

ORIENTING HOUSE AND LOT

● The sun has an extended arc and is high overhead at noon in summer. It has a much reduced arc and is low in the sky at noon in winter. A house needs protection from this overhead summer sun, but in winter the object is to capture all the sunshine possible.

● The direction a slope faces is important for solar orientation. Although other factors may outweigh this one in using land and placing the house, always consider the compass directions.

A south slope is very desirable.

Select an east slope in preference to a west slope.

Don't pick a north slope if you can help it.

A southeast slope is the best of all.

Don't put a house in a valley bottom, keep it up on the slope.

● Use a roof overhang on the south side of a house. An overhang on any other side may serve another purpose, but it is a protection against summer sun only when facing a generally south exposure.

● Use something upright on the west side, such as planting or garage to protect house against summer afternoon sun-heat.

● Screen the northwest direction to protect against cold winter wind. Some ways of doing this are the use of evergreen trees, high ground to the north, the garage, or perhaps the house next door. In summer let the south breeze get at the house.

● In the South, below 35° latitude, use an open type house to catch the summer breeze. Maximum outdoor living can be practiced for a major part of the year. Wide, overhead cover should be freely used to protect both enclosed and open areas of the house from intense summer heat.

● Large glass windows are really suitable only on the south side. Reduce the size of windows on the north side. Unprotected west windows are the worst of all, because of hot summer sun.

● A few feet below ground, the temperature is cool in summer and warm in winter. Don't sell short the basement, especially if you have a slope, one side can then be located at grade level. It then becomes a comfortable and desirable ground floor. In some sections of the South, however, such as the Gulf Coast, the living areas of the house must often be raised well above the ground, due to dampness and insects at ground level.

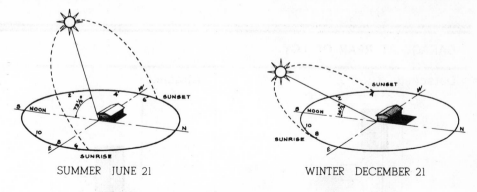

SUMMER JUNE 21   WINTER DECEMBER 21

POSITION OF SUN AT NOON FOR 40° N. LATITUDE

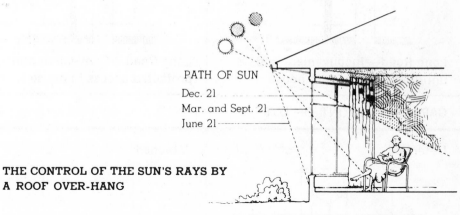

PATH OF SUN

Dec. 21
Mar. and Sept. 21
June 21

THE CONTROL OF THE SUN'S RAYS BY A ROOF OVER-HANG

SHADE LINE AT NOON—SOUTH SIDE

● Warm air is lighter than cold air and will rise. Provide for cool air to come into the house near the ground and allow warm air to escape high in rooms, or in the attic.

SOURCE: House and Site United. Housing and Home Finance Agency, Wash. D. C. 1952

(Plans are diagramatic and not to scale)

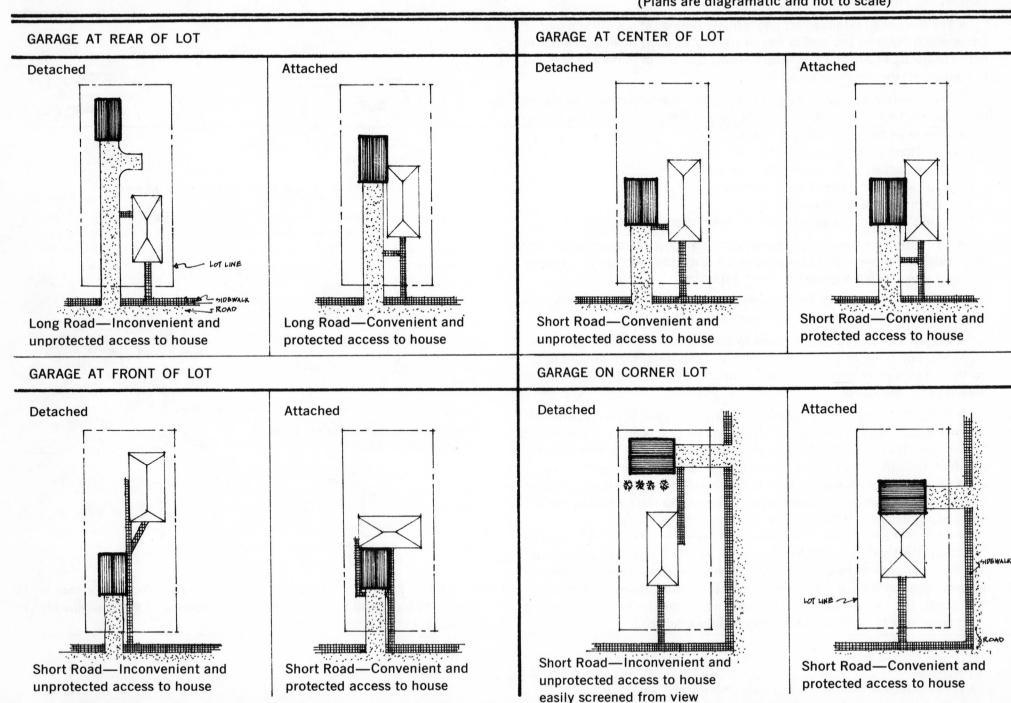

GARAGE AT REAR OF LOT

Detached

Long Road—Inconvenient and unprotected access to house

Attached

Long Road—Convenient and protected access to house

GARAGE AT CENTER OF LOT

Detached

Short Road—Convenient and unprotected access to house

Attached

Short Road—Convenient and protected access to house

GARAGE AT FRONT OF LOT

Detached

Short Road—Inconvenient and unprotected access to house

Attached

Short Road—Convenient and protected access to house

GARAGE ON CORNER LOT

Detached

Short Road—Inconvenient and unprotected access to house easily screened from view

Attached

Short Road—Convenient and protected access to house

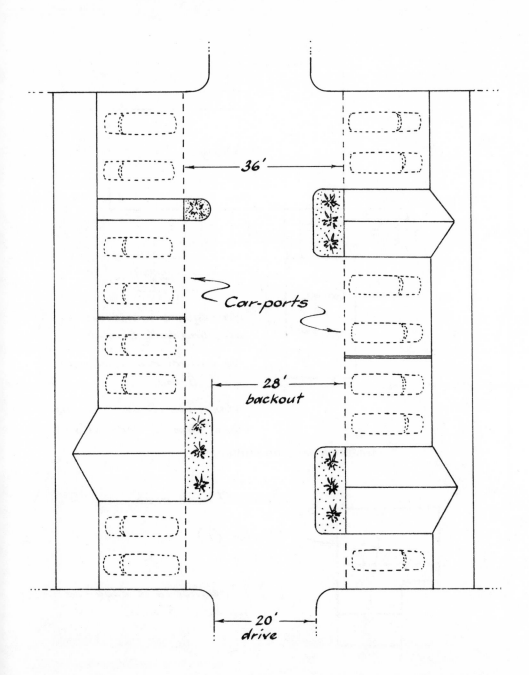

GENERAL

Driveways shall be provided on the site where necessary for convenient access to the living units, garage compounds, parking areas, service entrances of buildings, collection of refuse and all other necessary services. Driveways shall enter public streets at safe locations.

DRIVEWAY CIRCULATION

Driveways shall be planned for convenient circulation suitable for traffic needs and safety. Culs-de-sac shall be provided with adequate paved vehicular turning space, usually a turning circle of at least 80 feet in diameter, except for short straight service driveways with light traffic.

DRIVEWAYS WIDTHS

Driveways shall have two traffic lanes for their entire length, usually 18 feet in addition to any parking space, except that a single lane may be used for short straight service driveways where two-way traffic is not anticipated.

Garages, carports and parking bays shall be set back at least 8 feet from the nearest edge of any moving traffic lane to the extent necessary to provide sight lines for safe entry into the traffic way.

SOURCE: Minimum Property Requirements, FHA, Dept. of Housing and Urban Development, Washington, D. C.

Wall or window (2)

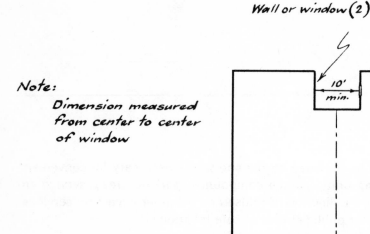

Note:

Dimension measured from center to center of window

2 family dwelling

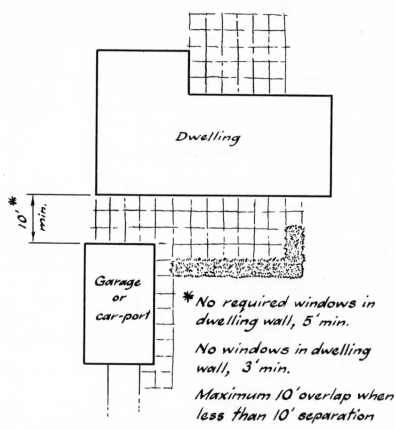

10' min.

Dwelling

Garage or car-port

* *No required windows in dwelling wall, 5' min.*

No windows in dwelling wall, 3' min.

Maximum 10' overlap when less than 10' separation

Distance between buildings

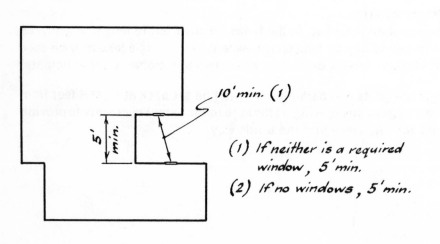

10' min. (1)

5' min.

(1) If neither is a required window, 5' min.

(2) If no windows, 5' min.

Outer courts

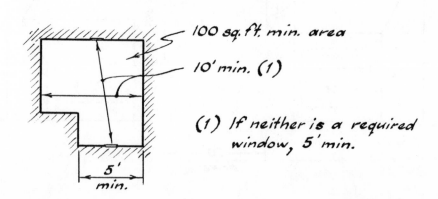

100 sq. ft. min. area

10' min. (1)

5' min.

(1) If neither is a required window, 5' min.

Inner courts

SOURCE: Minimum Property Requirements, FHA, Dept. of Housing and Urban Development, Washington, D. C.

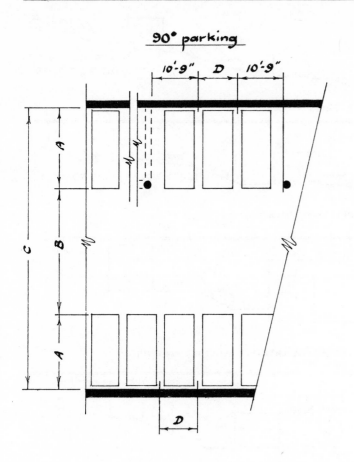

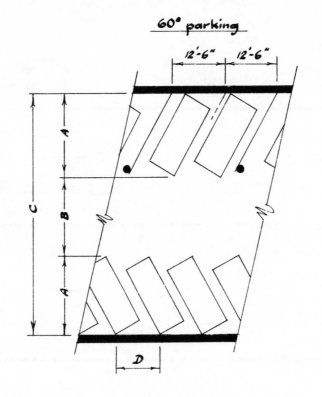

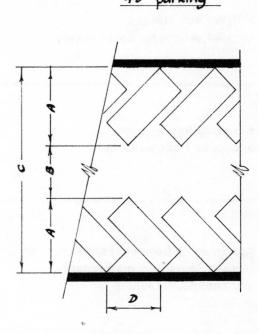

	Dimensions					
	Tenant parking			Attendant parking		
Space	45°	60°	90°	45°	60°	90°
Stall depth perpendicular to aisle (A)	17'-6"	19'-0"	18'-0"	17'2"	18'-10"	18'0"
Aisle width .... (B)	12'-8"	18'-0"	29'-0"	12'-8"	17'-4"	22'-0"
Unit parking depth .... (C)	47'-8"	56'-0"	65'-0"	47'-0"	55'-0"	58'-0"
Stall width parallel to aisle .... (D)	12'-8"	10'-6"	9'-0"	11'-4"	9'-3"	8'-0"

Note: Where 45° and 60° parking is necessary, one way traffic should be planned.

Garages shall be located for convenient access. This requirement applies both to vehicular access and to pedestrian access. Means of easy access by tenants from living units to garages is required.

SOURCE: *Minimum Property Requirements, FHA, Dept. of Housing and Urban Development, Wash., D. C.*

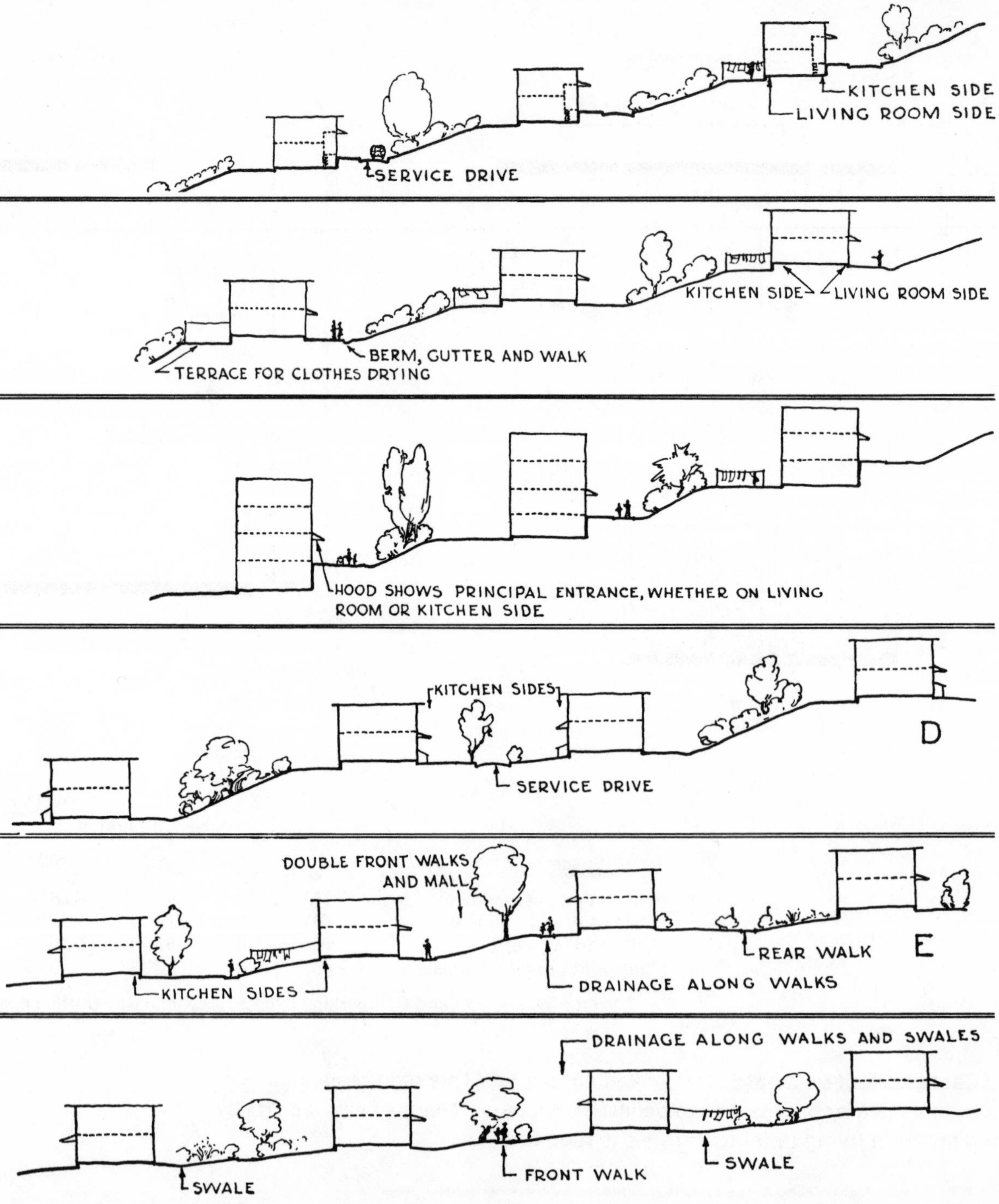

Hillside Row Houses
parallel service for coal delivery

KITCHEN SIDE
LIVING ROOM SIDE
SERVICE DRIVE

Standard Row Houses
access by front walks only

KITCHEN SIDE — LIVING ROOM SIDE
BERM, GUTTER AND WALK
TERRACE FOR CLOTHES DRYING

Apartments: Basement stories are for storage, laundries, maintenance and community rooms

HOOD SHOWS PRINCIPAL ENTRANCE, WHETHER ON LIVING ROOM OR KITCHEN SIDE

Row Houses
parallel service

KITCHEN SIDES
SERVICE DRIVE
D

Row Houses, end service, showing two methods of grading for surface drainage

DOUBLE FRONT WALKS AND MALL
REAR WALK
E
KITCHEN SIDES
DRAINAGE ALONG WALKS

DRAINAGE ALONG WALKS AND SWALES
SWALE
FRONT WALK
SWALE

50   100

SOURCE: Public Housing Design, Federal Public Housing Authority, U. S. Gov. Printing Office—1946

The following table gives desirable limits for slopes on different types of areas. Deviations may be warranted by especially favorable conditions, such as porous soils, mild climates, or light rainfall; also if local experience indicates that other gradients are satisfactory.

Failure to provide positive pitch away from buildings and to give open areas adequate slopes has necessitated costly regrading and reconstruction work on numerous projects. The trouble has been due in part to inaccurate construction, but incomplete or poorly conceived plans have been a contributing cause.

Of two basic design methods, one provides for drainage mainly across grassed areas, generally through "swales", until the water reaches streets, drives, or storm sewer inlets. This scheme, requiring the flow of water from walks onto lawns, is not altogether effective when slopes are inadequate and finished grading is not accurately executed, or if the turf is above the walk level. Swale drainage occasionally is carried under walks by small culverts (six- to eight-inch pipes or boxes). These are slight hazards and frequently become stopped. The other method employs walks to a considerable extent as drainage channels. This scheme has met some objection; nevertheless, it generally is more economical and practical than the use of swales, and it has been used far more widely. Moreover, when walks have been given proper cross and longitudinal slopes, with sewer inlets provided at points of concentrated storm water flow, there has been no serious inconvenience or complications.

DESIRABLE SLOPES

	Percent Slope	
	Maximum	Minimum
Streets, service drives and parking areas ..	8.00	[1]0.50
Collector and approach walks	[2]10.00	0.50
Entrance walks	[3]4.00	1.00
Ramps	15.00	....
Paved play and sitting areas	2.00	0.50
Paved laundry yards	5.00	0.50
Paved gutters	....	0.50
Project lawn areas	[4]25.00	1.00
Tenant yards	10.00	1.00
Grassed playgrounds	4.00	0.50
Swales	[5]10.00	[6]1.00
Grassed banks	4 to 1 slope	
Planted banks	2 to 1 slope (3 to 1 preferable)	

[1] 0.75% for dished section.

[2] Less where icy conditions may occur frequently.

[3] Slopes up to 10% or more are satisfactory provided walks are long enough to employ a curved profile, so that a slope not exceeding 4% can be used adjoining the building platform. See also preceding note.

[4] Steepest grade recommended for power mower.

[5] Less for drainage areas of more than approximately ½ acre.

[6] 2.00% preferable in all cases, particularly so where swales cross walks.

SOURCE: Public Housing Design, National Housing Agency, Federal Public Housing Agency—1946

The row house has long been advocated for rental housing for urban families with children as a good compromise between the desirability of a detached single-family house and the economic necessity of multifamily units. It is decidedly preferable from the viewpoint of the tenants because of greater livability. The results of surveys in both public and private housing indicate that families want to have direct access to the house, an individual yard or garden, and a place for small children to play close to the house where they can be easily supervised. These are features which the row house can provide.

From the management point of view, row house projects can be designed for maximum tenant maintenance of land area. They can also be designed for either individual heating installations or a central heating plant. Individual heating installations, though of higher operating cost to the tenant, result in lower maintenance cost to the management.

PRIVATE GARDEN

Privacy is an important factor in row house design. All house types show, therefore, a 2-foot extension of the party walls beyond the face of the building on either side. Sitting-out terraces on the garden side are separated by wing-walls, 6 feet long and 6 feet high. These wing-walls do not have to be of masonry material, although preferably they should be of a permanent rather than of a temporary nature.

PUBLIC ACCESS

Another arrangement which insures more privacy is the concentration of services from the front. The problem of refuse collection is solved by means of a masonry enclosure, 3 feet wide, 4 feet high, and 10 feet long for two living units. Access doors to the enclosure are from the side facing the building, away from street view. A flower box built into the top of the enclosure makes the appearance pleasing and attractive to the passer-by. A hose-bib connection facilitates cleaning and reduces odors to a minimum.

An entry-space for each living unit presents another privacy feature and is absolutely necessary for service-from-the-front planning. The conventional direct entrance from the street into the living room reduces privacy and is the cause of annoyance to many housewives.

THE 20-FOOT ROW HOUSE

Plan Type A has a gross floor area of 1,000 square feet. Living-dining areas are combined into one room, 12- by 19-feet. This room should face

SOURCE: Technical Bulletin, HHFA, May June— 1950

THE 20FT. ROW HOUSE

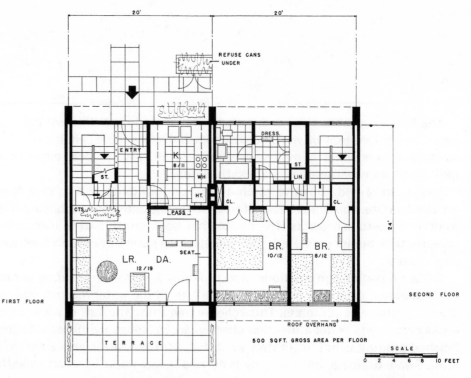

south. The dining area has direct communication with the kitchen by means of a pass, and can be screened off from the living area with a curtain, bookshelves, a permanent plywood screen, or other media. A large coat closet, 2 feet by 6 feet 6 inches, separates the stairhall from the living room. Its height can be held to 6 feet if an effect of greater spaciousness for the whole living area is desired. The space under the stairs is used for storage.

In addition to accommodating standard equipment, the kitchen provides space for a heater, water heater, and washing machine. If individual heat is planned, duct work is reduced to a minimum. If central heat is provided, the kitchen will gain 3 more feet of counter and cabinet space. On the second floor are two bedrooms, the bathroom (tub on opposite side from the window), and a small dressing alcove with a storage closet. Bedroom window sills are high so that furniture can be placed under them. All plumbing is concentrated in one wall. One flue services the heater and hot water heater. Hot water lines are short. The outdoor terrace, linking garden to living room, can be used in complete privacy.

THE 25FT. ROW HOUSE

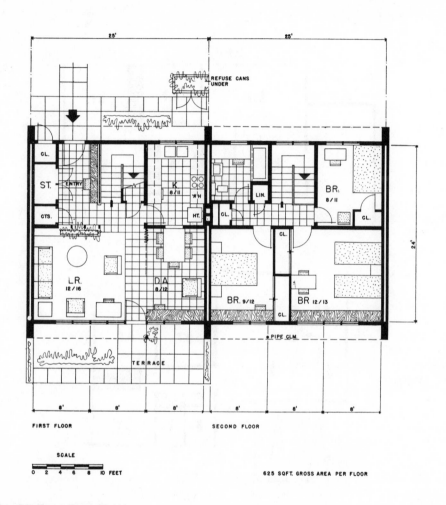

FIRST FLOOR   SECOND FLOOR

SCALE
0 2 4 6 8 10 FEET

625 SQFT. GROSS AREA PER FLOOR

THE 30FT. ROW HOUSE

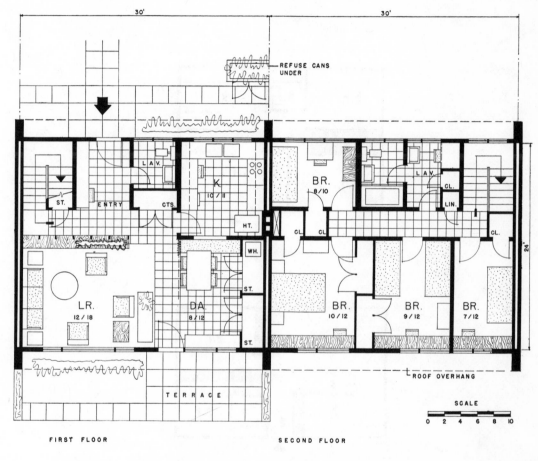

FIRST FLOOR   SECOND FLOOR

SCALE
0 2 4 6 8 10

750 SQFT. GROSS AREA PER FLOOR

The 25-Foot Row House

Plan Type A has a gross floor area of 1,250 square feet. Living and dining are combined into one spacious room facing the garden side and should have south orientation. Two of the three bedrooms on the second floor will then have south orientation, also. Storage closets are ample and include a large storage space off the entry, as well as a smaller one accessible from the outside, for tools and deliveries. Mechanical installations are similar to those of the 20-foot row house.

SOURCE: Technical Bulletin, HHFA May July—1950

The 30-Foot Row House

Plan Type A has a gross floor area of 1,500 square feet. The basic arrangement of rooms is similar to the preceding row house types, except for the addition of a first-floor lavatory off the entry. Three of the four bedrooms upstairs face the same direction as the living-dining combination downstairs. This direction should be generally south.

THE MINIMUM PLAN

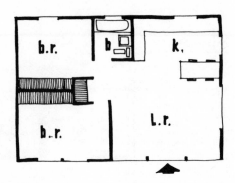

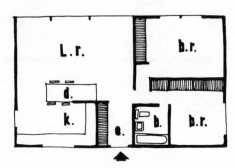

THE SIMPLE AND OFFSET RECTANGLE

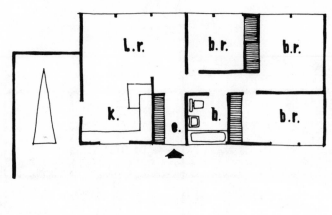

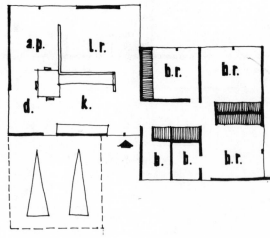

The most common plan developed by the tract builder has been the simple one-story rectangle. The box shape, with a minimum of exterior walls and concentrated plumbing, was easy and cheap to build and was readily sold in a period of extreme housing shortage. Today, however, the minimum two bedroom plan is inadequate for all but a few families.

The original rectangular plan may be expended by the simple addition of a third bedroom into one of the layouts most popular with builders.

A further modification is the offset rectangle plan which reduces circulation space, provides a possible garden terrace in the rear of the house, and allows for greater interest on the street elevation. The addition of a family, or all-purpose, room gives greater flexibility and use to the living area, while the second bath off the master bedroom adds an essential requirement in a house of this size.

SOURCE: D. Q. Jones and F. Emmons, Builder's Homes for Better Living, Reinhold Publishing Corp., N. Y.

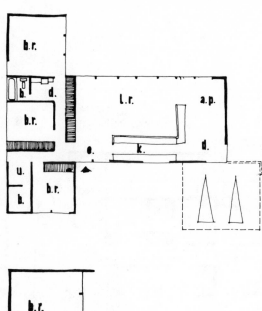

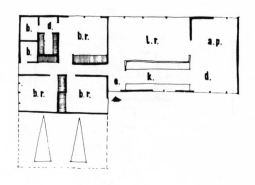

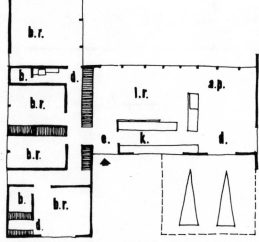

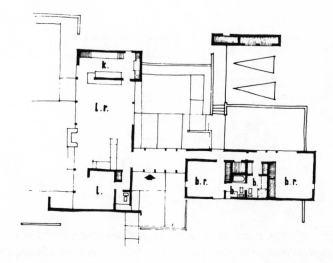

These plans are adaptations of the offset rectangle plan. They allow greater flexibility of layout, good separation of living and sleeping areas, and compact circulation. Interesting street elevations are possible with many variations. From a structural standpoint they may be a little more costly to build because of greater exterior wall area and irregular roof framing plan.

SOURCE: D. Q. Jones and F. Emmons, Builder's Homes for Better Living, Reinhold Publishing Corp., N. Y.

One additional advantage in a plan type such as the "T" or "L", where the sleeping and living areas are separate sections, is that a four bedroom sleeping unit can easily be substituted for the three bedroom unit previously shown. This allows a builder to combine one or more standardized living units with either three or four bedroom sleeping units as required.

THE "H" AND "U" PLANS

THE UTILITY CORE PLAN

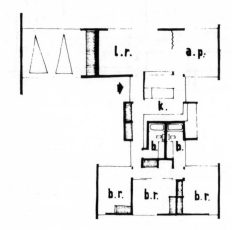

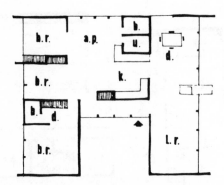

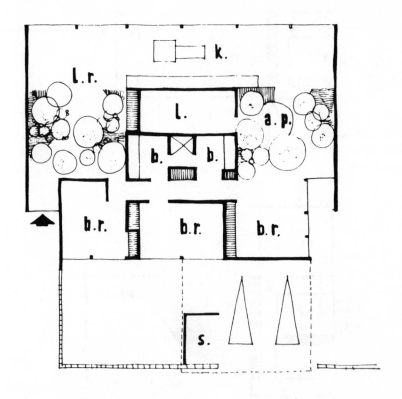

The "H" and "U" type plans divide living and sleeping units into separate sections. This layout is especially applicable to a utility core concept in which the kitchen becomes part of the connecting link. Excellent separation of activities is achieved, and useful patios are afforded shelter and privacy. In addition, each room can receive cross ventilation. The chief disadvantage of these types is in the long perimeter walls (almost fifty percent more than the same space in a simple rectangle), resulting in higher construction cost as well as increased expense of heating and air conditioning.

The rectangular utility core plan has several advantages. The house may be almost square and very compact, with a good concentration of utilities. In addition, the core acts as a buffer between the sleeping and living zones. The problems of this plan include the difficulty of properly relating the kitchen, garage and main entrances, and the excessive circulation space that is often required. This can be helped by opening up the exterior walls and actually using the lot as circulation and access in areas of mild climate.

SOURCE: D. Q. Jones and F. Emmons, Builder's Homes for Better Living, Reinhold Publishing Corp., N. Y.

THE IN-LINE PLAN

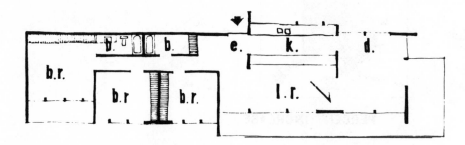

The in-line plan is an excellent solution for many unusual site conditions. On a narrow lot it allows access to side patios and outdoor areas; on steep hillsides it allows the maximum economy of construction and land usage. It can have good circulation (at the expense of a long corridor) and the same good orientation for all the rooms.

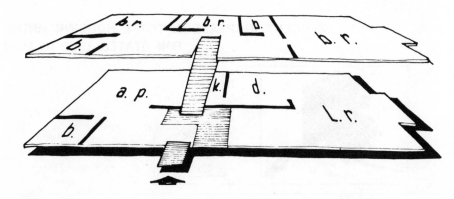

The plan may be adapted to a two-story house, where it helps to concentrate circulation and utilities, while retaining the advantage of providing the best orientation for both floors.

THE SPLIT LEVEL PLAN

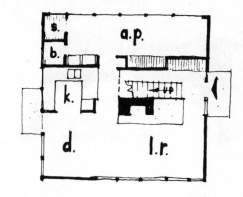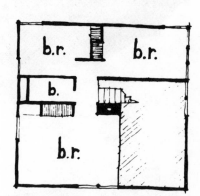

The split-level plan produces a maximum of total interior area for a house of small over-all size, and its separate levels can give greater privacy and interest in each area. It is very adaptable to sloping lots, and helps to solve the problems of deep foundations in northern climates. However, it may require a somewhat complicated framing system, and is difficult to relate to outdoor areas without special terracing or grading.

PERCENT INCREASE IN TOTAL U. S. DWELLING UNITS, 1940–1960

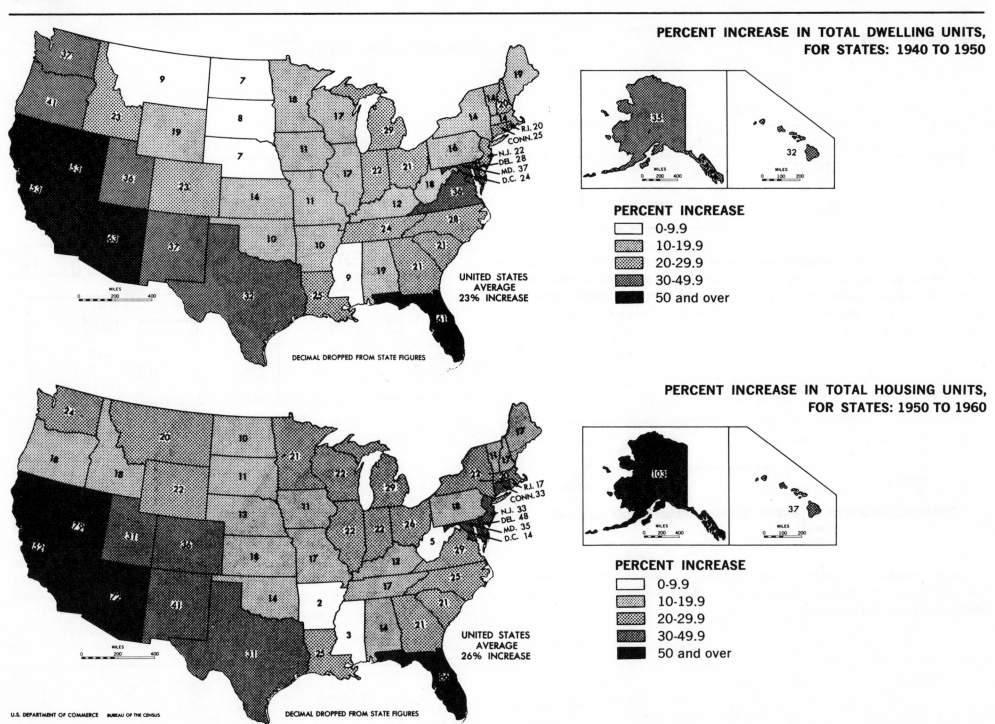

PERCENT INCREASE IN TOTAL DWELLING UNITS, FOR STATES: 1940 TO 1950

R.I. 20
CONN. 25
N.J. 22
DEL. 28
MD. 37
D.C. 24

UNITED STATES AVERAGE 23% INCREASE

DECIMAL DROPPED FROM STATE FIGURES

PERCENT INCREASE

- 0-9.9
- 10-19.9
- 20-29.9
- 30-49.9
- 50 and over

PERCENT INCREASE IN TOTAL HOUSING UNITS, FOR STATES: 1950 TO 1960

R.I. 17
CONN. 33
N.J. 33
DEL. 48
MD. 35
D.C. 14

UNITED STATES AVERAGE 26% INCREASE

DECIMAL DROPPED FROM STATE FIGURES

PERCENT INCREASE

- 0-9.9
- 10-19.9
- 20-29.9
- 30-49.9
- 50 and over

U.S. DEPARTMENT OF COMMERCE   BUREAU OF THE CENSUS

84

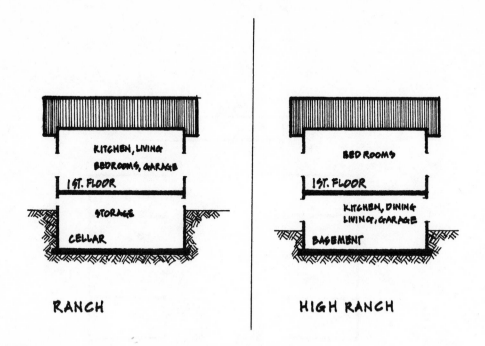

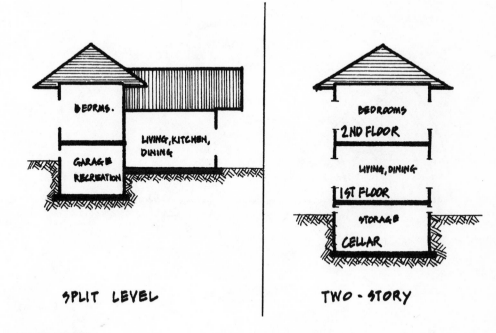

RANCH

The Ranch-type house is the traditional one-story house. All activities, cooking, dining, living and sleeping are on one level close to the ground. The house may or may not have a cellar, which is generally used for storage or minor activities. Older houses had high pitched roofs for expansion. The newer houses have low pitched roofs without provisions for expansion. This is the simplest type of construction.

HIGH RANCH

The High Ranch is similar to a ranch except that the main level is raised out of the ground allowing light and air into the basement. This lower level is then utilized as additional living space. One of the kitchen-dining-living areas can be located there, or the space can be used for additional bedrooms. The major advantage of this type of house over the traditional ranch is the utilization of the lower level for living purposes rather than storage or incidental use.

SPLIT-LEVEL

The split-level house separates the living activities into three levels. The kitchen-dining-living is the main level close to the ground. The sleeping level is located ½ level above the main level. The garage-recreation room-utility level is ½ level below the main level. The main advantage is the partial separation of activities and greater privacy. Disadvantages are the up and down stair movement and more complicated construction.

TWO-STORY

The two-story house is characteristic of most older houses. The lower level contains the kitchen-dining-living areas. The upper floor contains the sleeping areas. This type of house most often has a cellar for storage. The main advantage is the complete separation of living and sleeping activities for maximum privacy. The major disadvantage is the up and down stair movement. Construction is more complicated than the ranch type house. Also, there is less lot coverage than the other types.

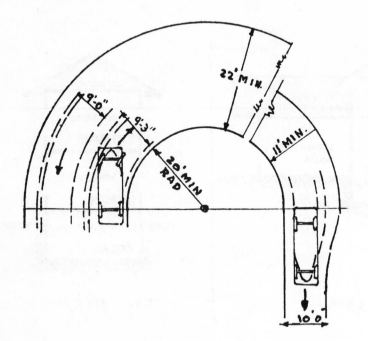

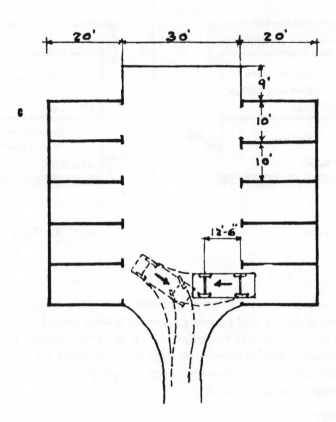

A. 180° turns

Garage compound

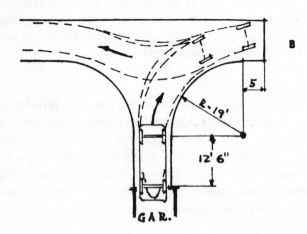

Tee turn out of garage

SOURCE: Eugene Henry Klaber, Housing Design, Reinhold Publishing Corp.—1954

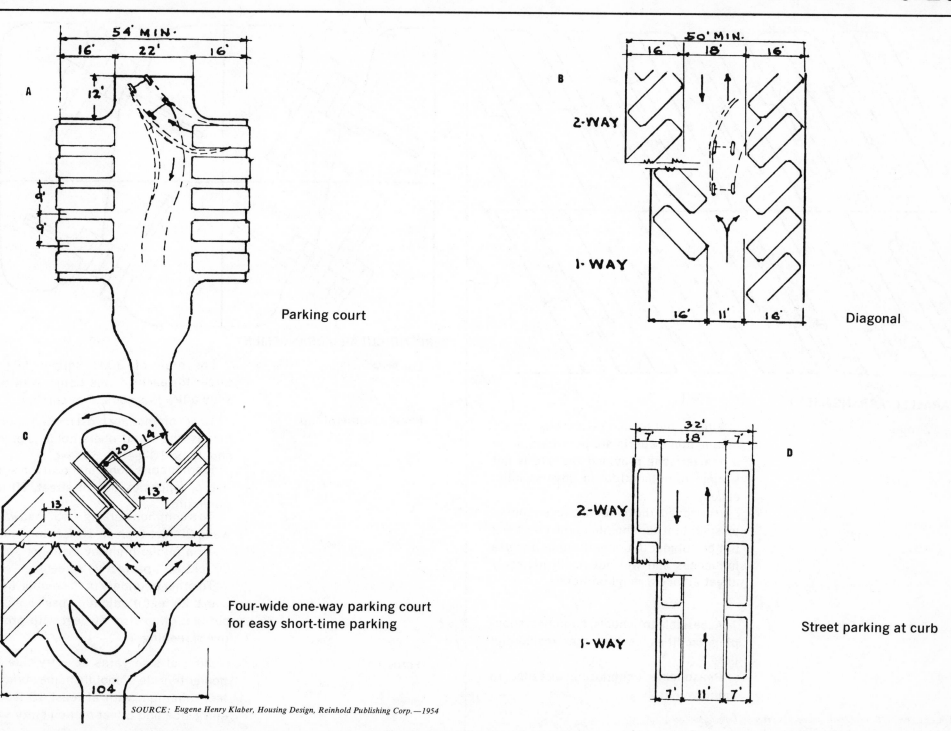

A — Parking court

B — Diagonal

C — Four-wide one-way parking court for easy short-time parking

D — Street parking at curb

SOURCE: *Eugene Henry Klaber, Housing Design, Reinhold Publishing Corp.—1954*

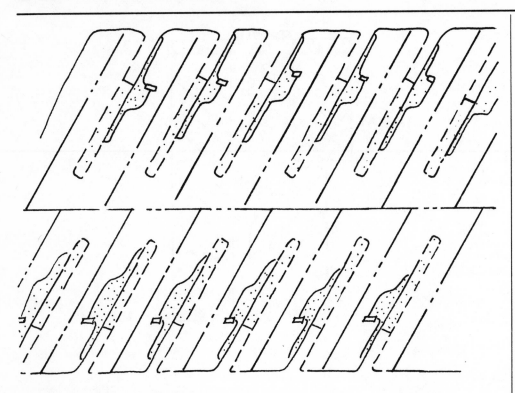

PARALLEL ARRANGEMENT

Zoning

Site should be in a residential zone if mobile home courts are permitted, or in a heavier zone provided the site is not subject to unhealthful or adverse influences.

If unzoned, the location chosen should be such that the mobile home court will not be subject to unhealthful or adverse influences and will not itself adversely affect adjacent neighborhoods.

Community Facilities

Accessible to schools, churches, shopping facilities as for other residential uses.

Reasonable commuting distance to employment.

SOURCE: Federal Housing Administration, Land Planning Bulletin 5, Washington, D. C.

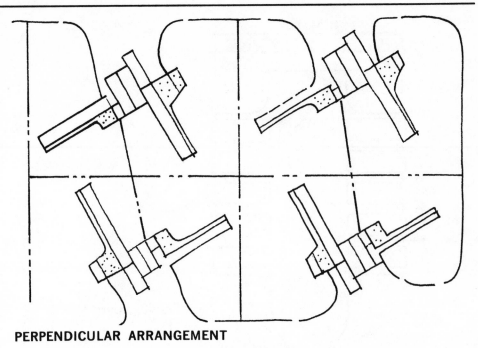

PERPENDICULAR ARRANGEMENT

Lot Area

Lot area of 3000 square feet or larger for each mobile home, with possibly a few lots somewhat smaller.

Mobile Home Stand

To accommodate most modern mobile homes, the stand where home is placed should be 10 feet by 50 feet.

From mobile home stand to the stand line on opposite side of street, 60 feet minimum.

To a common parking area, roadway or walk, 20 feet typical, 10 feet minimum.

To a public highway or major street, 50 feet with protective screening.

To other boundary of the mobile home court: 25 feet if adjoining uses are compatible; otherwise, 50 feet with protective screening.

Yards

Sum of side yards at entry side and non-entry side of mobile home stand, 32 feet minimum with at least 15 feet on entry side and 5 feet on non-entry side.

CREATION AND AUTHORITY.—The Department of Housing and Urban Development was established by the Department of Housing and Urban Development Act of September 9, 1965 (79 Stat. 667; 5 U. S. C. 642). The act, which became effective November 9, 1965, transferred to and vested in the Secretary of Housing and Urban Development all of the funtions, powers, and duties of the housing and Home Finance Agency (including the Community Facilities Administration and the Urban Renewal Administration), of the Federal Housing Administration and the Public Housing Administration, and of the heads and other officers also transferred to the Department the Federal National Mortgage Association.

PURPOSE.—The Declaration of Purpose of the Department of Housing and Urban Development Act declares that "the general welfare and security of the Nation and the health and living standards of our people require, as a matter of national purpose, sound development of the Nation's communities and metropolitan areas in which the vast majority of its people live and work.

"To carry out such purpose, and in recognition of the increasing importance of housing and urban development in our national life, the Congress finds that establishment of an executive department is desirable to achieve the best administration of the principal programs of the Federal Government which provide assistance for housing and for the development of the Nation's communities; to assist the President in achieving maximum coordination of the various Federal activities which have a major effect upon urban community, suburban, or metropolitan development; to encourage the solution of problems of housing, urban development, and mass transportation through State, county, town, village, or other local and private action, including promotion of interstate, regional, and metropolitan cooperation; to encourage the maximum contributions that may be made by vigorous private homebuilding and mortgage lending industries to housing, urban development, and the national economy; and to provide for full and appropriate consideration, at the national level, of the needs and interests of the Nation's communities and of the people who live and work in them."

ORGANIZATION.—The Secretary of Housing and Urban Development established the organization of the Department and assigned programs and functions to the respective organization units in Secretary's Organization Order 1, dated February 24, 1966. The internal structure is shown in the organization chart.

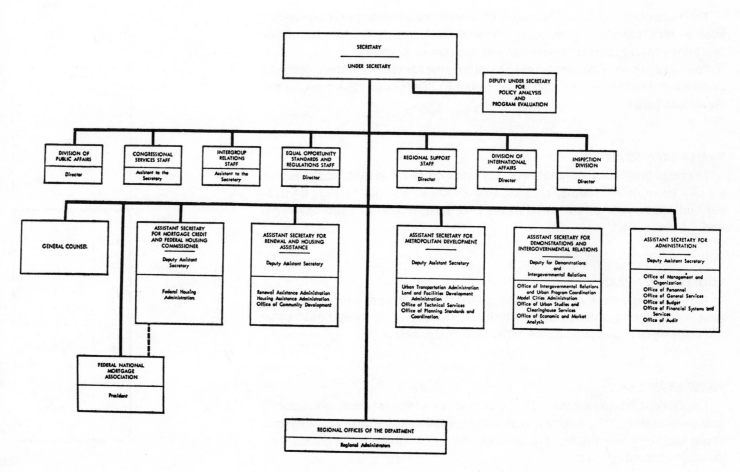

SOURCE: U. S. Government, Organization Manual—1966–67

The tenement house is characteristic of most slum areas in urban centers such as New York City. Although most were built during the second half of the 19th century, a substantial percentage still exist today.

The typical floor plan progressed through several stages of development, generally defined as type A) "Railroad" Plan B) "Dumbbell" Plan, and C) the "New-Law" plan.

"RAILROAD" PLAN

This was built full from lot line to lot line and covered 90% of the entire lot. All the interior rooms, ranging from 8 to 12 rooms, had no light or ventilation. Privies were located in the rear yard. Height of building were 6 and 7 stories high.

"DUMBBELL" PLAN

The buildings were similar to the Railroad Plan except that side courts were introduced providing some additional light and air. Additional toilet facilities were introduced on each floor, in the public hall.

"NEW-LAW" PLAN

The typical lot was increased to 50 ft. width and the lot coverage reduced to approximately 70%. Larger courts permitted some light and air in all rooms. Toilet facilities were included in each apartment. Rooms were still small and the units poorly laid out.

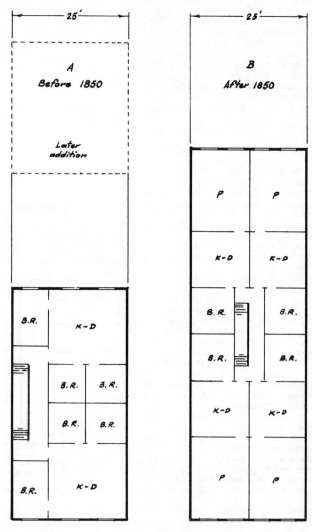

RAILROAD

Lot size—25' x 100'
Lot coverage—90%
Height of building—6 7 stories
Apts. per floor—4

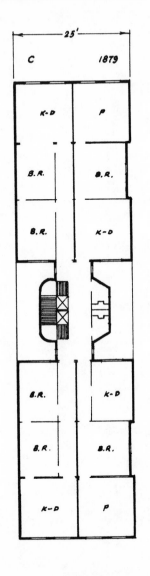

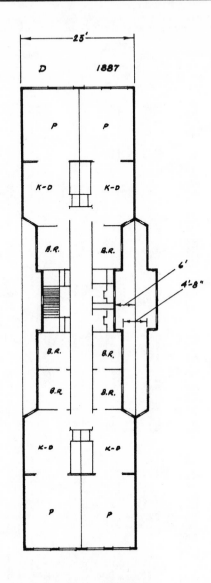

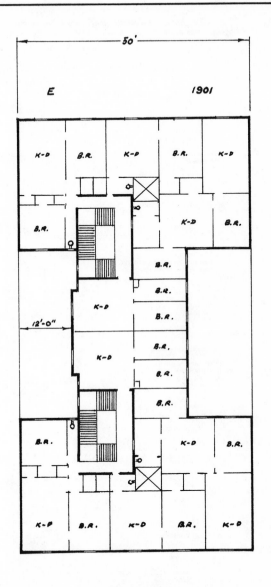

DUMBBELL **MODIFIED DUMBBELL** **NEW LAW**

Lot size—25' x 100'
Lot coverage—90%
Height of building—5 6 stories
Apts. per floor—4

Lot size—50' x 100'
Lot coverage—70%
Height of building—5 6 stories
Apts. per floor—7 8

—Percentage distribution of number of rooms, number of bedrooms, number of bathrooms, number of stories, basements, garages, water supply, sewage disposal, age of mortgagor, annual family income, annual total effective income, effective income as a percent of family income, 1-family homes, sec. 203, selected years

Percentage distribution	New homes							Existing homes						
	1965	1964	1963	1962	1960	1955	1950	1965	1964	1963	1962	1960	1955	1950
Number of rooms:														
4 rooms or less	5.7	5.7	6.2	5.0	3.4	16.0	56.0	11.9	12.9	14.8	14.6	16.7	24.5	29.1
5 rooms	40.8	41.6	45.1	49.9	56.8	57.7	31.9	39.0	40.6	40.6	40.2	39.7	39.9	34.9
6 rooms	34.9	35.3	33.3	32.1	31.3	24.6	11.5	33.8	32.9	32.0	32.2	31.7	26.9	25.3
7 rooms or more	18.6	17.4	15.4	13.0	8.5	1.7	.6	15.3	13.6	12.6	13.0	11.9	8.7	10.7
Average number of rooms	5.7	5.7	5.6	5.6	5.5	5.1	4.6	5.6	5.5	5.4	5.5	5.4	5.2	5.2
Number of bedrooms:														
2 bedrooms or less	4.2	4.3	4.8	5.3	5.1	20.4	NA	23.8	26.3	29.0	29.3	33.7	44.4	NA
3 bedrooms	78.6	80.0	81.2	83.8	87.8	73.8	NA	65.0	63.3	61.8	61.6	57.9	48.5	NA
4 bedrooms or more	17.2	15.7	14.0	10.9	7.1	5.8	NA	11.2	10.4	9.2	9.1	8.4	7.1	NA
Average number of bedrooms	3.2	3.1	3.1	3.1	3.0	2.9	NA	2.9	2.8	2.8	2.8	2.8	2.6	NA
Number of bathrooms:														
1 bathroom	34.2	38.5	40.1	42.0	47.5	NA	NA	62.5	64.5	67.4	68.3	76.5	NA	NA
1½ or 2 bathrooms	60.3	57.4	56.0	55.3	51.0	NA	NA	35.4	33.8	31.0	30.4	22.6	NA	NA
More than 2 bathrooms	5.5	4.1	3.9	2.7	1.5	NA	NA	2.1	1.7	1.6	1.3	.9	NA	NA
Stories:														
1 story	84.2	85.5	88.3	88.2	89.6	NA	NA	80.3	80.7	80.4	79.6	75.8	NA	NA
2 stories or more	10.7	9.3	6.4	6.8	4.9	NA	NA	16.8	16.7	17.3	18.2	22.5	NA	NA
Split level	5.1	5.2	5.3	5.0	5.5	NA	NA	2.9	2.6	2.3	2.2	1.7	NA	NA
Basements:														
Full basement	20.8	24.6	23.5	23.8	27.7	NA	NA	35.4	35.7	35.0	35.6	41.4	NA	NA
Part basement	4.7	5.2	4.7	5.7	5.4	NA	NA	3.7	4.1	4.0	5.2	6.2	NA	NA
No basement—slab on ground	47.5	46.9	48.8	51.7	44.6	NA	NA	24.1	23.2	22.6	22.0	17.8	NA	NA
No basement—crawl space	27.0	23.3	23.0	18.8	22.3	NA	NA	36.8	37.0	38.4	37.2	34.6	NA	NA
Garage:														
No garage	17.7	20.1	20.7	21.5	26.0	30.2	51.3	21.5	23.0	23.5	24.5	28.6	20.1	29.4
Carport	26.5	22.6	24.4	16.7	20.8	NA	NA	13.2	12.6	12.2	9.1	9.5	NA	NA
Garage	55.8	57.3	54.9	61.8	53.2	69.8	48.7	65.3	64.4	64.3	66.4	61.9	79.9	70.6
Water supply:														
Public main	97.0	95.9	95.0	95.2	94.2	NA	NA	96.4	96.1	95.3	95.0	94.9	NA	NA
Community system	2.2	2.7	3.3	3.8	4.3	NA	NA	1.0	1.0	1.0	1.3	1.4	NA	NA
Individual well	.8	1.4	1.7	1.0	1.5	NA	NA	2.6	2.9	3.7	3.7	3.7	NA	NA
Sewage disposal:														
Public sewer	88.4	86.2	84.4	81.1	76.9	NA	NA	83.3	83.4	81.8	77.6	76.1	NA	NA
Community sewer	3.2	3.6	4.2	4.5	4.9	NA	NA	.9	1.0	.9	1.2	1.1	NA	NA
Individual septic tank	7.5	9.3	10.2	11.8	15.3	NA	NA	13.8	14.0	15.7	18.2	18.9	NA	NA
Individual cesspool	.9	.9	1.2	2.6	2.9	NA	NA	2.0	1.6	1.6	3.0	3.9	NA	NA
Age of mortgagor:														
Less than 25 years	16.6	16.2	15.9	14.6	12.9	NA	NA	16.7	16.2	15.1	13.7	12.5	NA	NA
25 to 29 years	28.8	28.8	27.5	25.7	25.4	NA	NA	28.6	27.9	26.0	23.9	24.2	NA	NA
30 to 34 years	18.0	17.5	18.4	20.3	22.3	NA	NA	16.6	16.6	17.4	18.9	21.3	NA	NA
35 to 39 years	14.1	14.4	14.7	15.4	17.0	NA	NA	13.5	14.0	14.7	15.4	16.7	NA	NA
40 to 44 years	9.7	9.7	10.5	10.7	10.4	NA	NA	9.7	10.2	10.8	11.9	11.4	NA	NA
45 to 49 years	6.3	6.7	6.3	6.5	6.5	NA	NA	6.9	7.3	7.8	8.1	7.5	NA	NA
50 to 59 years	5.4	5.5	5.0	5.4	4.6	NA	NA	6.9	6.8	7.1	6.9	5.7	NA	NA
60 years and over	1.1	1.2	1.7	1.4	.9	NA	NA	1.1	1.0	1.1	1.2	.7	NA	NA
Average age............years	33.0	33.2	33.4	33.7	33.6	NA	NA	33.4	33.6	34.1	34.5	34.1	NA	NA
Median age............years	31.3	31.4	31.8	32.4	32.6	NA	NA	31.4	31.8	32.6	33.3	33.1	NA	NA
Annual family income:														
Less than $4,000	0.3	0.5	0.6	1.1	0.5	NA	NA	0.5	0.8	1.0	1.2	1.4	NA	NA
$4,000 to $4,999	1.8	3.1	3.5	5.2	4.6	NA	NA	2.9	3.9	4.7	5.5	7.0	NA	NA
$5,000 to $5,999	7.2	8.5	10.1	12.2	12.6	NA	NA	7.6	9.6	11.3	12.8	15.0	NA	NA
$6,000 to $6,999	14.3	15.4	16.6	17.2	19.4	NA	NA	14.6	15.9	17.0	17.4	19.3	NA	NA
$7,000 to $7,999	15.8	15.9	15.9	15.9	17.5	NA	NA	15.8	16.0	15.7	15.9	16.3	NA	NA
$8,000 to $8,999	13.7	13.6	13.8	13.7	13.8	NA	NA	13.2	13.3	13.0	12.8	12.7	NA	NA
$9,000 to $9,999	13.6	13.2	12.8	12.4	11.8	NA	NA	13.2	12.7	12.1	11.6	10.6	NA	NA
$10,000 to $11,999	17.2	15.5	14.5	12.7	11.4	NA	NA	16.3	14.4	13.5	12.3	10.3	NA	NA
$12,000 to $14,999	11.3	10.0	8.5	6.8	5.8	NA	NA	11.0	9.4	8.2	7.4	5.3	NA	NA
$15,000 and over	4.8	4.3	3.7	2.8	2.6	NA	NA	4.9	4.0	3.5	3.1	2.1	NA	NA
Average family income	$9,273	$9,003	$8,752	$8,382	$8,252	NA	NA	$9,172	$8,833	$8,587	$8,372	$7,934	NA	NA
Median family income	$8,777	$8,484	$8,237	$7,899	$7,733	NA	NA	$8,651	$8,291	$8,023	$7,824	$7,447	NA	NA
Annual total effective income:														
Less than $4,000	1.1	1.6	1.8	2.1	1.3	11.2	55.6	1.7	2.2	2.4	2.7	3.0	10.6	42.8
$4,000 to $4,999	4.3	6.0	6.4	8.3	7.6	26.5	24.0	6.2	7.7	8.3	9.1	11.3	24.6	24.1
$5,000 to $5,999	12.2	13.7	14.5	16.0	17.0	21.0	9.7	13.1	15.2	16.2	17.2	19.4	19.9	11.9
$6,000 to $6,999	19.3	19.4	18.5	18.8	21.2	16.8	5.8	19.4	19.7	18.7	18.9	19.8	16.5	9.4
$7,000 to $7,999	16.9	16.2	15.9	15.9	17.1	10.6	2.5	16.4	15.9	15.2	15.2	15.0	11.3	4.9
$8,000 to $8,999	12.2	11.7	12.8	13.1	12.6	5.6	1.0	11.3	11.0	11.8	11.6	11.1	6.2	2.1
$9,000 to $9,999	11.3	11.0	10.2	9.6	9.2	3.7	.6	10.7	10.1	9.3	8.9	7.9	4.3	1.7
$10,000 to $11,999	12.2	11.0	11.6	10.1	8.7	2.7	.4	11.2	9.8	10.3	9.6	7.7	3.3	1.3
$12,000 to $14,999	7.7	7.0	5.8	4.4	3.9	1.3	.3	7.3	6.2	5.6	5.0	3.5	2.2	1.2
$15,000 and over	2.8	2.4	2.5	1.7	1.4	.6	.1	2.7	2.2	2.2	1.9	1.3	1.1	.6
Average total effective income	$8,349	$8,108	$7,991	$7,705	$7,584	$5,975	$4,213	$8,147	$7,853	$7,741	$7,593	$7,243	$6,177	$4,837
Median total effective income	$7,777	$7,572	$7,546	$7,289	$7,168	$5,484	$3,861	$7,580	$7,325	$7,295	$7,135	$6,784	$5,669	$4,274
Effective income as a percent of family income:														
100	48.6	52.0	62.5	64.1	62.6	NA	NA	44.1	46.7	60.7	62.6	60.9	NA	NA
90–99	25.5	23.9	20.7	18.7	18.8	NA	NA	26.5	24.6	20.5	19.0	18.7	NA	NA
Less than 90	25.9	24.1	16.8	17.2	18.6	NA	NA	29.4	28.7	18.8	18.4	20.4	NA	NA

NA   Not available.

SOURCE: *Annual Report—1965, U. S. Department of Housing and Urban Development*

SUB-DIVISIONS AND LAND DEVELOPMENT

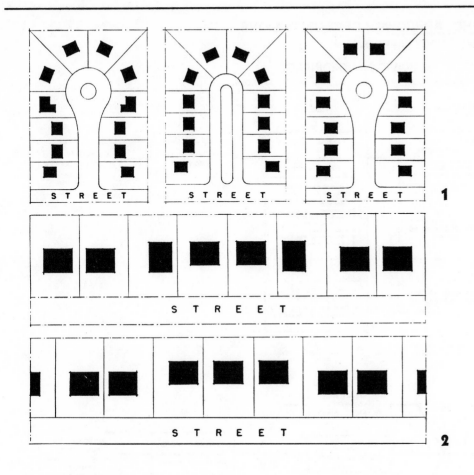

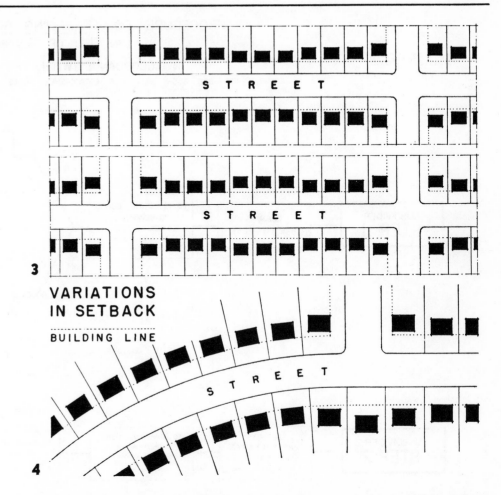

VARIATIONS IN SETBACK

1. The location of houses on culs-de-sac should result in a well-arranged group of dwellings with an appearance of spaciousness. Especial care is required to avoid an unpleasant angular relationship of individual houses to those on either side. Congested appearance is avoided if not more than five houses front on the turnaround.

2. Variations in grouping of houses to further avoid monotony can be obtained by varying the widths of side yards. Where all houses on the street are located in the center of each lot, there is a monotonous regularity in spacing even though the exteriors are varied in design. Variations in the widths of side yards should be so arranged that an appearance of openness results through the increased space between groups of dwellings. Setback and side-yard variations should be considered in relation to the design of individual houses.

SOURCE: Principles of Planning Small Houses, Technical Bulletin *4 Federal Housing Administration

3. When streets are straight and all houses are set back equidistant from the street line, a monotonous street appearance usually results. This can be avoided by varying the setback of the houses from the street. The setback should apply to groups of houses and the variation from the required building line should seldom exceed ten feet—less than ten feet usually being desirable. Variation in the location of houses to preserve existing trees or other natural features of the site also will avoid monotony in street appearance.

4. When streets are decidedly curved, monotony resulting from locating houses equidistant from the street line is generally overcome due to the changing vista of houses built to a curving setback line. However, slight variations in setback of house groups may also be desirable.

PROCEDURE FOR <u>PLANNING BOARD APPROVAL</u> OF SUBDIVISIONS
(IN LIEU OF GOVERNING BODY APPROVAL)

<u>ALTERNATE "A"</u>

IN ACCORDANCE WITH THE LOCAL SUBDIVISION ORDINANCE
PROVIDED SUCH ORDINANCE ESTABLISHES RULES, REGULATIONS AND STANDARDS FOR PLAT APPROVAL

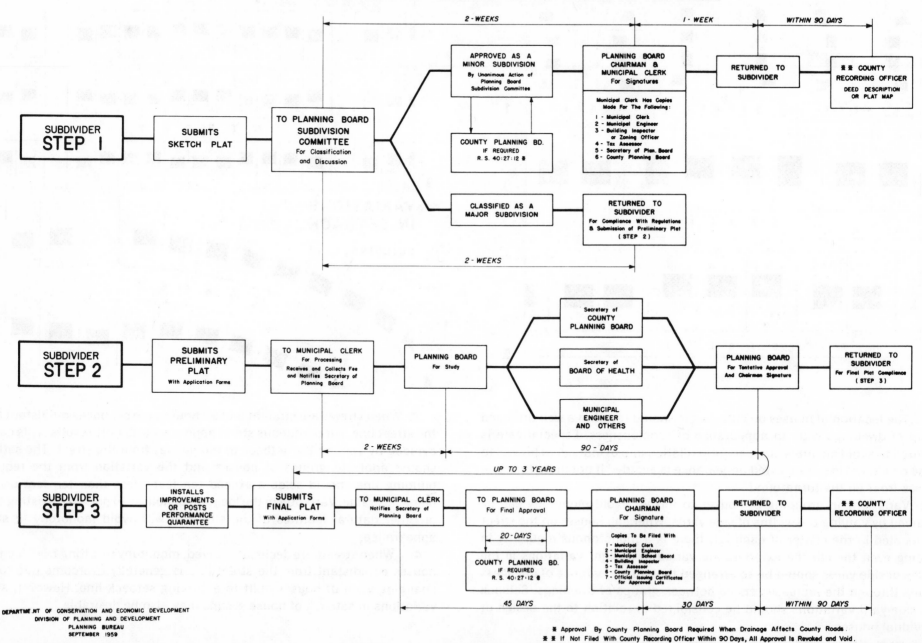

DEPARTMENT OF CONSERVATION AND ECONOMIC DEVELOPMENT
DIVISION OF PLANNING AND DEVELOPMENT
PLANNING BUREAU
SEPTEMBER 1959

※ Approval By County Planning Board Required When Drainage Affects County Roads.
※ ※ If Not Filed With County Recording Officer Within 90 Days, All Approval Is Revoked and Void.

PROCEDURE FOR GOVERNING BODY APPROVAL OF SUBDIVISIONS
AFTER FAVORABLE REFERRAL BY THE PLANNING BOARD

ALTERNATE "B"

IN ACCORDANCE WITH THE LOCAL SUBDIVISION ORDINANCE
PROVIDED SUCH ORDINANCE ESTABLISHES RULES, REGULATIONS AND STANDARDS FOR PLAT APPROVAL

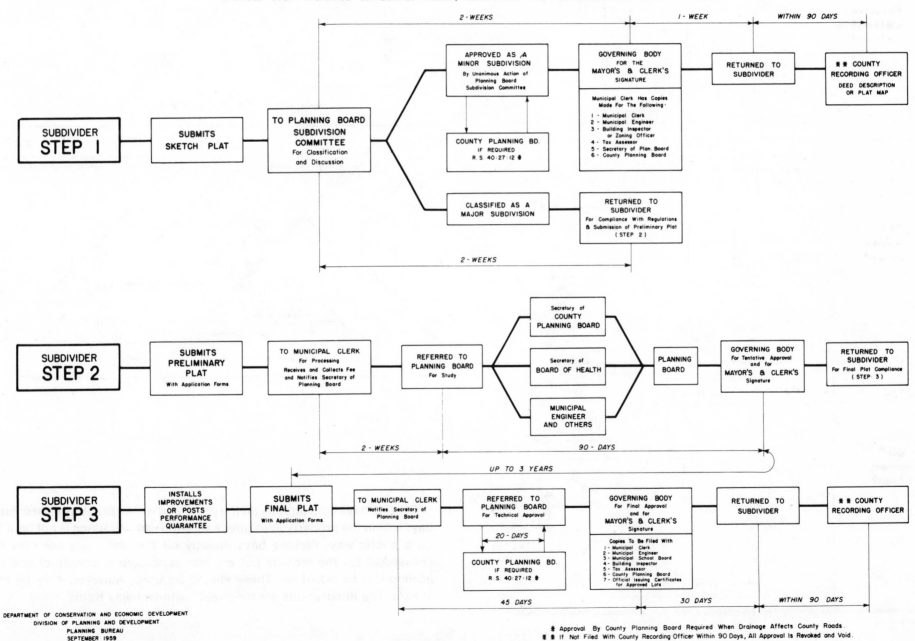

DEPARTMENT OF CONSERVATION AND ECONOMIC DEVELOPMENT
DIVISION OF PLANNING AND DEVELOPMENT
PLANNING BUREAU
SEPTEMBER 1959

✱ Approval By County Planning Board Required When Drainage Affects County Roads.
✱✱ If Not Filed With County Recording Officer Within 90 Days, All Approval Is Revoked and Void.

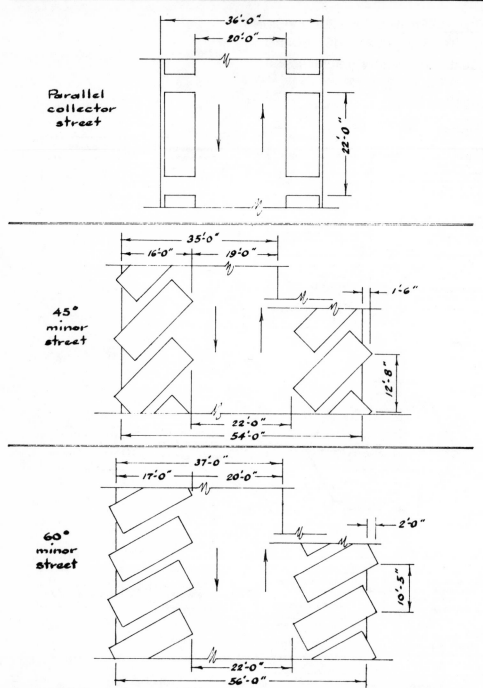

Parallel collector street

45° minor street

60° minor street

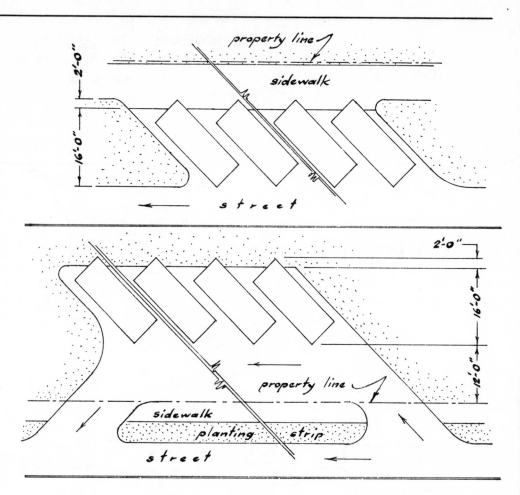

property line

sidewalk

street

sidewalk

planting strip

street

property line

Parking bays both directly off the street and within property limits. Parking bays within the property lines offer a solution where parking is not permitted on a public way. Parking bays directly off the street are not only more convenient for the tenants but are less expensive to construct and more economical to maintain. These should be used, however, only on minor streets. The illustrations are for streets with two-way traffic.

SOURCE: *Minimum Property Standards, for 1 and 2-Family Houses, FHA, Dept. of Housing and Urban Development, Washington, D. C.*

COMPUTING CHART

TO FIND THE TOTAL COST OF AN IMPROVED LOT
(RAW LAND AND STREET IMPROVEMENTS)

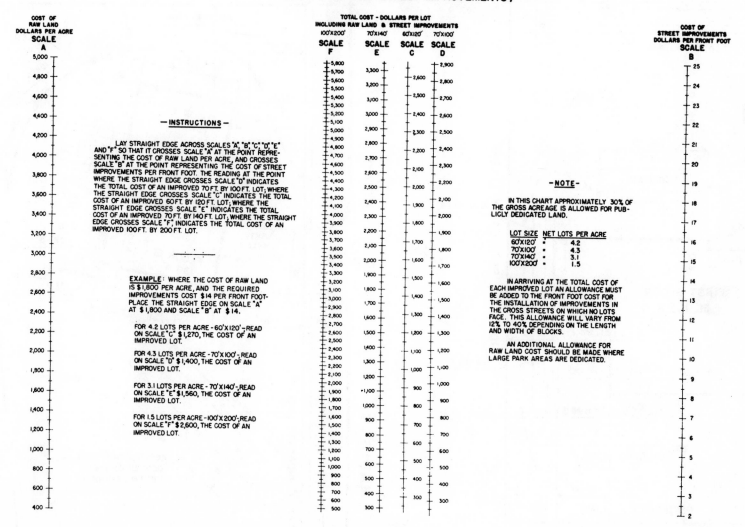

COST OF RAW LAND DOLLARS PER ACRE SCALE A

TOTAL COST - DOLLARS PER LOT INCLUDING RAW LAND & STREET IMPROVEMENTS

100'X200' SCALE F — 70'X140' SCALE E — 60'X120' SCALE C — 70'X100' SCALE D

COST OF STREET IMPROVEMENTS DOLLARS PER FRONT FOOT SCALE B

—INSTRUCTIONS—

LAY STRAIGHT EDGE ACROSS SCALES "A", "B", "C", "D", "E" AND "F" SO THAT IT CROSSES SCALE "A" AT THE POINT REPRESENTING THE COST OF RAW LAND PER ACRE, AND CROSSES SCALE "B" AT THE POINT REPRESENTING THE COST OF STREET IMPROVEMENTS PER FRONT FOOT. THE READING AT THE POINT WHERE THE STRAIGHT EDGE CROSSES SCALE "D" INDICATES THE TOTAL COST OF AN IMPROVED 70 FT. BY 100 FT. LOT; WHERE THE STRAIGHT EDGE CROSSES SCALE "C" INDICATES THE TOTAL COST OF AN IMPROVED 60 FT. BY 120 FT. LOT; WHERE THE STRAIGHT EDGE CROSSES SCALE "E" INDICATES THE TOTAL COST OF AN IMPROVED 70 FT. BY 140 FT. LOT; WHERE THE STRAIGHT EDGE CROSSES SCALE "F", INDICATES THE TOTAL COST OF AN IMPROVED 100 FT. BY 200 FT. LOT.

EXAMPLE : WHERE THE COST OF RAW LAND IS $1,800 PER ACRE, AND THE REQUIRED IMPROVEMENTS COST $14 PER FRONT FOOT—PLACE THE STRAIGHT EDGE ON SCALE "A" AT $1,800 AND SCALE "B" AT $14.

FOR 4.2 LOTS PER ACRE - 60'X120'—READ ON SCALE "C" $1,270, THE COST OF AN IMPROVED LOT.

FOR 4.3 LOTS PER ACRE - 70'X100'—READ ON SCALE "D" $1,400, THE COST OF AN IMPROVED LOT.

FOR 3.1 LOTS PER ACRE - 70'X140'—READ ON SCALE "E" $1,560, THE COST OF AN IMPROVED LOT.

FOR 1.5 LOTS PER ACRE - 100'X200'—READ ON SCALE "F" $2,600, THE COST OF AN IMPROVED LOT.

—NOTE—

IN THIS CHART APPROXIMATELY 30% OF THE GROSS ACREAGE IS ALLOWED FOR PUBLICLY DEDICATED LAND.

LOT SIZE	NET LOTS PER ACRE
60'X120'	4.2
70'X100'	4.3
70'X140'	3.1
100'X200'	1.5

IN ARRIVING AT THE TOTAL COST OF EACH IMPROVED LOT AN ALLOWANCE MUST BE ADDED TO THE FRONT FOOT COST FOR THE INSTALLATION OF IMPROVEMENTS IN THE CROSS STREETS ON WHICH NO LOTS FACE. THIS ALLOWANCE WILL VARY FROM 12% TO 40% DEPENDING ON THE LENGTH AND WIDTH OF BLOCKS.

AN ADDITIONAL ALLOWANCE FOR RAW LAND COST SHOULD BE MADE WHERE LARGE PARK AREAS ARE DEDICATED.

SOURCE: Federal Housing Administration, Washington, D. C.

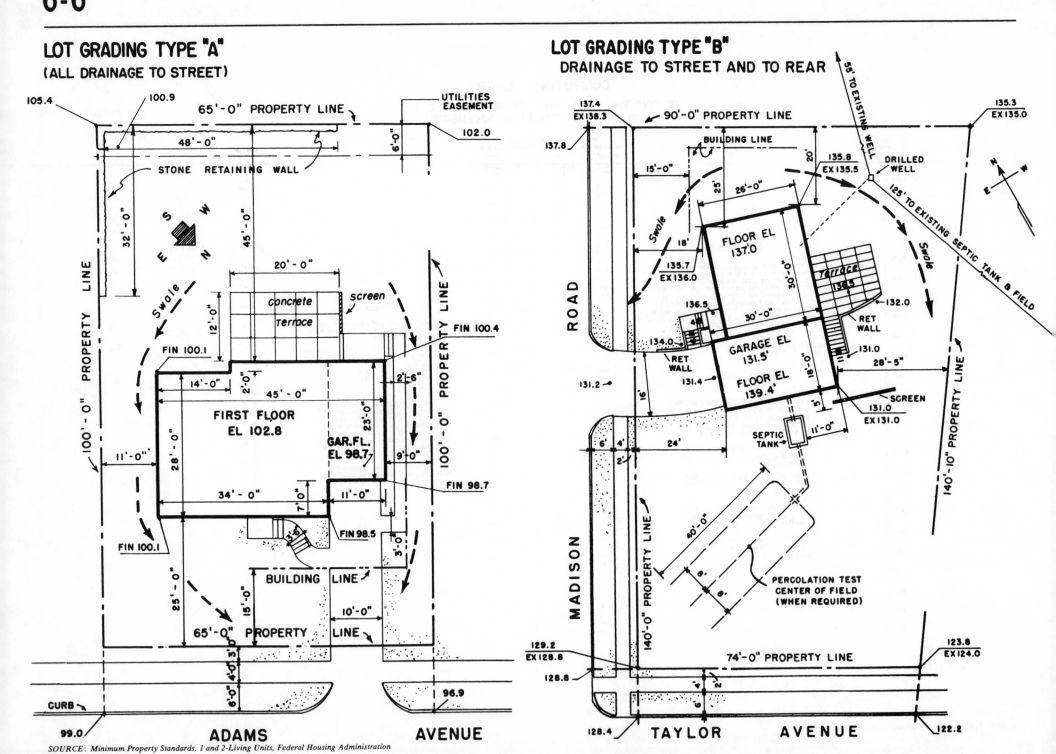

LOT GRADING TYPE "A"
(ALL DRAINAGE TO STREET)

LOT GRADING TYPE "B"
DRAINAGE TO STREET AND TO REAR

SOURCE: Minimum Property Standards, 1 and 2-Living Units, Federal Housing Administration

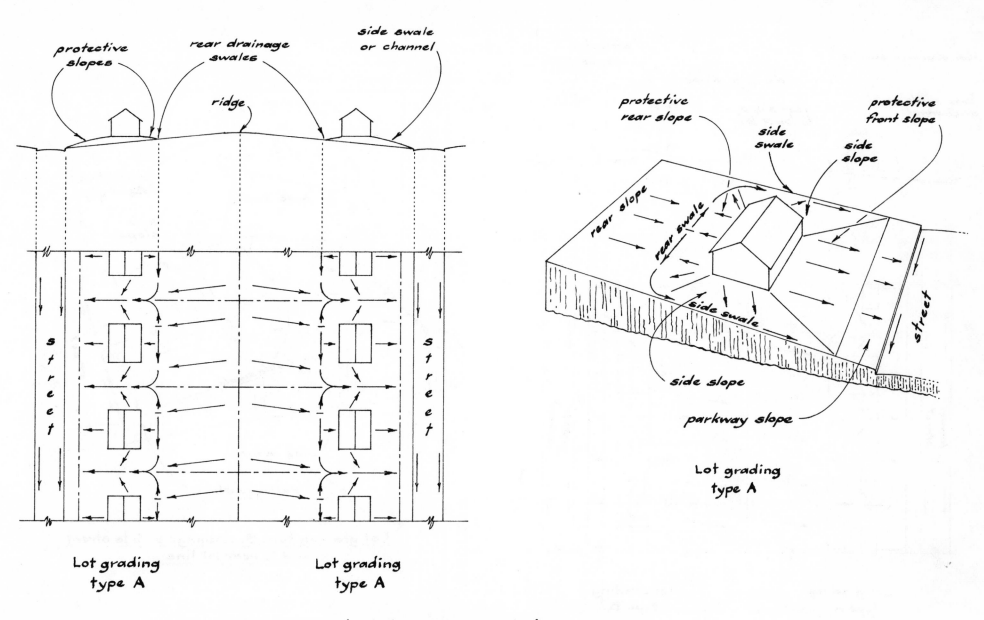

protective
slopes

rear drainage
swales

side swale
or channel

ridge

street

street

Lot grading
type A

Lot grading
type A

protective
rear slope

side
swale

side
slope

protective
front slope

rear slope

rear swale

side swale

side slope

street

side slope

parkway slope

Lot grading
type A

Lot grading type A, all drainage to street
ridge along rear lot lines

SOURCE: Minimum Property Requirements, Federal Housing Administration, Washington, D. C.

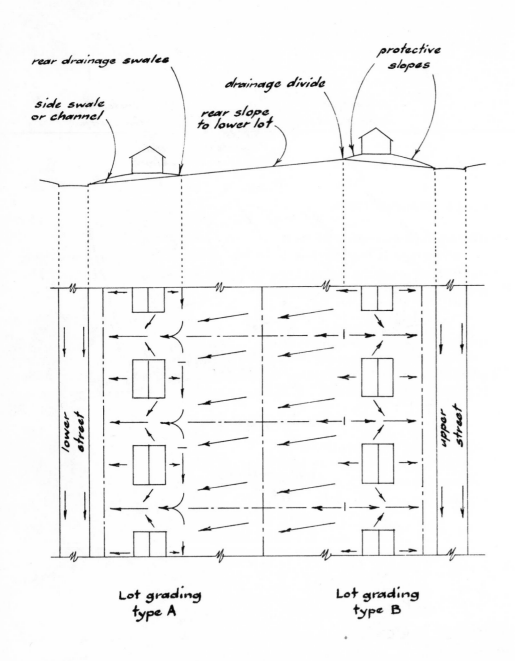

rear drainage swales

side swale
or channel

drainage divide

rear slope
to lower lot

protective
slopes

lower street

upper street

Lot grading
type A

Lot grading
type B

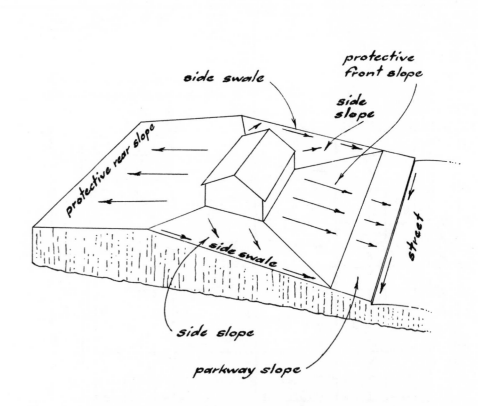

side swale

protective
front slope

side
slope

protective rear slope

side swale

street

side slope

parkway slope

Lot grading type B, drainage both to street
and to rear lot line

SOURCE: *Minimum Property Requirements, Federal Housing Administration, Washington, D. C.*

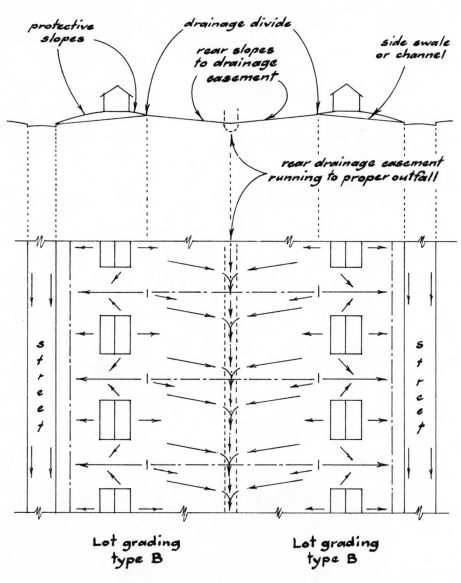

protective slopes

drainage divide

rear slopes to drainage easement

side swale or channel

rear drainage easement running to proper outfall

s t r e e t

s t r e e t

Lot grading type B

Lot grading type B

Valley along rear lot lines

BLOCK GRADING TYPES

Grading Type A—(see plate 6–7)

This method is the simplest of all the methods. It provides for a ridge (high point) along the rear lot lines, then each lot is sloped down directly to the street, independent of other lots.

Grading Type B—(see plate 6–8)

This method provides for drainage to a valley (low point) along rear lot lines. The front portion is drained towards the street. The drainage along the rear lot lines will require an easement to properly handle the runoff.

Grading Type C—(see plate 6–10)

This method is similar to type B except that the drainage runs to side swales or channels. From the side of the house the water flows back to the rear lot line.

SOURCE: *Minimum Property Requirements, Federal Housing Administration, Washington, D. C.*

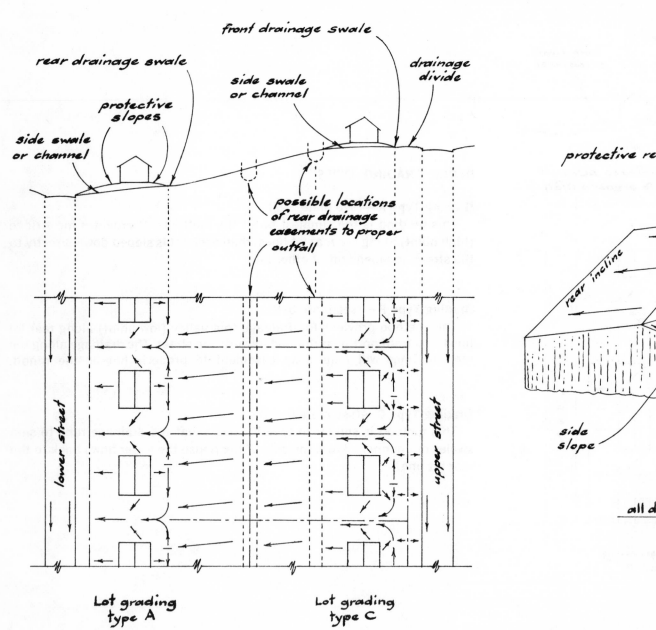

rear drainage swale

front drainage swale

protective slopes

side swale or channel

drainage divide

side swale or channel

possible locations of rear drainage easements to proper outfall

lower street

upper street

Lot grading type A

Lot grading type C

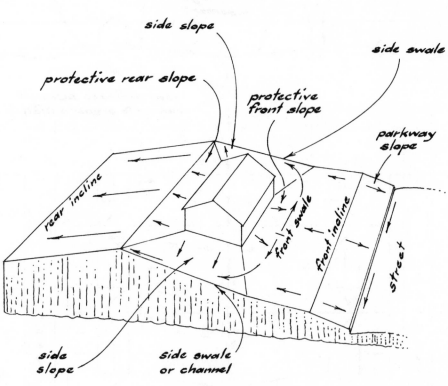

side slope

protective rear slope

protective front slope

side swale

parkway slope

rear incline

front swale

front incline

street

side slope

side swale or channel

Lot grading type C
all drainage to rear lot line

SOURCE: Minimum Property Requirements, Federal Housing Administration, Washington, D. C.

TYPES OF STREETS

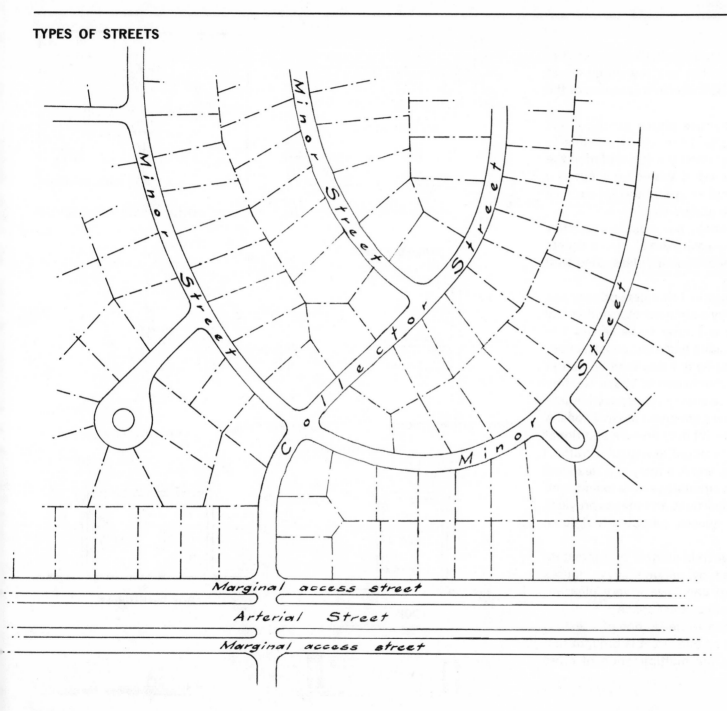

The term **"street"** means a way for vehicular traffic, whether designated as a street, highway, thoroughfare, parkway, throughway, road, avenue, boulevard, lane, place, or however otherwise designated:

1. **Arterial streets and highways** are those which are used primarily for fast or heavy traffic. Right-of-way width 80—120 feet.

2. **Collector streets** are those which carry traffic from minor streets to the major system of arterial streets and highways, including the principal entrance streets of a residential development and streets for circulation within such a development. Right-of-way width 60—80 feet.

3. **Minor streets** are those which are used primarily for access to the abutting properties. Right-of-way width 50—60 feet.

4. **Marginal access streets** are minor streets which are parallel to and adjacent to arterial streets and highways; and which provide access to abutting properties and protection from through traffic. Right-of-way width 40 feet.

5. **Alleys** are minor ways which are used primarily for vehicular service access to the back or the side of properties otherwise abutting on a street.

SOURCE: Control of Land Sub-Division, NYS Dept. of Commerce, Albany. N. Y.

Nomenclature adopted by the Association of State Highway Officials

TYPICAL

The pattern of streets and lots set out by the land subdivider provides the framework for groups of houses. Many interesting and individual street arrangements can be devised by considering the shape and contours of the land and by properly routing traffic.

The grid street plan is a handicap to effective house grouping and can only be obtained by occasional set-backs and the use of planting to conceal the monotony of the plan. On the other hand the street plan of the subdivision should be simple and straightforward; it should arise out of a reasonable and economical use of the space with an eye for the appearance and architectural effects of the buildings to be placed there.

Curved streets have a pleasant and natural effect, particularly when they are justified by topographical conditions. But excessive use of curved streets on flat land may be both dangerous and uneconomical unless done with careful planning.

The dead-end or cul-de-sac street provides the most complete privacy and traffic separation. The closure of the street clearly distinguishes an individual group of houses, and by limiting the number of houses to be served it is possible to use a street of economical dimensions and light construction. (The turning circle of a dead-end street should be not less than 80 feet in outside diameter. Also, in order to provide manoeuvring space for fire-fighting equipment and other emergencies there should be a space not less than 100 feet in diameter clear of trees and other permanent obstructions. A pedestrian lane from one turning circle to the next may provide additional egress; under normal circumstances this can be closed to vehicular traffic.)

The loop street provides the privacy, safety and economy of a dead-end street without the difficulties of turning; traffic circulates easily to and from a collector street. The loop street in various proportions and shapes provides interesting opportunities for the grouping of houses, particularly if some park space can be introduced.

The need to provide off-street parking suggests a number of interesting opportunities for small house groups served by parking bays. Houses grouped around a quadrangle or motor court can have a very pleasant character and are economical in the use of public street space.

In setting out a pattern of residential streets a T intersection of streets is safer than a cross intersection because traffic on one street is brought to a halt. The special hazard of the grid plan is the multiplication of cross intersections.

SOURCE: *Principles of Small House Grouping, Central Mortgage and Housing Corporation, Ottawa, Canada*

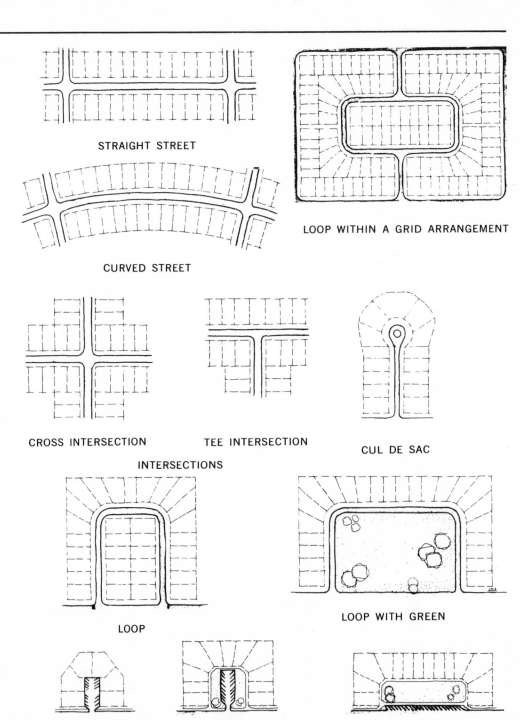

STRAIGHT STREET

LOOP WITHIN A GRID ARRANGEMENT

CURVED STREET

CROSS INTERSECTION   TEE INTERSECTION   CUL DE SAC

INTERSECTIONS

LOOP   LOOP WITH GREEN

SIX LOT ARRANGEMENT   MOTOR COURT   PARKING BAY

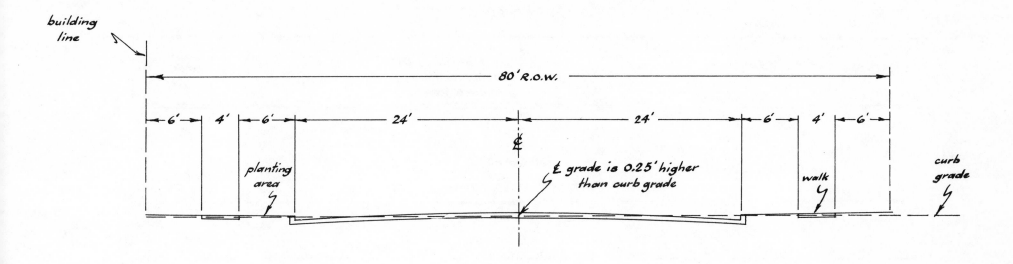

Secondary street
(residential)

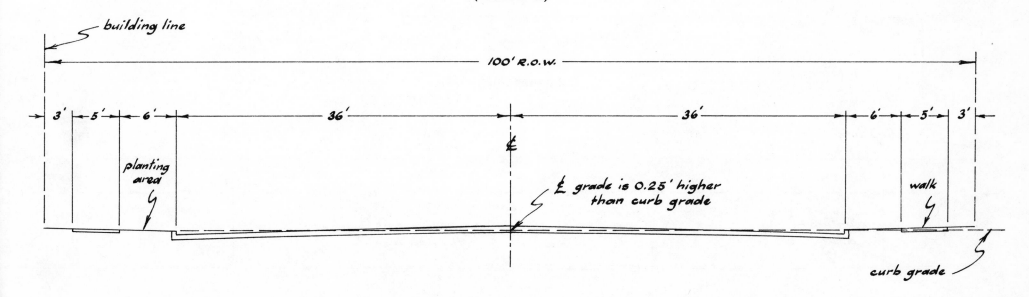

Major street

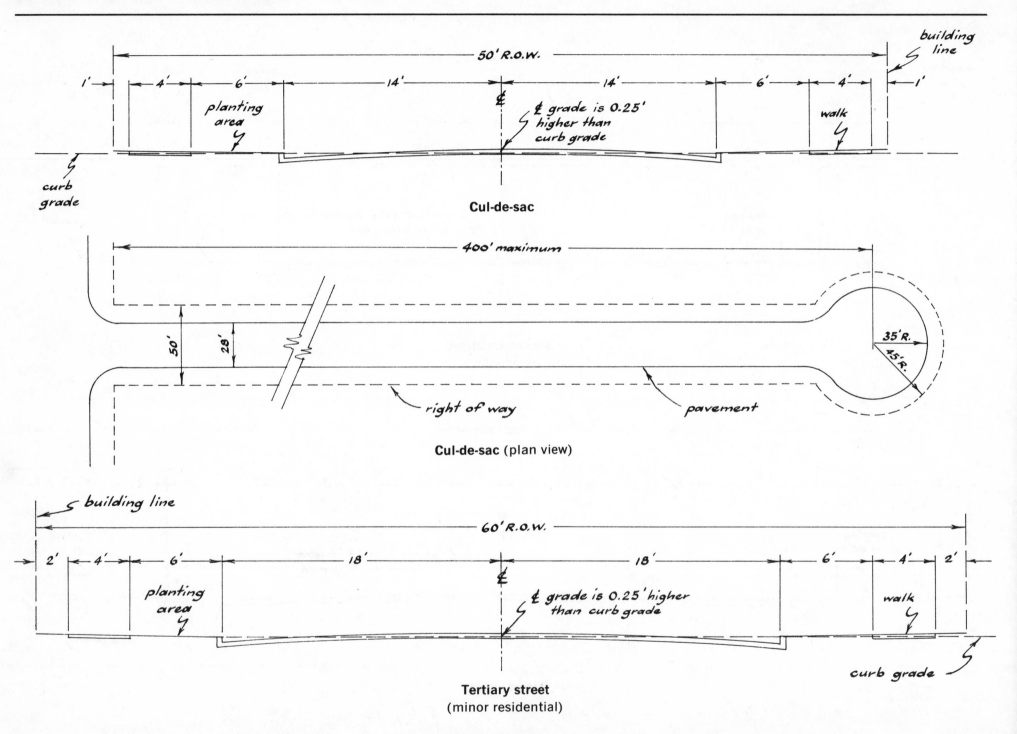

Cul-de-sac

50' R.O.W.

building line

1' 4' 6' 14' 14' 6' 4' 1'

planting area

℄ grade is 0.25' higher than curb grade

walk

curb grade

Cul-de-sac (plan view)

400' maximum

50' 28'

right of way   pavement

35' R.
45' R.

Tertiary street
(minor residential)

building line

60' R.O.W.

2' 4' 6' 18' 18' 6' 4' 2'

planting area

℄ grade is 0.25' higher than curb grade

walk

curb grade

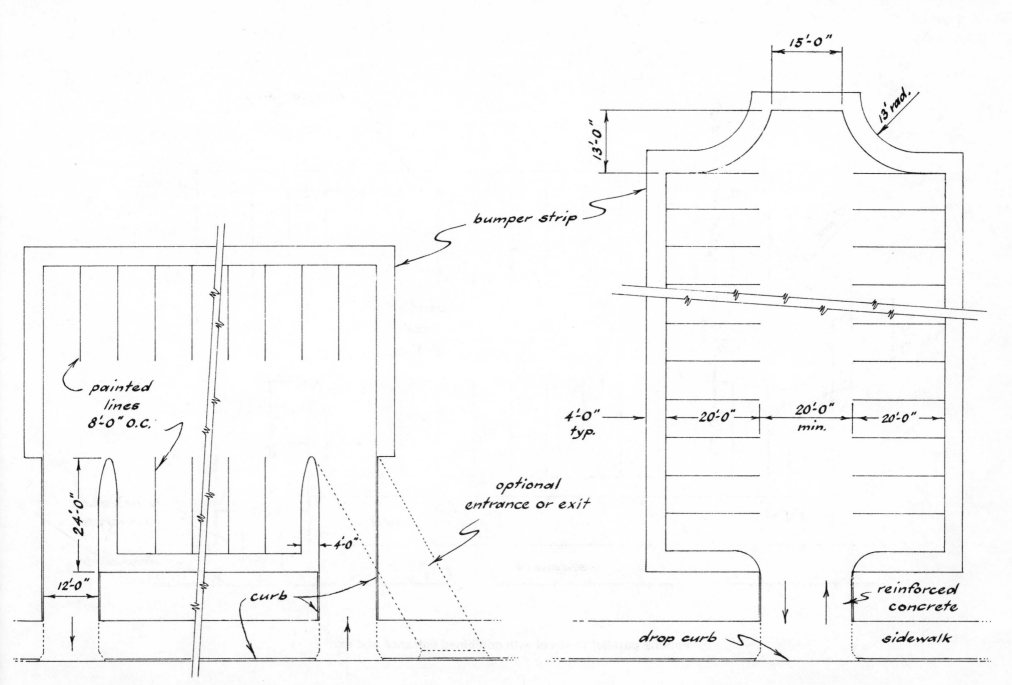

Parking parallel to street with separate entrance and exit

Parking—right angle to street

SOURCE: NYC Housing Authority, Memo to Architects—1952

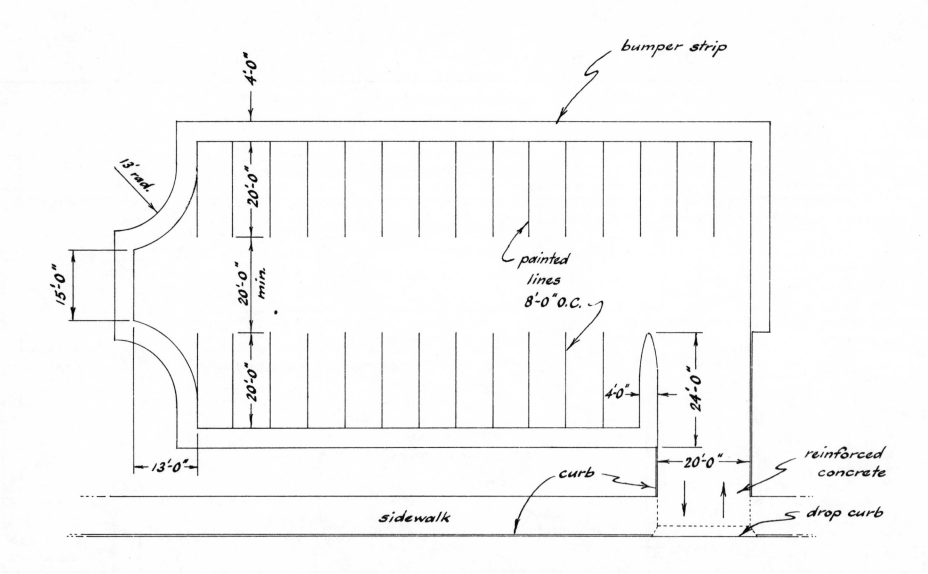

Parking parallel to street with combined entrance and exit

SOURCE: Memo to Architects, NYC Housing Authority—1952

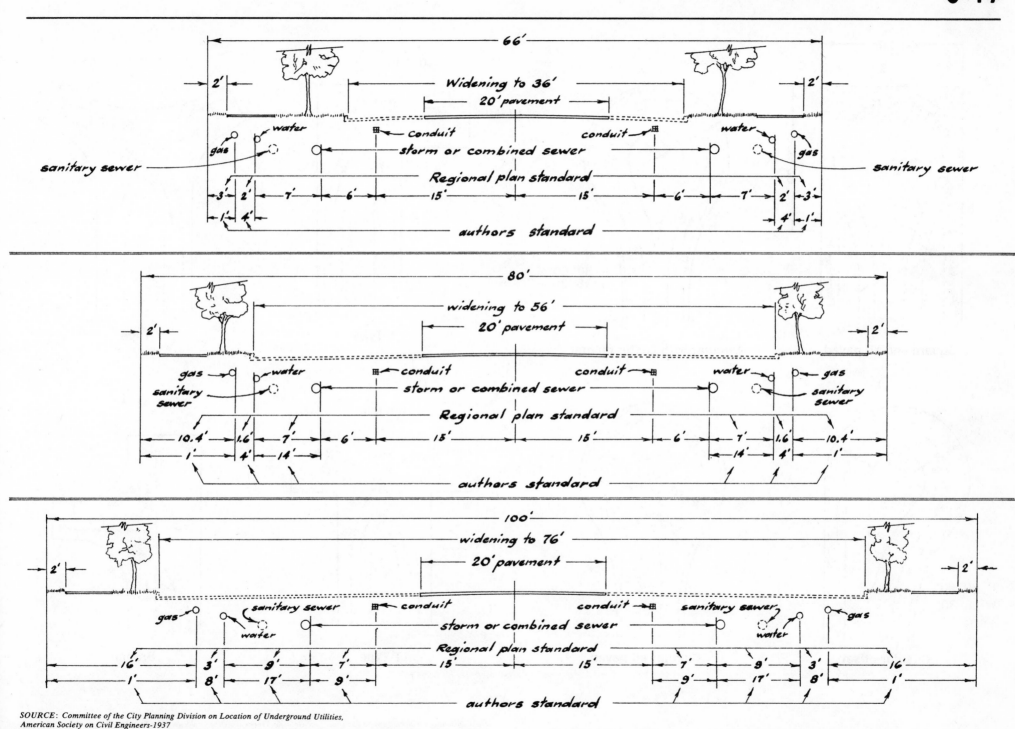

SOURCE: *Committee of the City Planning Division on Location of Underground Utilities,*
American Society on Civil Engineers-1937

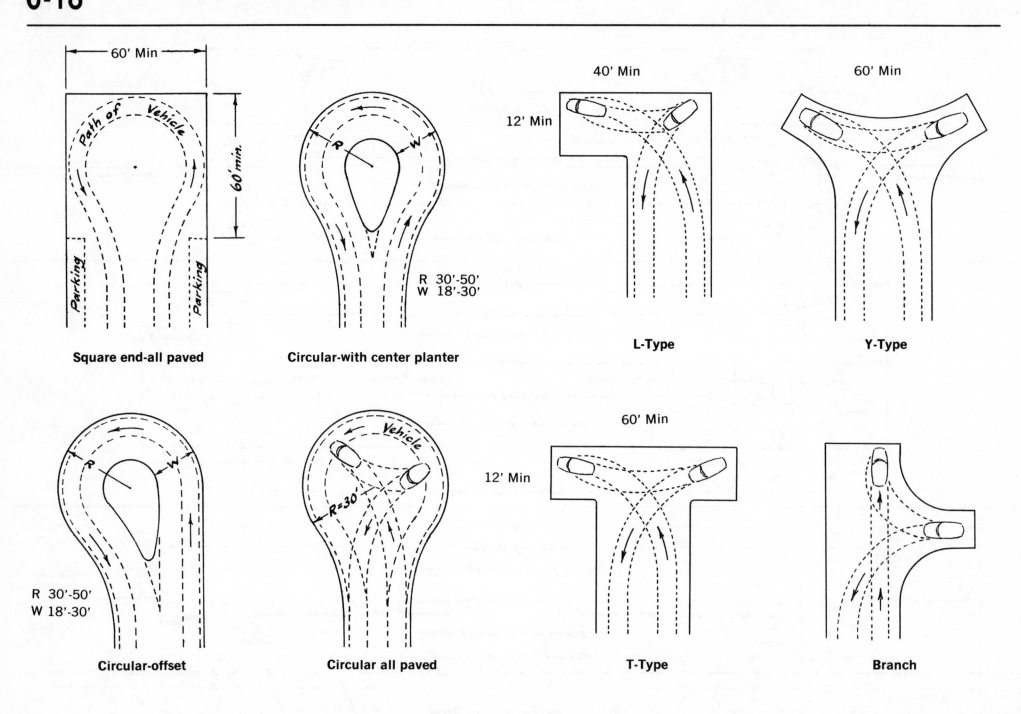

Square end-all paved

Circular-with center planter

R 30'-50'
W 18'-30'

L-Type

40' Min

12' Min

Y-Type

60' Min

Circular-offset

R 30'-50'
W 18'-30'

Circular all paved

R=30

T-Type

60' Min

12' Min

Branch

note - Dimensions Indicated are for Passenger Cars Only, for Trucks and Other Vehicles, Sizes Must be Increased Accordingly.

STREET AND AVENUE SYSTEM

One of the simplest systems employed in naming streets is to give the name "street" to streets running generally east-west and the name "avenue" to streets running generally north-south or vice-versa. Such a system could be applied whether streets are given name designations or number designations. The assignment of the word "street" to streets running in one direction and the word "avenue" to streets running in the opposite direction has the advantage of limiting the address search to either north-south or east-west streets.

Whether streets are given name designations or number designations is of not too much concern. It is quickly apparent that streets given number designations such as First Ave. Second Ave. etc., are easier to locate than streets named after birds, trees, states, etc. As a general rule, however, a city would not give number designations to both north-south and east-west streets. Number designation for streets running in one direction and same designation for streets running in the opposite direction is commonplace. The system becomes more workable when the streets and avenues are named in such a way that the name of the street informs one of its approximate location in relation to other streets and in relation to the base lines. For example, if north-south public ways were designated as "avenues" and named after states and the furthermost avenues in the western edge of the city were given names of states which began with the letter "A" (Arizona, Arkansas, etc.) progressing down the alphabet to the letters "X" and "Y" "Z" on the eastern edge of the city, then "Arkansas Ave." would indicate that the street ran north-south and that it was in the far western part of the city.

A disadvantage of the street and avenue naming system is that it is too general to enable streets to be located easily and quickly in large cities. The use of alphabetical street naming order does not readily lend itself to change.

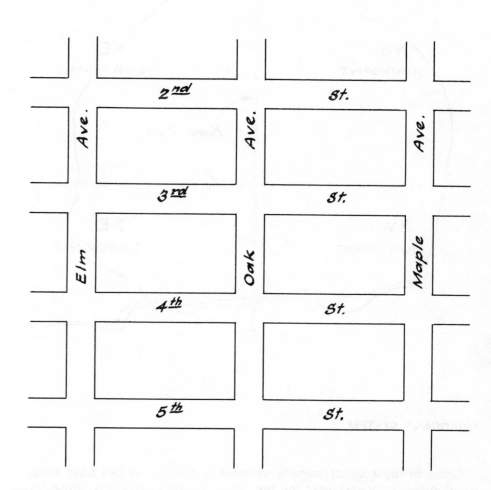

SOURCE: *A Guide to Street Naming and Property Numbering, Southern Association of State Planning and Development Agencies-1952*

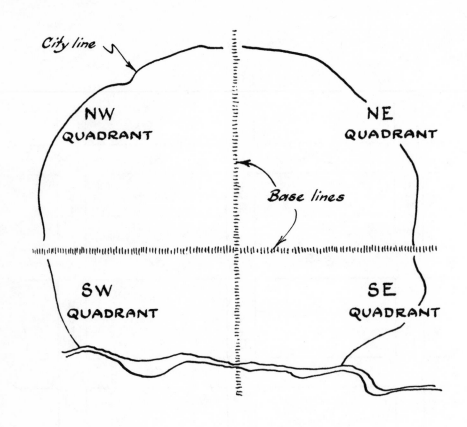

QUADRANT SYSTEM

Basic to most street naming systems is the use of two **base lines**—running generally east-west and the other running generally north-south—which divide the city into four quadrants. The base lines are actually the extension of the intersecting lines which form the point of reference. By incorporating directional letters as part of the street name, any street is easily located as far as the quadrant in which it lies. For example, it is observed that Elm St. lies to the north, and to the east of the base lines.

SOURCE: *A Guide to Street Naming and Property Numbering, Southern Association of State Planning and Development Agencies-1952*

It is therefore in the northeast quadrant, and the correct name of the street would be Elm N. E. Also streets running generally in one direction, say, east-west, could be given the suffix "street" and streets running generally in the opposite direction would be known as "avenues". An address of "339 Elm Ave. N. E." would inform one that the house faces a public way running north-south, located in the northeast quadrant and approximately 1/3 of a block beyond the third block north of the base line.

The specific purpose of a uniform and orderly street system is to enable one to find a street (and a street number) as quickly and easily as possible. When a system is to be adopted, it should be as simple as possible, and should allow for systematic expansion of the system as the community grows. A system which is not flexible and does not make allowances for future growth is hardly worth the effort, since within a comparatively short time the addition of new streets will create anew the confusion which the reform was supposed to correct.

The coordinate of Lyman St. Numbering System was developed by Richard R. Lyman, a civil engineer, some 23 years ago. Mr. Lyman was appointed to serve on a committee established to devise a method of numbering streets in a city so that it would be possible for a traveler to find an address in a city without the aid of a map. In this guide the system developed by Mr. Lyman is called the coordinate system because any address is a coordinate of two values—some value or distance along one base line and some distance along the other base line.

The coordinate system is similar to other street naming systems which utilize two base lines, or reference lines which run approximately at right angles to each other. These base lines form the division lines between north, south, east and west. Under the coordinate system, streets are given numbers instead of names and the numbers are in fact street names.

The illustration shows how streets are numbered (or named) by hundreds—100 for each block away from the two axes. Streets parallel to the north of the base line labeled E. W. are given the designation ''north'' as part of the street number; streets parallel to and south of the E. W. base line are given the designation ''south''. In a similar manner ''east'' and ''west'' designations are given streets parallel to the N. S. base line. It will be observed that the E. W. base line runs along the center line of the street numbered ''O East'' and ''O West'' and likewise, the N. S. base line runs along the center line of the street numbered ''O North'' and O South''.

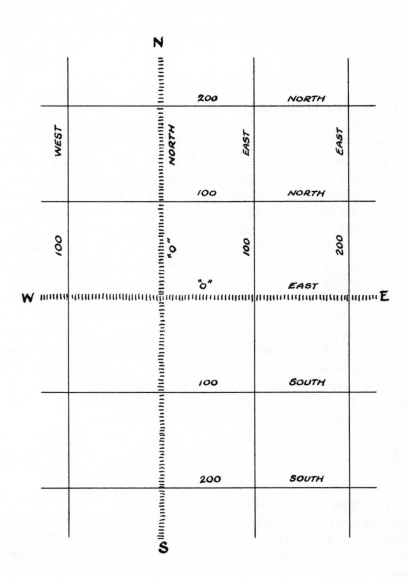

SOURCE: A Guide to Street Naming and Property Numbering, Southern Association of State Planning and Development Agencies-1952

After streets have been named systematically a plan must be worked out for numbering property which buts the streets. Systematic property numbering is of questionable value unless the property numbering plan is integrated with street naming.

BASE LINES AND GRID LINES

Fundamental to a property numbering system is the establishment of a point of reference to which all property is related. This point of reference is usually established near the center of the city, and may be thought of as the intersection of two imaginary lines. from such a point outward in four directions—north, south, east and west—property is numbered as it relates to the reference point. The reference point is, of course, identical with the intersection of the base lines established for street naming.

It is axiomatic that every property numbering system is based upon some point of reference. Without such reference point property numbers could have no sequence or order. Parallel to these base lines, "grid lines", or "correction lines" are established to divide property into blocks for numbering purposes. The grid lines indicate the division between block number changes where property numbers change from one hundred to the next higher hundred. The residents of most American cities are accustomed to a gridiron street pattern with parallel streets more or less equal distance apart. Such a street pattern easily lends itself to establishment of block number changes at street intersections and most people have long accustomed themselves to such a system.

PROPERTY NUMBERING INTERVALS

The property or front footage along the street is given a number rather than a particular structure. This principle is in recognition of the fact that there is no good way of knowing how many structures will eventually be built on vacant land within blocks, and that any numbering scheme which attempted to number structures consecutively leaves no flexibility to accommodate change.

SOURCE: A Guide to Street Naming and Property Numbering, Southern Association of State Planning and Development Agencies-1952

By assigning a property number to an interval of front footage along the street a system is established whereby change and growth are conveniently handled. This number interval may be selected to fit the particular need. In central business districts where lots are customarily smaller, a small interval may be needed; low density residential areas may more suitably be assigned numbers according to a greater interval. An interval of 20 feet, maybe 50 feet, may fit the requirements for a particular residential area; business areas and very dense residential areas may require a smaller interval, say, ten or fifteen feet. As a general rule, it is wise to select a property numbering interval of short length, say, ten feet for business areas and perhaps 20 to 25 feet for other areas. Haphazard changes in the interval length should be avoided since a particular house number on one street should correspond in location to a house similarly situated on a parallel street on the other side of the city.

ASSIGNMENT OF HOUSE NUMBERS

Once the numbering interval has been selected assignment of numbers to existing structures can be made by measuring the number of intervals from the grid line nearest the base line and actually assigning to each building the number of the interval in which the front entrance falls.

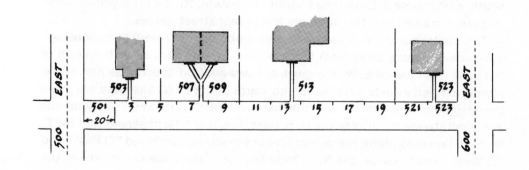

Measurements are made from grid line nearest the base line. Numbers are assigned to FRONT ENTRANCE.

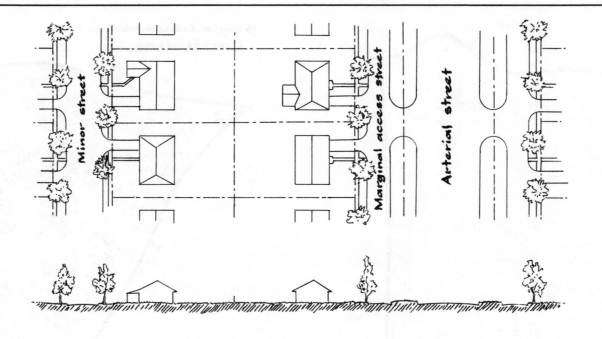

Houses front on
arterial street—
access from
marginal access street

When houses must front on an arterial street, a marginal access street should be provided for these houses. This will eliminate any conflict between through and local circulation.

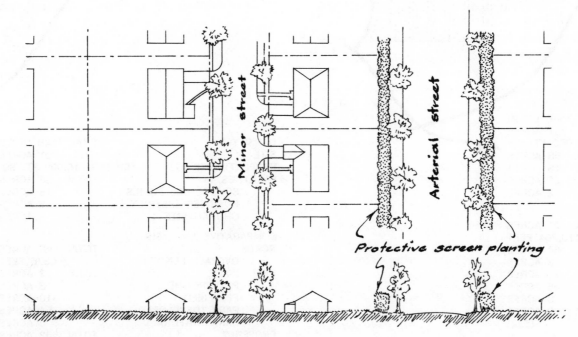

Houses front on
minor street—
access from
minor street only

Houses should always front on a minor street. If the subdivision is properly designed, there will be a minimum of traffic on the minor street providing a maximum of privacy and safety.

SOURCE: Land Subdivision Regulations, Housing and Home Finance Agency, Washington, D. C.

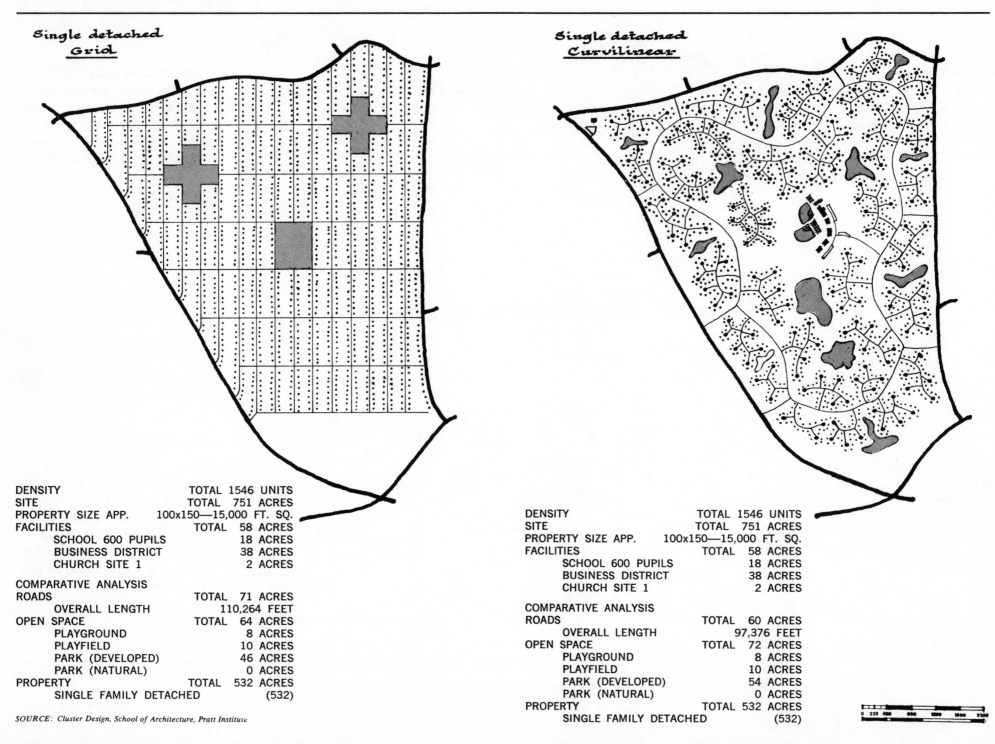

Single detached Grid

Single detached Curvilinear

DENSITY	TOTAL 1546 UNITS
SITE	TOTAL 751 ACRES
PROPERTY SIZE APP.	100x150—15,000 FT. SQ.
FACILITIES	TOTAL 58 ACRES
SCHOOL 600 PUPILS	18 ACRES
BUSINESS DISTRICT	38 ACRES
CHURCH SITE 1	2 ACRES

COMPARATIVE ANALYSIS		
ROADS	TOTAL	71 ACRES
OVERALL LENGTH		110,264 FEET
OPEN SPACE	TOTAL	64 ACRES
PLAYGROUND		8 ACRES
PLAYFIELD		10 ACRES
PARK (DEVELOPED)		46 ACRES
PARK (NATURAL)		0 ACRES
PROPERTY	TOTAL	532 ACRES
SINGLE FAMILY DETACHED		(532)

SOURCE: Cluster Design, School of Architecture, Pratt Institute

DENSITY	TOTAL 1546 UNITS
SITE	TOTAL 751 ACRES
PROPERTY SIZE APP.	100x150—15,000 FT. SQ.
FACILITIES	TOTAL 58 ACRES
SCHOOL 600 PUPILS	18 ACRES
BUSINESS DISTRICT	38 ACRES
CHURCH SITE 1	2 ACRES

COMPARATIVE ANALYSIS		
ROADS	TOTAL	60 ACRES
OVERALL LENGTH		97,376 FEET
OPEN SPACE	TOTAL	72 ACRES
PLAYGROUND		8 ACRES
PLAYFIELD		10 ACRES
PARK (DEVELOPED)		54 ACRES
PARK (NATURAL)		0 ACRES
PROPERTY	TOTAL	532 ACRES
SINGLE FAMILY DETACHED		(532)

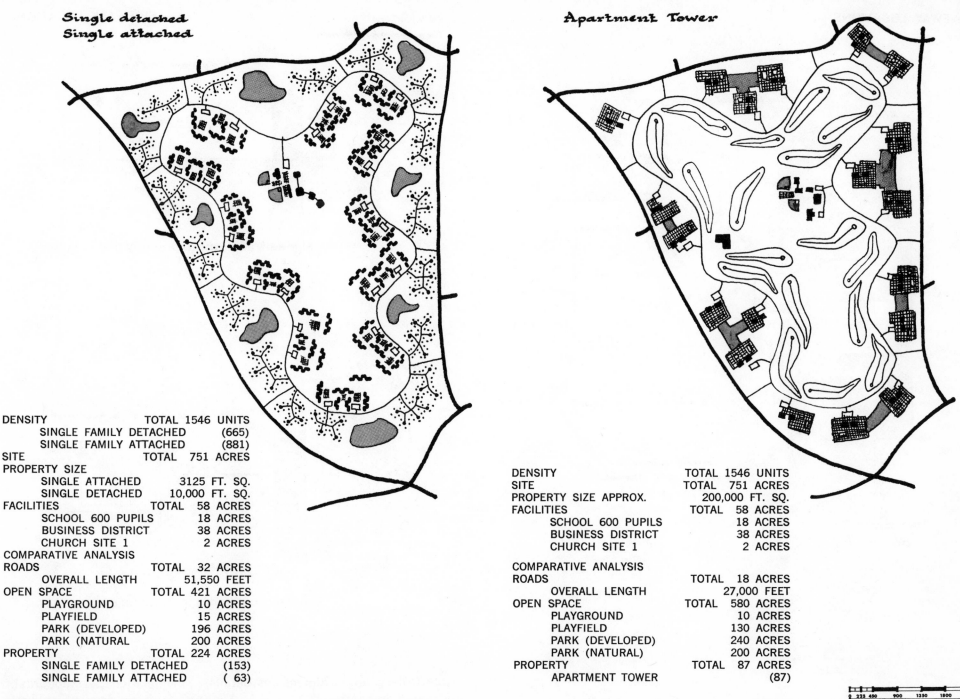

Single detached
Single attached

Apartment Tower

DENSITY   TOTAL 1546 UNITS
        SINGLE FAMILY DETACHED   (665)
        SINGLE FAMILY ATTACHED   (881)
SITE   TOTAL 751 ACRES
PROPERTY SIZE
        SINGLE ATTACHED   3125 FT. SQ.
        SINGLE DETACHED   10,000 FT. SQ.
FACILITIES   TOTAL 58 ACRES
        SCHOOL 600 PUPILS   18 ACRES
        BUSINESS DISTRICT   38 ACRES
        CHURCH SITE 1   2 ACRES
COMPARATIVE ANALYSIS
ROADS   TOTAL 32 ACRES
        OVERALL LENGTH   51,550 FEET
OPEN SPACE   TOTAL 421 ACRES
        PLAYGROUND   10 ACRES
        PLAYFIELD   15 ACRES
        PARK (DEVELOPED)   196 ACRES
        PARK (NATURAL   200 ACRES
PROPERTY   TOTAL 224 ACRES
        SINGLE FAMILY DETACHED   (153)
        SINGLE FAMILY ATTACHED   (63)

SOURCE: Cluster Design, School of Architecture, Pratt Institute

DENSITY   TOTAL 1546 UNITS
SITE   TOTAL 751 ACRES
PROPERTY SIZE APPROX.   200,000 FT. SQ.
FACILITIES   TOTAL 58 ACRES
        SCHOOL 600 PUPILS   18 ACRES
        BUSINESS DISTRICT   38 ACRES
        CHURCH SITE 1   2 ACRES

COMPARATIVE ANALYSIS
ROADS   TOTAL 18 ACRES
        OVERALL LENGTH   27,000 FEET
OPEN SPACE   TOTAL 580 ACRES
        PLAYGROUND   10 ACRES
        PLAYFIELD   130 ACRES
        PARK (DEVELOPED)   240 ACRES
        PARK (NATURAL)   200 ACRES
PROPERTY   TOTAL 87 ACRES
        APARTMENT TOWER   (87)

0 225 450   900   1350   1800   2250

DRIVEWAY LOCATIONS

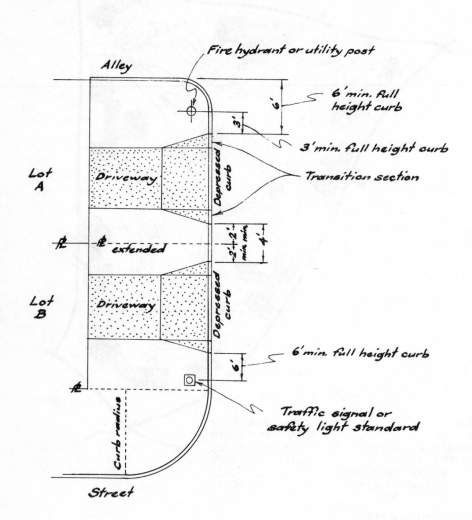

SIDEWALK LOCATIONS

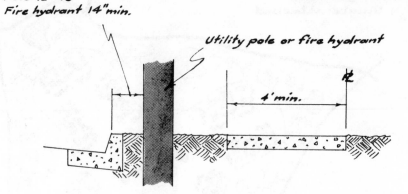

Sidewalk adjacent to property line

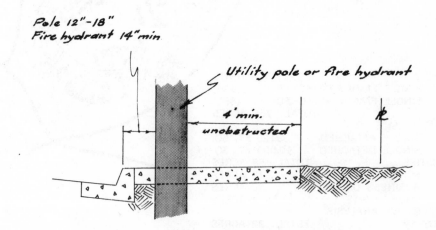

Sidewalk contiguous with curbing

Note: Other sidewalk dimensions, details, & specifications per standards of municipality in control.

SOURCE: Street and Urban Road Maintenance, Research Foundation, American Public Works Association

VEHICULAR CIRCULATION

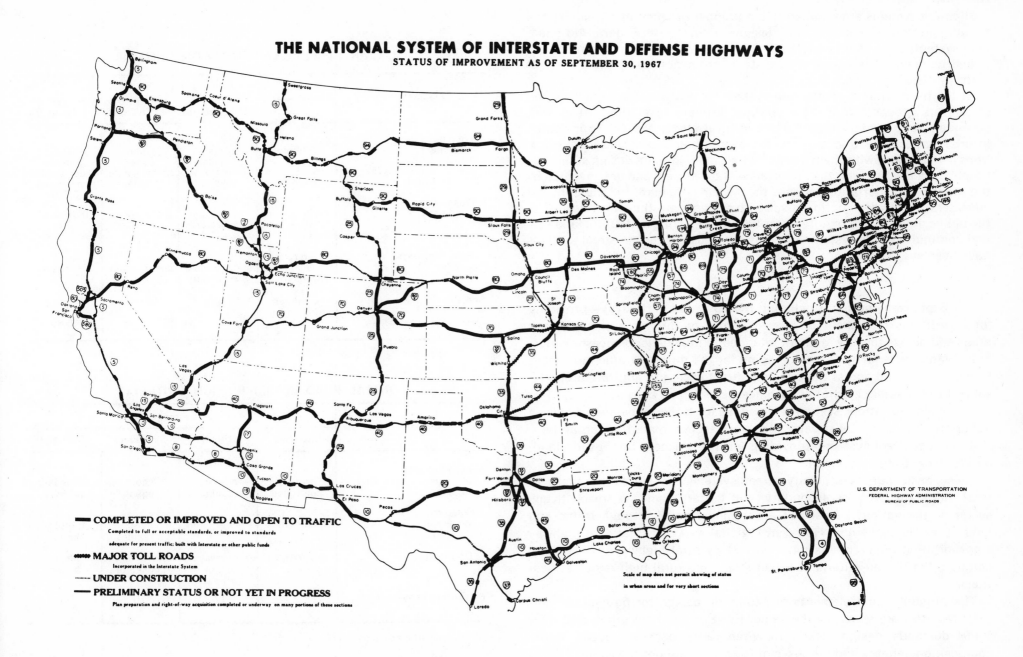

THE NATIONAL SYSTEM OF INTERSTATE AND DEFENSE HIGHWAYS
STATUS OF IMPROVEMENT AS OF SEPTEMBER 30, 1967

U.S. DEPARTMENT OF TRANSPORTATION
FEDERAL HIGHWAY ADMINISTRATION
BUREAU OF PUBLIC ROADS

Scale of map does not permit showing of status
in urban areas and for very short sections

COMPLETED OR IMPROVED AND OPEN TO TRAFFIC
Completed to full or acceptable standards, or improved to standards
adequate for present traffic; built with Interstate or other public funds

MAJOR TOLL ROADS
Incorporated in the Interstate System

UNDER CONSTRUCTION

PRELIMINARY STATUS OR NOT YET IN PROGRESS
Plan preparation and right-of-way acquisition completed or underway on many portions of these sections

HIGHWAY CLASSIFICATION

Highway systems are grouped into a number of different classifications for administrative, planning, and design purposes. The Federal Aid financing system, state-county-city's administrative systems, and commercial-industrial-residential-recreational systems are examples of the variety of highway classifications.

In the most basic classification system for design work, highways and streets are grouped into: (1) interstate, primary (excluding interstate), secondary, and tertiary road classes in rural areas, and (2) expressway, arterial, collector, and local road classes in urban areas. These classifications usually carry with them a set of suggested minimum design standards which are in keeping with the importance of the system and are governed by the specific transportation services the system is to perform. The principal consideration for designating roads into systems are the travel desires of the public, land-access requirements based on existing and future land use, and continuity of the system. Four basic purposes of urban street systems have been suggested:

1.   **Expressway system (including freeways and parkways)**—providing for expeditious movement of large volumes of through traffic between areas and across the city, and not intended to provide land-access service.

2.   **Major arterial system**—providing for the through traffic movement between areas and across the city, and direct access to abutting property; subject to necessary control of entrances, exists, and curb use.

3.   **Collect or street system**—providing for traffic movement between major arterials and local streets, and direct access to abutting property.

4.   **Local street system**—providing for direct access to abutting land, and for local traffic movements.

These basic purposes of city street systems are similar to those of rural interstate, primary, secondary, and tertiary highways, respectively, so far as the various degrees of accommodation of through traffic and land access is concerned. However, regional as well as national highway transportation requirements must be met by rural highways. The Tables compare the overall criteria of urban street and rural highway classifications.

The principles and elements of geometric design for both urban and rural facilities are generally the same. However, to meet urban and rural traffic demands, design details are often varied because speeds, traffic composition, lengths and purposes of trips, etc., are not the same.

SOURCE: *Standards for Street Facilities and Services, Procedure Manual 7A, National Committee on Urban Transportation, Public Administration Service, Chicago, 1958, p. 11.*

URBAN STREET CLASSIFICATION CRITERIA

Element	System			
	Expressway	Major Arterial	Collector	Local
Service function:				
Movement	primary	primary	equal	secondary
Access	none	secondary	equal	primary
Principal trip length	over 3 miles	over 1 mile	under 1 mile	under ½ mile
Use by transit	express	regular	regular	none, except C.B.D.
Linkage:				
Land uses	major generators & C.B.D.	secondary generators & C.B.D.	local areas	individual sites
Rural highways	interstate & state primary	state primary & secondary	county roads	none
Spacing	1-3 miles	1 mile	½ mile	....
Percentage of system	0-8	20-35		65-80

RURAL ROAD CLASSIFICATION CRITERIA*

Element	System			
	Interstate	Primary	Secondary	Tertiary
Service function:				
Movement	primary	primary	equal	secondary
Access	controlled	secondary	equal	primary
Linkage to:				
Geographic	major cities	smaller cities	smaller cities & regions	farm-to-market
Urban streets	expressways	expressways & major arterials	major arterials & collectors	collectors & local
Percentage of system	2	17	10	71

*Includes surfaced roads only.

Type of Facility	Function and Design Features	Spacing	Widths R.O.W.	Widths Pavement	Desirable Maximum Grades	Speed	Other Features
Freeways	Provide regional and metropolitan continuity and unity. Limited access; no grade crossings; no traffic stops.	Variable; related to regional pattern of population and industrial centers	200–300′	Varies; 12′ per lane; 8–10′ shoulders both sides of each roadway; 8′–60′ median strip.	3%	60 mph	Depressed, at grade, or elevated. Preferably depressed, through urban areas. Require intensive landscaping, service roads, or adequate rear lot building set-back lines (75′) where service roads are not provided.
Expressways	Provide metropolitan and city continuity and unity. Limited access; some channelized grade crossings and signals at major intersections. Parking prohibited.	Variable; generally radial or circumferential	200–250′	Varies 12′ per lane; 8-10′ shoulders; 8-30′ median strip.	4%	50 mph	Generally at grade. Requires landscaping and service roads or adequate rear lot building set-back lines (75′) where service roads are not provided.
Major Roads (Major Arterials)	Provide unity throughout contiguous urban area. Usually form boundaries for neighborhoods. Minor access control; channelized intersections; parking generally prohibited.	1½ to 2 miles	120–150′	84′ maximum for 4 lanes, parking and median strip.	4%	35–45 mph	Require 5′ wide detached sidewalks in urban areas, planting strips (5′–10′ wide or more) and adequate building set-back lines (30′) for buildings fronting on street; 60′ for buildings backing on street.
Secondary Roads (Minor Arterials)	Main feeder streets. Signals where needed; stop signs on side streets. Occasionally form boundaries for neighborhoods.	¾ to 1 mile	80′	60′	5%	35–40 mph	Require 5′ wide detached sidewalks, planting strips between sidewalks and curb 5′ to 10′ or more, and adequate building set-back lines (30′).
Collector Streets	Main interior streets. Stop signs on side streets.	¼ to ½ mile	64′	44′ (2–12′ traffic lanes; 2-10′ parking lanes)	5%	30 mph	Require at least 4′ wide detached sidewalks; vertical curbs; planting strips are desirable; building set-back lines 30′ from right of way.
Local Streets	Local service streets. Non-conducive to through traffic.	at blocks	50′	36′ where street parking is permitted.	6%	25 mph	Sidewalks at least 4′ in width for densities greater than 1 d.u./acre, and curbs and gutters.
Cul-de-sac	Street open at only one end, with provision for a turn-around at the other.	only wherever practical	50′ (90′ dia. turn-around)	30′–36′ (75′ turn-around)	5%		Should not have a length greater than 500 feet.

SOURCE: George Nez, Standards for New Urban Development—The Denver Background,
Reprinted by Permission of Urban Land, Vol 20, No 5 Urban Land Institute, 1200 18th Street, N. W., Wash. D. C.

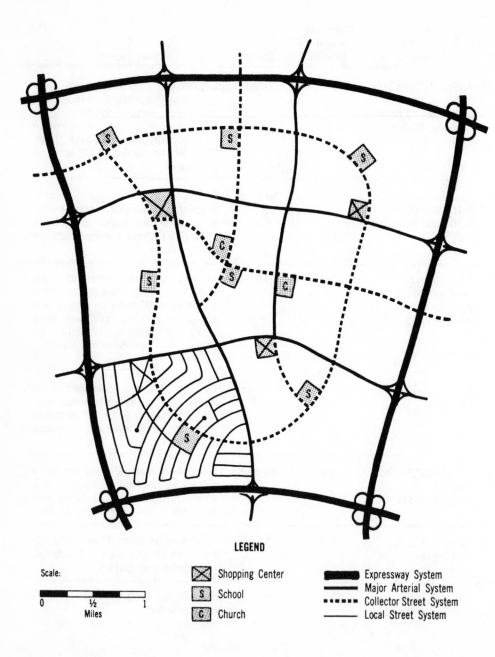

LEGEND

Scale:

0   ½   1

Miles

⊠ Shopping Center

Ⓢ School

Ⓒ Church

▬▬ Expressway System

─── Major Arterial System

▪▪▪▪ Collector Street System

── Local Street System

SUMMARY OF STREET CLASSIFICATION CRITERIA

Element	System			
	Expressway	Major Arterial	Collector	Local
Service Function				
movement	primary	primary	equal	secondary
access	none	secondary	equal	primary
principal trip length	over 3 miles	over 1 mile	under 1 mile	under 1/2 mile
use by transit	express	regular	regular	none, except C.B.D.
Linkage				
Land Uses	major generators & C.B.D.	secondary generators & C.B.D.	local areas	individual sites
Rural Highways	interstate & state primary	state primary & secondary	county roads	none
Spacing	1-3 miles	1 mile	1/2 mile	----
Percentage of System	0 - 8		20 - 35	65 - 80

SOURCE: Standards for Street Facilities and Services, Procedure Manual 7A, National Committee on Urban Transportation, Public Administration Service, Chicago, Ill. — 1958

TRAFFIC DESIGN ELEMENTS

Traffic element	Explanation and nation-wide percentage or factor
Average daily traffic: ADT	Average 24-hour volume for a given year; total for both directions of travel, unless otherwise specified. Directional or one-way ADT is an average 24-hour volume in one direction of travel only.
Current traffic	ADT composed of existing trips, including attracted traffic, that would use the improvement if opened to traffic today (current year specified.)
Future traffic	ADT that would use a highway in the future (future year specified). Future traffic may be obtained by adding generated traffic, normal traffic growth, and development traffic to current traffic, or by multiplying current traffic by the traffic projection factor.
Traffic projection factor	Future traffic divided by current traffic. General range, 1.5 to 2.5 for 20-year period.
Design hour volume: DHV	Future hourly volume for use in design (two-way unless otherwise specified), usually the 30th highest hourly volume of the design year (30HV) or equivalent, the approximate value of which can be obtained by the application of the following percentages to future traffic (ADT). The design hour volume, when expressed in terms of all types of vehicles, should be accompanied by factor T, the percentage of trucks during peak hours. Or, the design hour volume may be broken down to the number of passenger vehicles and the number of trucks.
Relation between DHV and ADT: K	DHV expressed as a percentage of ADT, both two-way; normal range 12 to 18. Or, DHV expressed as a percentage of ADT, both one-way; normal range, 16 to 24.
Directional distribution: D	One-way volume in predominant direction of travel expressed as a percentage of two-way DHV. General range, 50 to 80. Average, 67.
Composition of traffic: T	Trucks (exclusive of light delivery trucks) expressed as a percentage of DHV. Average 10 to 12.

DESIGN HOUR VOLUMES
TYPICAL TRAFFIC-FLOW DIAGRAMS

PLAN
-a-

ADT (1955) IN PARENTHESES
ADT (1975) — TWO-WAY FLOW
-b-

TWO-WAY DHV = K × ADT
K = 12%
DHV (1975) — TWO-WAY FLOW
-c-

ONE-WAY DHV = D × TWO-WAY DHV
D = 60%
DHV (1975) — DIRECTIONAL FLOW
-d-

TRUCK PERCENTAGE IN PARENTHESES

a.m. PEAK   p.m. PEAK

PLAN INDICATION
1,600 — p.m. PEAK
900 — a.m. PEAK
DESIGN VEHICLE-C43

DHV (1975) — DETAILS FOR INTERCHANGE

SOURCE: A Policy on Geometric Design of Rural Highways, American Association of State Highway Officials, Wash. D. C. 1954. A Policy of Arterial Highways in Urban Areas, American Association of State Highway Officials, Wash. D. C. 1960

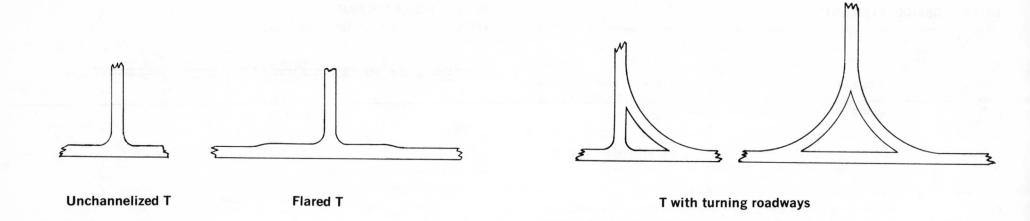

Unchannelized T   **Flared T**   **T with turning roadways**

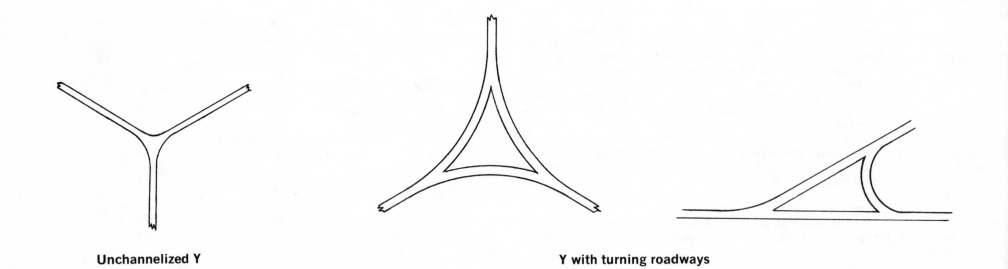

Unchannelized Y   **Y with turning roadways**

3 leg intersections

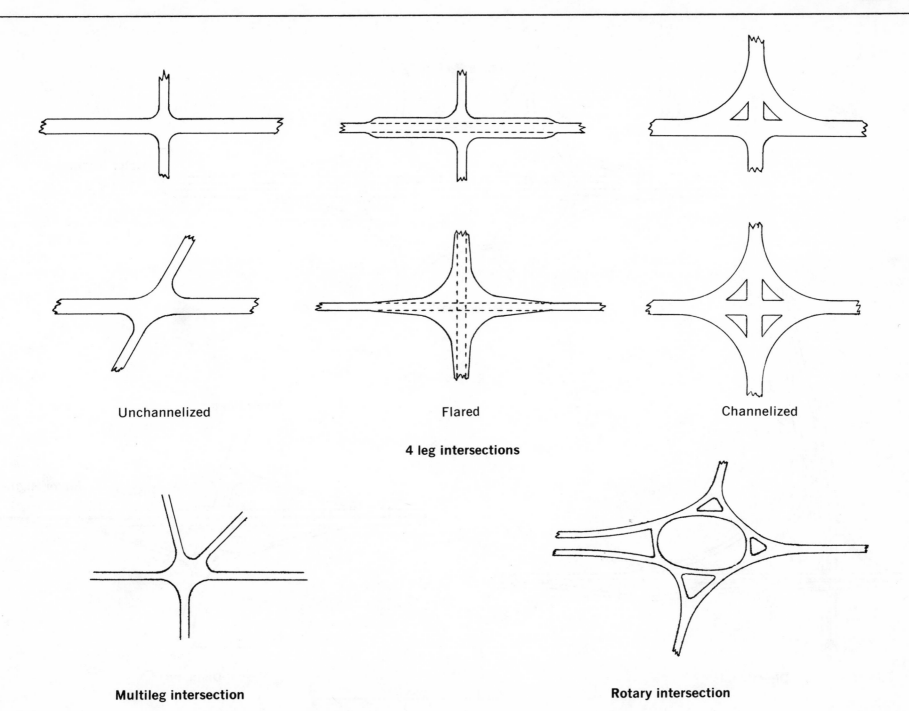

Unchannelized   Flared   Channelized

4 leg intersections

Multileg intersection   **Rotary intersection**

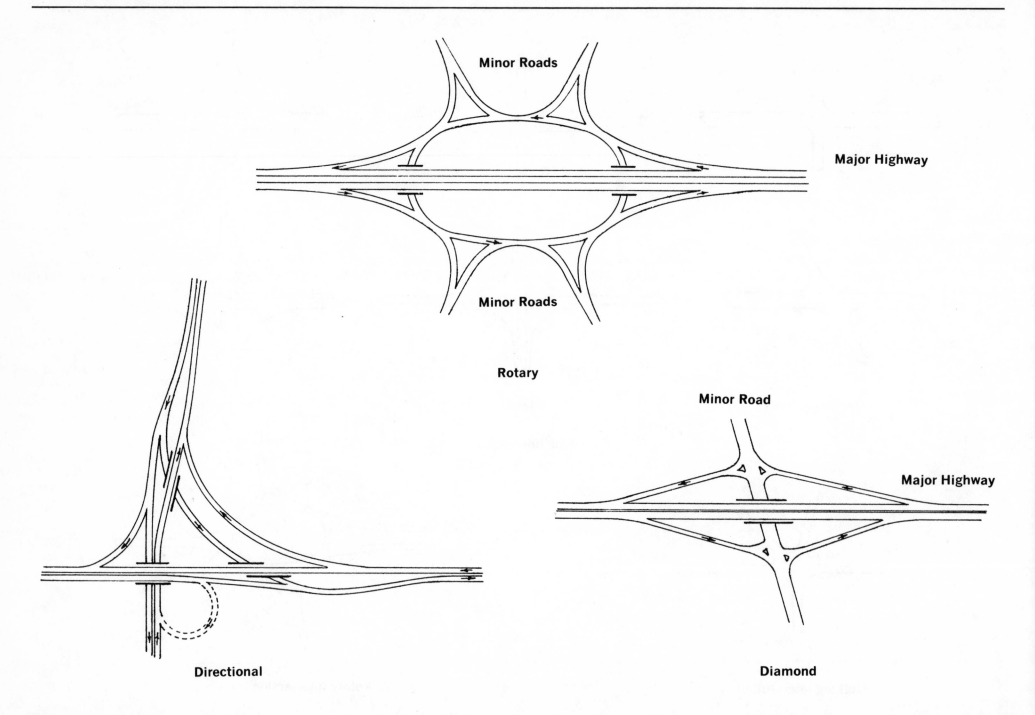

Minor Roads

Major Highway

Minor Roads

Rotary

Minor Road

Major Highway

Directional

Diamond

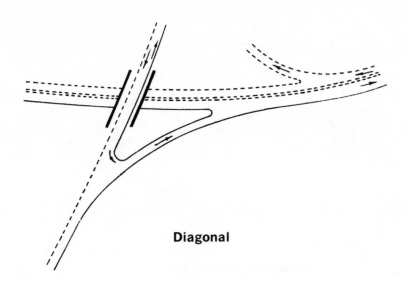

Diagonal

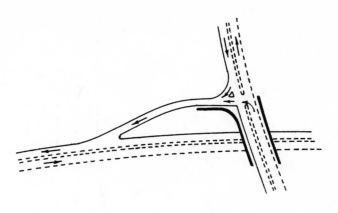

Parallel

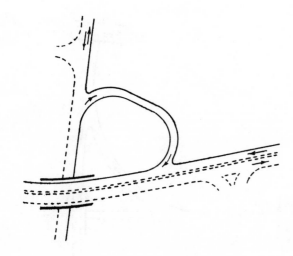

Loop

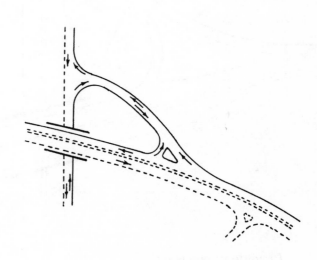

Cloverleaf: two-way

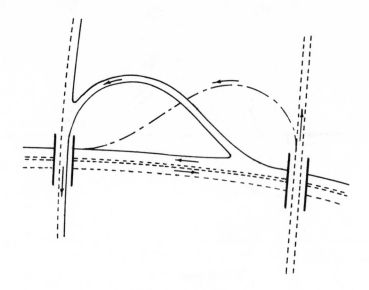

Semidirect connection

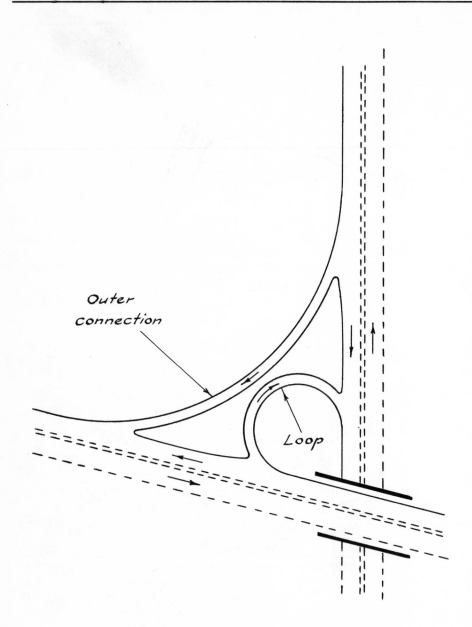

Outer connection

Loop

Cloverleaf: one-way

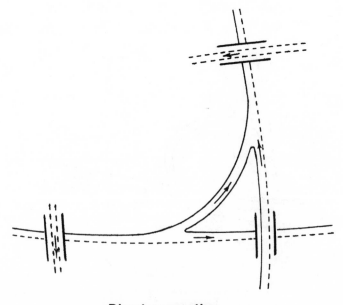

Direct connection

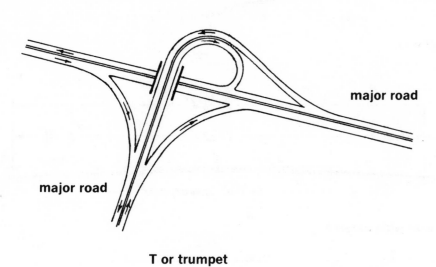

T or trumpet

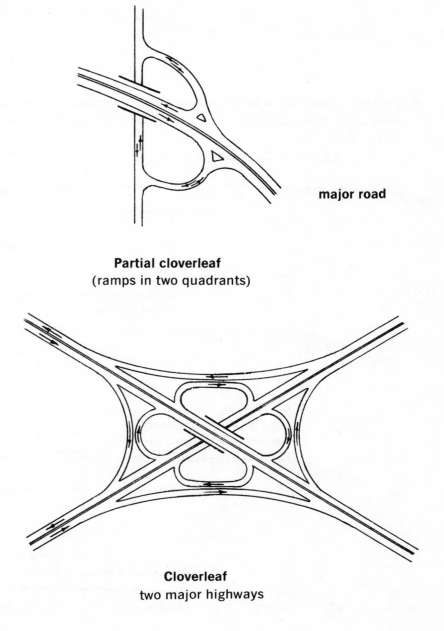

Partial cloverleaf
(ramps in two quadrants)

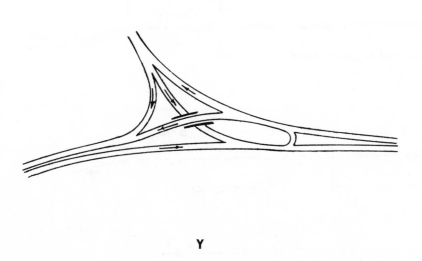

Y

all legs equal

Cloverleaf
two major highways

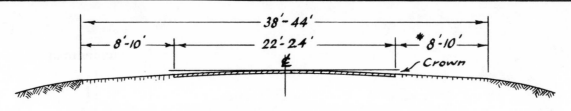

Typical 2-lane highway

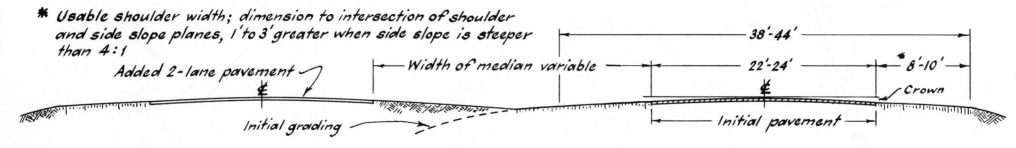

4-lane divided highway with wide median

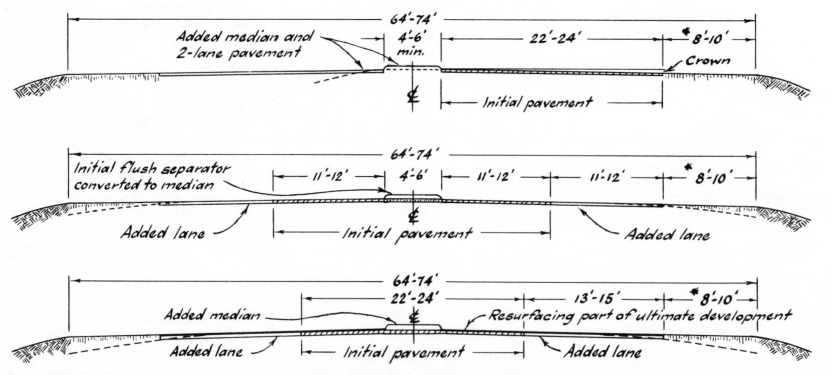

SOURCE: *A Policy on Geometric Design of Rural Highways,*
American Association of State Highway Officials, Wash. D. C. 1954

4-lane divided highway with narrow median

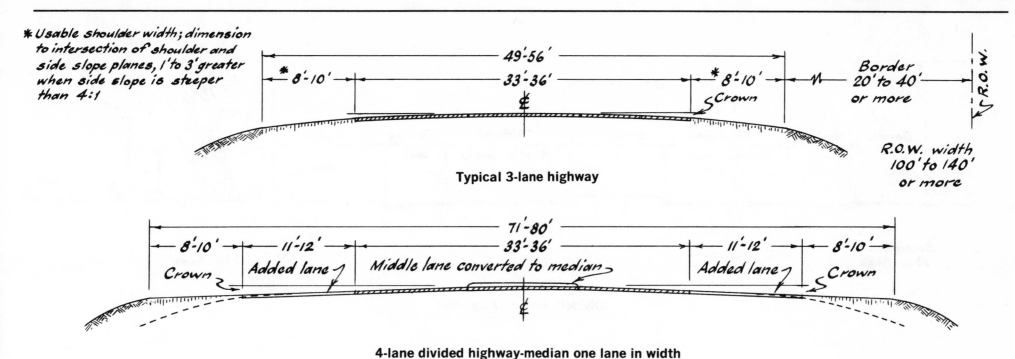

* *Usable shoulder width; dimension to intersection of shoulder and side slope planes, 1' to 3' greater when side slope is steeper than 4:1*

49'-56'

* 8'-10'   33'-36'   * 8'-10'

Crown   ₵

Border 20' to 40' or more

R.O.W.

R.O.W. width 100' to 140' or more

Typical 3-lane highway

71'-80'

8'-10'   11'-12'   33'-36'   11'-12'   8'-10'

Crown   Added lane   Middle lane converted to median   Added lane   Crown

₵

4-lane divided highway-median one lane in width

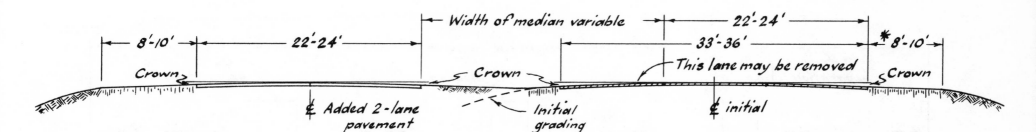

Width of median variable   22'-24'

8'-10'   22'-24'   33'-36'   * 8'-10'

Crown   Crown   This lane may be removed   Crown

₵ Added 2-lane pavement   Initial grading   ₵ initial

4-lane divided highway with wide median

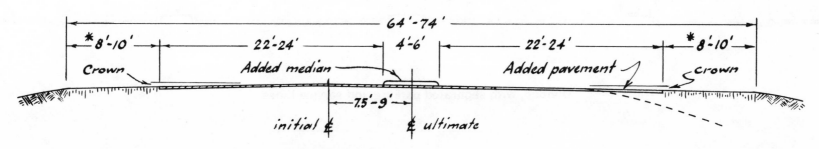

64'-74'

* 8'-10'   22'-24'   4'-6'   22'-24'   * 8'-10'

Crown   Added median   Added pavement   Crown

7.5'-9'

initial ₵   ₵ ultimate

4-lane divided highway with narrow median

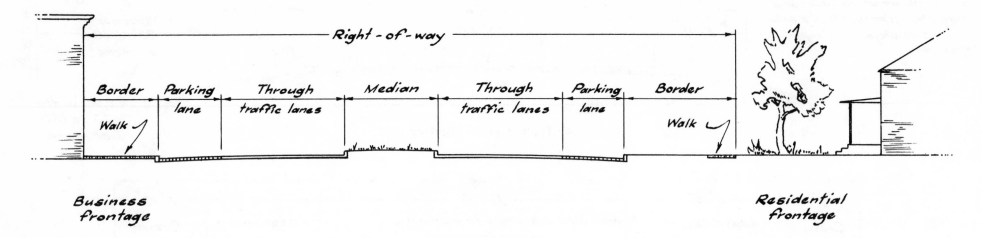

Divided, with parking lanes

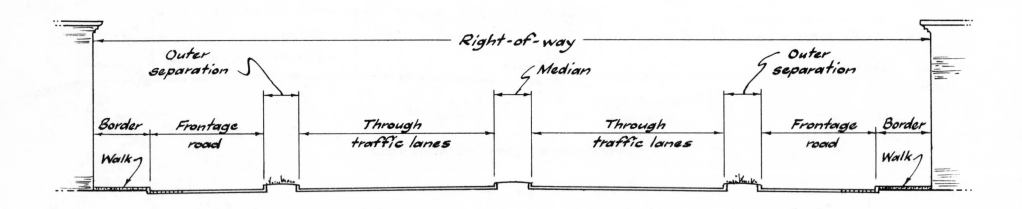

Divided, with separated parking and service lanes

SOURCE: A Policy on Arterial Highways in Urban Areas, American Association of State Highway Officials, Wash. D. C. 1960

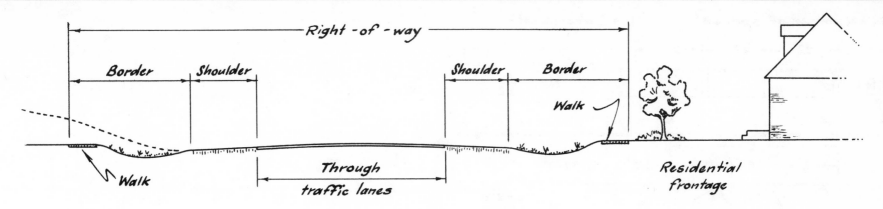

Shoulders, no curbs

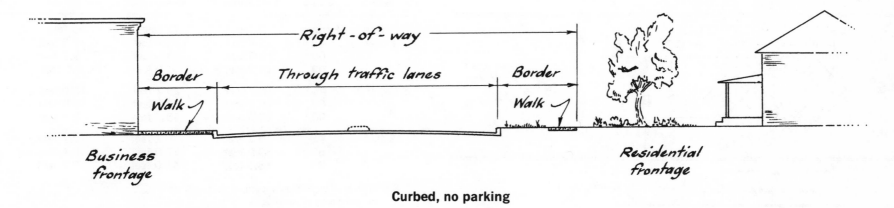

Curbed, no parking

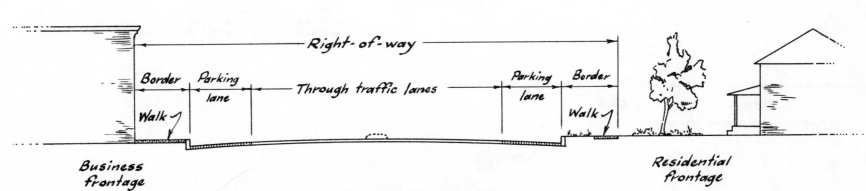

Curbed, with parking lanes

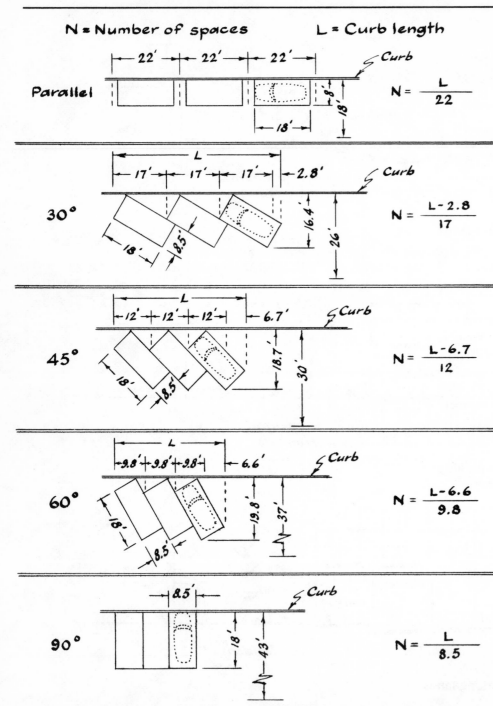

N = Number of spaces   L = Curb length

Parallel

$$N = \frac{L}{22}$$

30°

$$N = \frac{L - 2.8}{17}$$

45°

$$N = \frac{L - 6.7}{12}$$

60°

$$N = \frac{L - 6.6}{9.8}$$

90°

$$N = \frac{L}{8.5}$$

Street Space Used for Various Parking Positions*

Stall width	Position at curb	Width of street used when parked	Street width needed for parking plus maneuvering	Length of curb per car	Cars parked per 100 feet
7 feet	Parallel	7 feet	17 feet	22 feet	4.5
8 feet	45	18.4 feet	30.4 feet	11.3 feet	8.2
	60	19.6 feet	38.6 feet	9.2 feet	9.5
	90	18.0 feet	46.0 feet	8.0 feet	12.5
8 feet 6 in.	45	18.7 feet	29.7 feet	12.0 feet	7.8
	60	19.8 feet	37.8 feet	9.8 feet	9.5
	90	18.0 feet	43.0 feet	8.5 feet	11.5
9 feet	45	19.1 feet	30.1 feet	12.7 feet	7.37
	60	20.0 feet	37.0 feet	10.4 feet	9.0
	90	18.0 feet	41.0 feet	9.0 feet	11.1

* Based on stall widths as shown, including lines
  No overhang of curb
  Car length   18 feet
    width   6 feet 6 inches
    wheel base 10 feet 6 inches
    overall turning diameter 23 feet 3 inches

SOURCE: Solving Parking Problems, Bureau of Planning New York State Dept. of Commerce, Albany, N. Y.

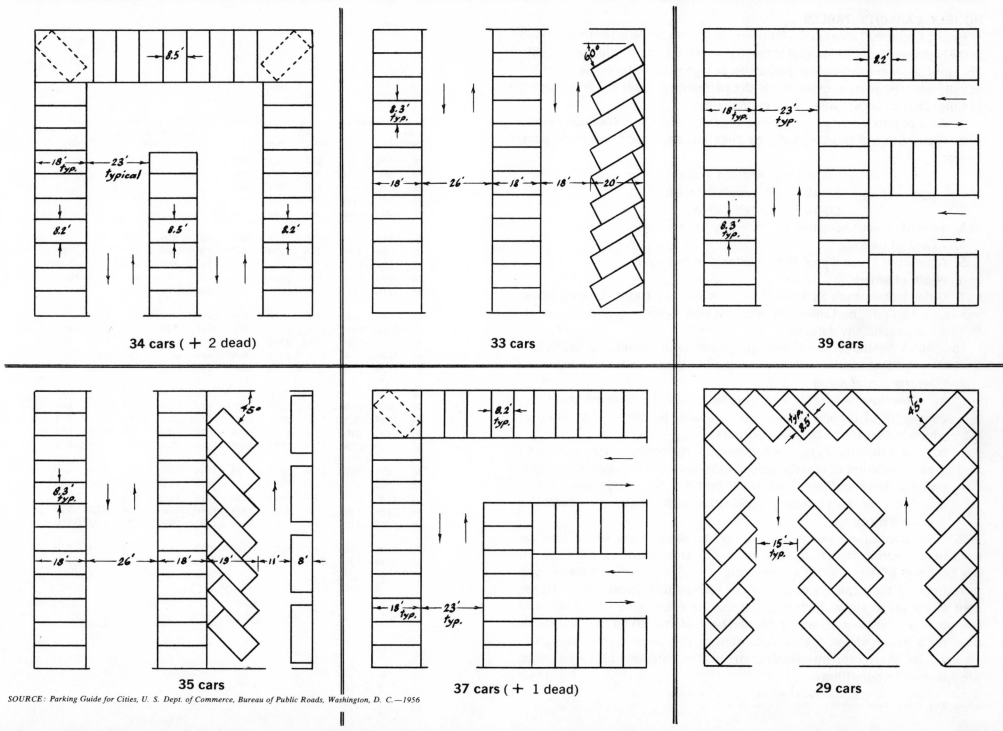

34 cars (+ 2 dead)

33 cars

39 cars

35 cars

37 cars (+ 1 dead)

29 cars

SOURCE: Parking Guide for Cities, U. S. Dept. of Commerce, Bureau of Public Roads, Washington, D. C.—1956

HOURLY CAPACITY TABLES

Hourly Capacity Tables in the following pages are based on data described in the Highway Capacity Manual of the Highway Research Board, dated 1950. The data show hourly volume capacities at signalized intersections, which usually limit the amount of traffic which can flow on a street in a given period of time. Capacities are affected principally by:

1. Area of city; i.e., downtown, intermediate, out-lying. (Defined below.)
2. Distribution of two-way traffic by direction, assumed to be, in the peak hours:

> 50-50 for downtown areas
> 55-45 for intermediate areas
> 60-40 for out-lying areas

3. Type of street operation; i.e., one-way or two-way
4. Extent of parking
5. Amount of green signal time available in the hour
6. Width of street
7. Other factors such as amount of truck and bus traffic, turning movements, and so on. The tables following assume average conditions for all factors not specifically defined.

The tables should be used with judgment, and conditions which are unusual will affect results. Tables are self-explanatory with these helps:

1. Description of Areas

   a. Downtown Area. An area devoted mainly to business purposes, consisting of closely spaced development, 50 per cent or more of which is devoted to business purposes.

   b. Intermediate Area. Area generally surrounding the downtown area, consisting of closely spaced development, possibly with multi-unit dwellings and less than 50 per cent devoted to business.

   c. Out-lying Area. Mainly residential with single unit dwellings more widely spaced.

2. The controlling percentages of green signal time which may be used in estimating street capacity for major streets are 45 per cent, 55 per cent and 65 per cent. If 45 per cent of the green signal time is used in estimating the capacity of one of the intersecting streets, then 45 per cent of the green signal time must be used in estimating the capacity of the other intersecting street. If 55 per cent of the green signal time is used for a major street, then 35 per cent of the green signal time must be used for the minor intersecting street. The interlocking percentages are enclosed in parenthesis.

SOURCE: Standards for Street Facilities and Services, Procedure Manual 7A, National Committee On Urban Transportation, Public Administration Service, Chicago, Ill, 1958

| Total Street Width | Downtown—Parking Prohibited Percent Green | | | | | Downtown—Parking Permitted Percent Green | | | | |
	45	(55 — 35)		(65 — 25)		45	(55 — 35)		(65 — 25)	
20	360	440	280	520	200	---	---	---	---	---
22	450	550	350	650	250	---	---	---	---	---
24	540	660	420	780	300	---	---	---	---	---
26	630	770	490	910	350	---	---	---	---	---
28	720	880	560	1040	400	---	---	---	---	---
30	810	990	630	1170	450	450	550	350	650	250
32	900	1100	700	1300	500	495	600	390	720	270
34	990	1210	770	1430	550	540	660	420	780	300
36	1080	1320	840	1560	600	585	710	460	850	320
38	1170	1430	910	1690	650	650	800	500	940	360
40	1260	1540	980	1820	700	700	850	550	1010	390
42	1350	1650	1050	1950	750	740	910	570	1070	410
44	1440	1760	1120	2080	800	790	960	620	1140	440
46	1530	1860	1200	2210	850	830	1010	650	1200	460
48	1600	1950	1250	2310	890	880	1070	690	1270	490
50	1665	2030	1300	2400	930	920	1120	720	1330	510
52	1755	2140	1370	2540	970	970	1180	760	1400	540
54	1820	2220	1420	2620	1020	1010	1230	790	1460	560
56	1890	2300	1480	2730	1050	1060	1290	830	1530	590
58	1960	2390	1530	2830	1090	1100	1340	860	1590	610
60	2025	2470	1580	2930	1120	1150	1400	900	1660	640
62	2070	2530	1610	2990	1150	1170	1430	910	1690	650
64	2140	2610	1670	3090	1190	1215	1480	950	1760	670
66	2180	2660	1700	3150	1210	1260	1540	980	1820	700
68	2230	2720	1740	3220	1240	1280	1560	1000	1850	710
70	2300	2800	1800	3320	1280	1330	1620	1040	1920	740
72	2340	2850	1830	3380	1300	1350	1650	1050	1950	750

Downtown—Parking One Side

Total Street Width	Percent Green				
	45	(55 — 35)		(65 — 25)	
20	----	----	----	----	---
22	----	----	----	----	---
24	----	----	----	----	---
26	----	----	----	----	---
28	----	----	----	----	---
30	700	850	550	1020	380
32	760	930	590	1090	430
34	830	1010	650	1200	460
36	900	1100	700	1300	500
38	955	1170	740	1380	530
40	1025	1250	800	1490	560
42	1080	1320	840	1560	600
44	1150	1400	900	1670	630
46	1190	1450	930	1720	660
48	1240	1520	960	1790	690
50	1295	1580	1010	1870	720
52	1350	1650	1050	1950	750
54	1390	1690	1090	2010	770
56	1440	1760	1120	2080	800
58	1490	1830	1150	2160	820
60	1530	1870	1190	2210	850
62	1580	1930	1230	2290	870
64	1620	1980	1260	2340	900
66	1660	2030	1290	2390	930
68	1710	2090	1330	2470	950
70	----	----	----	----	---
72	----	----	----	----	---

Downtown—Parking Prohibited

Percent Green				
45	(55 — 35)		(65 — 25)	
555	680	430	810	300
665	810	520	960	370
775	950	600	1120	430
880	1080	680	1280	480
970	1190	750	1400	540
1080	1320	840	1560	600
1170	1430	910	1690	650
1240	1520	960	1800	680
1330	1630	1030	1930	730
1420	1740	1100	2050	790
1490	1830	1150	2160	820
1580	1930	1230	2290	870
1660	2020	1300	2400	920
1730	2120	1340	2490	970
1820	2220	1420	2630	1010
1890	2310	1470	2730	1050
1960	2400	1520	2830	1090
2030	2480	1580	2930	1130
2110	2580	1640	3040	1180
----	----	----	----	----
----	----	----	----	----
----	----	----	----	----
----	----	----	----	----
----	----	----	----	----
----	----	----	----	----
----	----	----	----	----

Downtown—Parking Both Sides

Total Street Width	Percent Green				
	45	(55 — 35)		(65 — 25)	
20	----	----	----	----	---
22	----	----	----	----	---
24	----	----	----	----	---
26	----	----	----	----	---
28	----	----	----	----	---
30	----	----	----	----	---
32	----	----	----	----	---
34	----	----	----	----	---
36	----	----	----	----	---
38	----	----	----	----	---
40	830	1020	640	1190	470
42	880	1080	680	1270	490
44	930	1140	720	1340	520
46	980	1200	760	1410	550
48	1035	1260	810	1490	580
50	1075	1310	840	1550	600
52	1120	1370	870	1620	620
54	1160	1420	900	1680	640
56	1200	1470	930	1730	670
58	1240	1520	960	1790	690
60	1280	1570	990	1850	710
62	1320	1610	1030	1910	730
64	1370	1670	1070	1980	760
66	1390	1700	1080	2010	770
68	1420	1740	1100	2050	790
70	1450	1770	1130	2090	810
72	----	----	----	----	---

Total Street Width	Intermediate—Parking Prohibited Percent Green					Intermediate—Parking One Side Percent Green					Intermediate—Parking Both Sides Percent Green				
	45	(55 — 35)		(65 — 25)		45	(55 — 35)		(65 — 25)		45	(55 — 35)		(65 — 25)	
20	555	680	430	810	300	----	----	----	----	----	----	----	----	----	---
22	660	810	510	970	350	----	----	----	----	----	----	----	----	----	---
24	755	920	590	1090	420	----	----	----	----	----	----	----	----	----	---
26	840	1030	650	1220	460	----	----	----	----	----	----	----	----	----	---
28	920	1120	720	1320	520	----	----	----	----	----	----	----	----	----	---
30	990	1210	770	1430	550	735	900	570	1070	400	----	----	----	----	---
32	1060	1300	820	1530	590	830	1020	640	1200	460	----	----	----	----	---
34	1110	1360	860	1600	620	900	1100	700	1300	500	----	----	----	----	---
36	1185	1450	920	1710	660	975	1190	760	1410	540	----	----	----	----	---
38	1240	1510	970	1790	690	1030	1250	810	1480	580	----	----	----	----	---
40	1290	1570	1010	1870	710	1090	1340	840	1580	600	850	1040	660	1230	470
42	1350	1650	1050	1950	750	1155	1410	900	1670	640	900	1100	700	1300	500
44	1420	1740	1100	2050	790	1210	1470	950	1740	680	960	1170	750	1380	540
46	1470	1800	1140	2120	820	1260	1540	980	1820	700	1010	1240	780	1460	560
48	1510	1850	1170	2180	840	1310	1600	1020	1900	720	1060	1300	820	1530	590
50	1565	1910	1220	2260	870	1365	1670	1060	1970	760	1110	1370	850	1610	610
52	1620	1980	1260	2340	900	1420	1740	1100	2060	780	1165	1430	900	1680	650
54	1670	2040	1300	2410	930	1460	1790	1130	2110	810	1225	1490	960	1770	680
56	1710	2090	1330	2470	950	1510	1850	1160	2180	830	1280	1560	1000	1850	710
58	1755	2140	1370	2530	980	1555	1890	1220	2240	870	1315	1610	1020	1900	730
60	1800	2200	1400	2600	1000	1610	1950	1270	2320	900	1365	1670	1060	1970	760
62	----	----	----	----	----	1640	1990	1290	2350	930	1410	1720	1100	2030	790
64	----	----	----	----	----	1680	2050	1310	2410	950	1455	1780	1130	2100	810
66	----	----	----	----	----	1730	2110	1350	2500	960	1490	1830	1150	2150	830
68	----	----	----	----	----	1785	2170	1400	2570	1000	1535	1870	1200	2220	850
70	----	----	----	----	----	----	----	----	----	----	1585	1930	1240	2290	880
72	----	----	----	----	----	----	----	----	----	----	----	----	----	----	---

SOURCE: Standards for Street Facilities and Services, Procedure Manual 7A, National Committee
on Urban Transportation, Public Administration Service, Chicago, Ill. 1958

Total Street Width	Intermediate—Parking Prohibited Percent Green					Intermediate—Parking Permitted Percent Green				
	45	(55 — 35)		(65 — 25)		45	(55 — 35)		(65 — 25)	
20	325	400	250	470	180	---	---	---	---	---
22	410	500	320	590	230	---	---	---	---	---
24	490	600	380	710	270	---	---	---	---	---
26	580	700	460	830	330	---	---	---	---	---
28	660	800	520	950	370	---	---	---	---	---
30	735	900	570	1060	410	450	540	360	650	250
32	820	1000	640	1180	460	490	590	390	710	270
34	900	1100	700	1300	500	550	670	430	800	300
36	980	1200	760	1420	540	590	720	460	350	330
38	1045	1270	820	1510	580	660	800	520	950	370
40	1100	1340	860	1590	610	700	850	550	1010	390
42	1165	1420	910	1680	650	735	890	580	1060	410
44	1230	1500	960	1770	690	800	970	630	1160	440
46	1270	1550	990	1830	710	840	1020	660	1210	470
48	1310	1600	1020	1890	730	900	1100	700	1300	500
50	1355	1650	1060	1950	760	945	1160	730	1370	520
52	1390	1700	1080	2000	780	980	1200	760	1420	540
54	1435	1740	1130	2070	800	1045	1270	820	1510	580
56	1470	1790	1150	2120	820	1090	1330	850	1570	610
58	1510	1840	1180	2180	840	1145	1400	890	1650	640
60	1535	1870	1200	2220	850	1185	1450	920	1710	660
62	1555	1890	1220	2240	870	1230	1500	960	1770	690
64	1595	1940	1250	2300	890	1270	1550	990	1830	710
66	1620	1970	1270	2330	910	1315	1600	1030	1890	740
68	1640	2000	1280	2360	920	1355	1650	1060	1950	760
70	1660	2020	1300	2390	930	1400	1700	1100	2020	780
72	1680	2050	1310	2420	940	1430	1740	1120	2070	790

Total Street Width	Outlying or Rural Percent Green						
	45	(55 — 35)		(65 — 25)		(75 — 16.7)	
20	300	370	230	430	170	500	110
22	370	450	290	540	200	620	140
24	455	560	350	660	250	760	170
26	530	650	410	760	300	880	190
28	560	680	440	810	310	940	200
30	635	780	490	920	350	1070	230
32	715	880	550	1030	400	1190	260
34	785	960	610	1130	440	1320	290
36	840	1030	650	1210	470	1410	310
38	900	1100	700	1300	500	1500	330
40	960	1180	740	1380	540	1600	350
42	1015	1240	790	1460	570	1690	370
44	1070	1310	830	1540	600	1790	400
46	1110	1360	860	1600	620	1850	410
48	1160	1420	900	1670	650	1940	430
50	1200	1470	930	1730	670	2020	440
52	1235	1510	960	1780	690	2060	460
54	1270	1560	980	1830	710	2120	470
56	1315	1610	1020	1880	730	2200	480
58	1350	1660	1040	1940	760	2260	490
60	1370	1680	1060	1970	770	2290	500
62	1400	1710	1090	2020	780	2350	520
64	1430	1750	1110	2060	800	2380	520
66	1440	1760	1120	2070	810	2410	530
68	1460	1790	1130	2100	820	2450	540
70	1480	1810	1150	2130	830	2470	550
72	1500	1840	1160	2160	840	2510	550

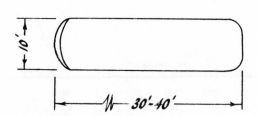

Typical bus dimensions ....
For smaller buses - use lower dimensions
For larger buses - use higher dimensions

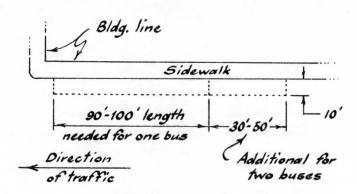

Near-side bus stop

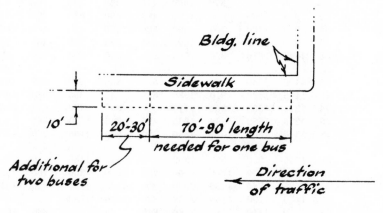

Far-side bus stop

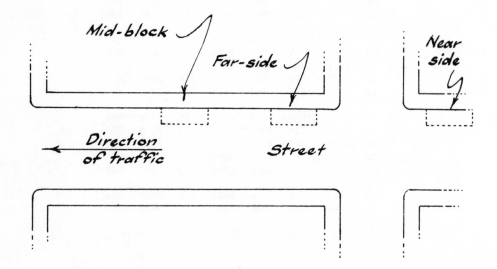

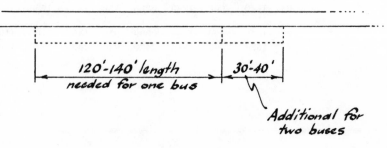

Mid-block

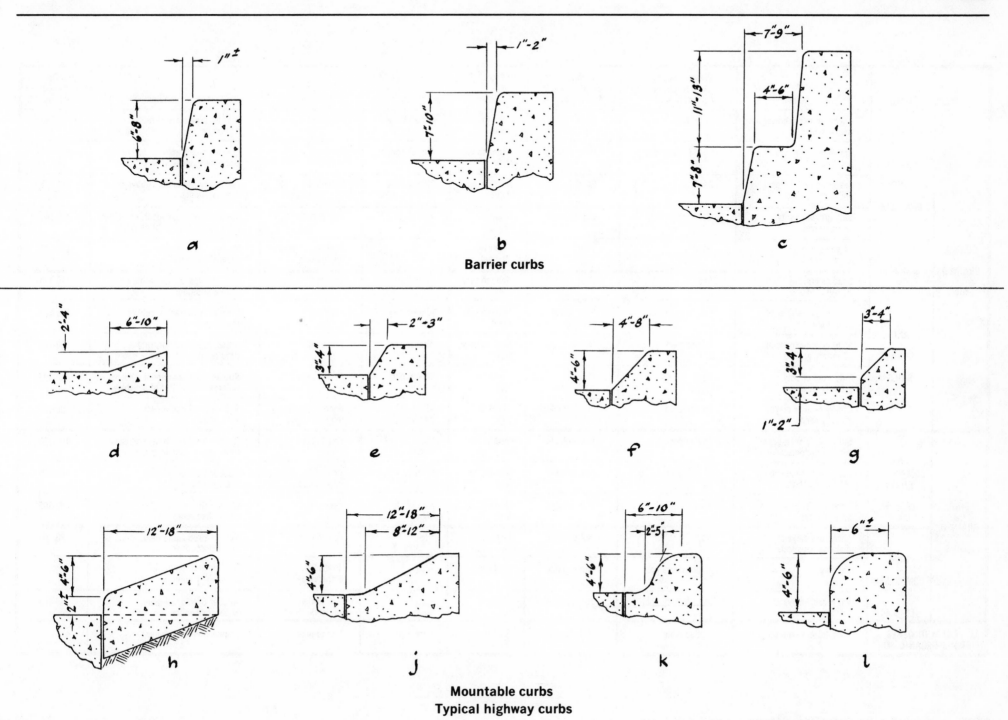

Barrier curbs

Mountable curbs
Typical highway curbs

Major Divisions		Name	Value as Foundation When Not Subject to Frost Action	Value as Base Directly Under Wearing Surface	Potential Frost Action	Compressibility and Expansion	Drainage Characteristics	Compaction Equipment	Unit Dry Weight Lb. Per Cu. Ft.
COARSE GRAINED SOILS	GRAVEL AND GRAVELLY SOILS	Gravel or sandy gravel, well-graded	Excellent	Good	None to very slight	Almost none	Excellent	Crawler type tractor, rubber tired equipment, steel wheeled roller	125-140
		Gravel or sandy gravel, poorly-graded	Good to excellent	Poor to fair	None to very slight	Almost none	Excellent	Crawler type tractor, rubber tired equipment, steel wheeled roller	120-130
		Gravel or sandy gravel, uniformly graded	Good	Good	None to very slight	Almost none	Excellent	Crawler type tractor, rubber tired equipment	115-125
		Silty gravel or silty sandy gravel	Good to excellent	Fair to good	Slight to medium	Very slight	Fair to poor	Rubber tired equipment, sheepsfoot roller, close control of moisture	130-145
		Clayey gravel or clayey sandy gravel	Good	Poor	Slight to medium	Slight	Poor to practically impervious	Rubber tired equipment, sheepsfoot roller	120-140
	SAND AND SANDY SOILS	Sand or gravelly sand, well-graded	Good	Poor	None to very slight	Almost none	Excellent	Crawler type tractor, rubber tired equipment	110-130
		Sand or gravelly sand, poorly-graded	Fair to good	Poor to not suitable	None to very slight	Almost none	Excellent	Crawler type tractor, rubber tired equipment	105-120
		Sand or gravelly sand, uniformly graded	Fair to good	Not suitable	None to very slight	Almost none	Excellent	Crawler type tractor, rubber tired equipment	100-115
		Silty sand or silty gravelly sand	Good	Poor	Slight to high	Very slight	Fair to poor	Rubber tired equipment, sheepsfoot roller; close control of moisture	120-135
		Clayey sand or clayey gravelly sand	Fair to good	Not suitable	Slight to high	Slight to medium	Poor to practically impervious	Rubber tired equipment, sheepsfoot roller	105-130
FINE GRAINED SOILS	LOW COMPRESSIBILITY LL < 50	Silts, sandy silts, gravelly silts, or diatomaceous soils	Fair to poor	Not suitable	Medium to very high	Slight to medium	Fair to poor	Rubber tired equipment, sheepsfoot roller; close control of moisture	100-125
		Lean clays, sandy clays, or gravelly clays	Fair to poor	Not suitable	Medium to high	Medium	Practically impervious	Rubber tired equipment, sheepsfoot roller	100-125
		Organic silts or lean organic clays	Poor	Not suitable	Medium to high	Medium to high	Poor	Rubber tired equipment, sheepsfoot roller	90-105
	HIGH COMPRESSIBILITY LL > 50	Micaceous clays or diatomaceous soils	Poor	Not suitable	Medium to very high	High	Fair to poor	Rubber tired equipment, sheepsfoot roller	80-100
		Fat clays	Poor to very poor	Not suitable	Medium	High	Practically impervious	Rubber tired equipment, sheepsfoot roller	90-110
		Fat organic clays	Poor to very poor	Not suitable	Medium	High	Practically impervious	Rubber tired equipment, sheepsfoot roller	80-105
PEAT AND OTHER FIBROUS ORGANIC SOILS		Peat, humus, and other	Not suitable	Not suitable	Slight	Very high	Fair to poor	Compaction not practical	—

SOURCE: Adapted from U. S. Army Corps of Engineers, Engineering Manual, Part XII, Chapter 2, Appendix "A"

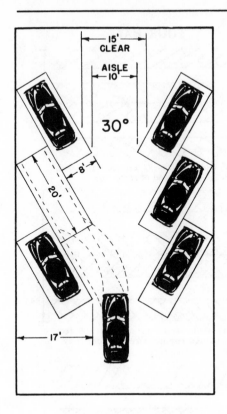

30-DEGREE ANGLE

gives you easy parking but takes a lot of space.

Cars per 100 lineal feet of double bay . . . 12

Area required per car in double bay . . . 425 sq. ft.

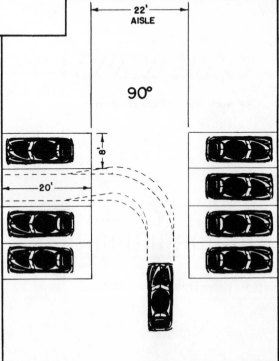

60-DEGREE ANGLE

is most popular method. Parks a lot of cars with easy access.

Cars per 100 lineal feet of double bay . . . 20

Area required per car in double bay . . . 330 sq. ft.

45-DEGREE ANGLE

gives you easy parking also but will park more cars.

Cars per 100 lineal feet of double bay . . . 16

Area required per car in double bay . . . 388 sq. ft.

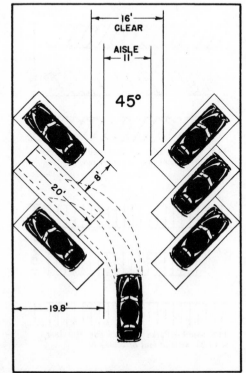

90-DEGREE ANGLE

Handles the most cars but difficult for some drivers. Permits two-way traffic flow.

Cars per 100 lineal feet of double bay . . . 25

Area required per car in double bay . . . 268 sq. ft.

SOURCE: *Solving Parking Problems, Bureau of Planning, Department of Commerce, State of N. Y.*

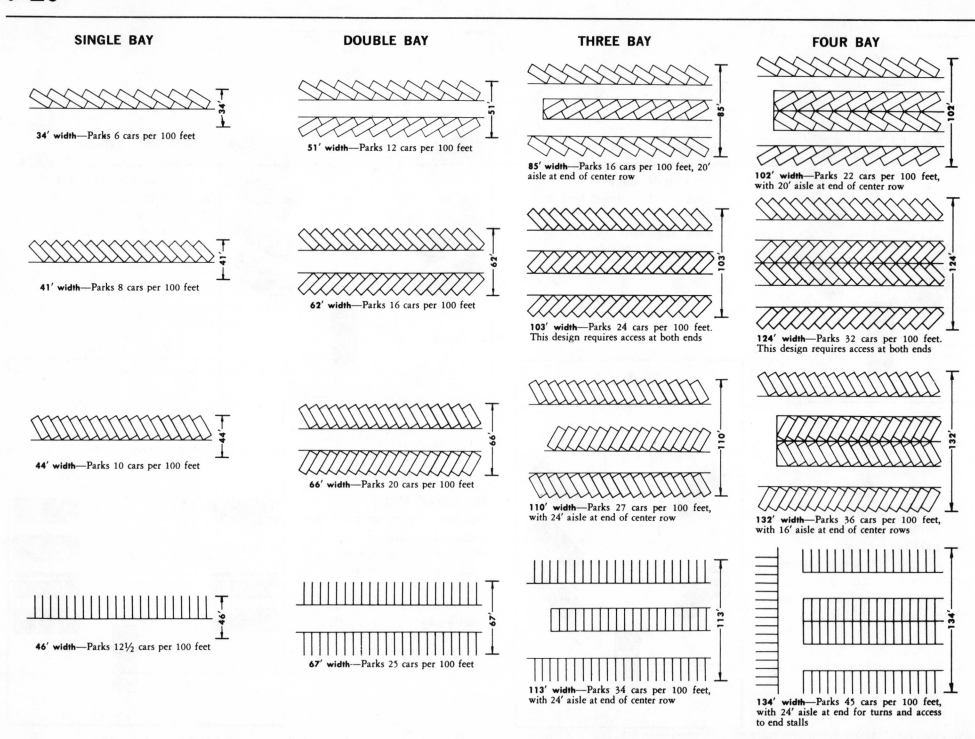

SINGLE BAY

34′ width—Parks 6 cars per 100 feet

41′ width—Parks 8 cars per 100 feet

44′ width—Parks 10 cars per 100 feet

46′ width—Parks 12½ cars per 100 feet

DOUBLE BAY

51′ width—Parks 12 cars per 100 feet

62′ width—Parks 16 cars per 100 feet

66′ width—Parks 20 cars per 100 feet

67′ width—Parks 25 cars per 100 feet

THREE BAY

85′ width—Parks 16 cars per 100 feet, 20′ aisle at end of center row

103′ width—Parks 24 cars per 100 feet. This design requires access at both ends

110′ width—Parks 27 cars per 100 feet, with 24′ aisle at end of center row

113′ width—Parks 34 cars per 100 feet, with 24′ aisle at end of center row

FOUR BAY

102′ width—Parks 22 cars per 100 feet, with 20′ aisle at end of center row

124′ width—Parks 32 cars per 100 feet. This design requires access at both ends

132′ width—Parks 36 cars per 100 feet, with 16′ aisle at end of center rows

134′ width—Parks 45 cars per 100 feet, with 24′ aisle at end for turns and access to end stalls

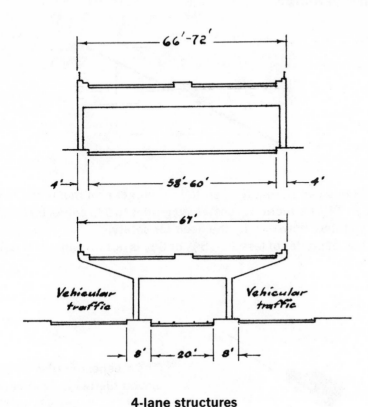

4-lane structures

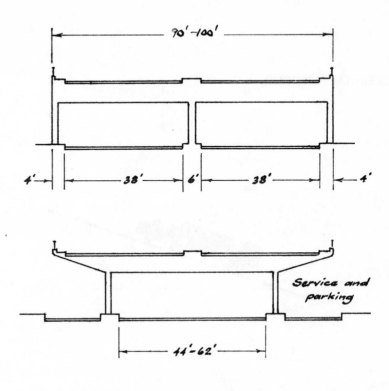

6-lane structures

ADVANTAGES

1. Elevated construction does not generally affect the existing street system.

2. Elevated construction usually requires less right-of-way than a depressed highway.

3. An elevated highway can be easily drained and does not require extensive relocation of existing utilities.

4. An elevated highway generally is less costly than an on-grade or depressed highway in built-up urban areas.

DISADVANTAGES

1. Elevated highways may affect light, air, or view of adjacent development.

2. Elevated highway ramps are upgrade for traffic entering and downgrade for traffic leaving the highway. This is contrary to traffic deceleration and acceleration requirements.

3. An elevated highway can easily become a visual obstacle if not properly related to the surrounding urban environment.

PASSENGER VEHICLES

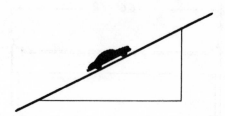

Automobiles can normally operate in high gear on maximum sustained grades up to 7%. Reduction of sustained grades to 5% or 6% for automobile traffic is justified, however, by the need for safety.

Reduction of grades of less than 5% or 6% is not warranted for passenger traffic only.

COMMERCIAL VEHICLES

Haveavy trucks can normally operate in high gear on maximum sustained grades up to 3%. Passing facilities (added lanes or long sight distance) should be provided on mixed traffic roads where grades cannot be reduced to 3%.

Either speed or pay load must be drastically reduced on sustained grades of over 3%.

6% is the maximum sustained grade for safe operation of trucks and automobiles. On mountain roads, in high altitudes and areas subject to frequent ice, snow, sleet and fog the maximum safe sustained grade is about 5% for all vehicles.

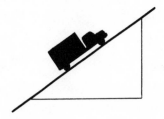

The steepest grades on existing paved highways or streets in the U. S. A. are 9% to 12% for highways and 30% to 32% for urban streets.

The average commercial vehicle can ascend a continuous 17% grade in low gear; use only for ramps, access, driveways.

ROAD DRAINAGE

ROADS

The minimum grade for good ditch drainage is 0.50%. 1% is preferable and 0.25% is the absolute minimum.

STREETS

The minimum grade for good gutter drainage is 0.30%. With great care in construction an absolute minimum of 0.10% may be used.

MAXIMUM DITCH GRADES—DRAINAGE

1% to 3%—sodded ditches
2% to 5%—ditch checks,
sod or paved ditch of concrete,
bitum. or rubble.

Silty soils will erode on grades over 1%. Most soils will erode on grades over 2%.

MOTOR-VEHICLE REGISTRATIONS, 1950 TO 1966, AND DRIVERS LICENSES, 1966, BY STATES

[**In thousands, except as indicated.** Motor-vehicle registrations include publicly owned vehicles; for uniformity, figures have been adjusted to a calendar-year basis as registration years in States differ; figures represent net numbers where possible, excluding re-registrations and nonresident registrations]

STATE	AUTOMOBILES, TRUCKS, AND BUSES								DRIVERS LICENSES, 1966		
					1966			Motor-cycles (incl. official),[1] 1966		Percent	
	1950	1955	1960	1965	Total	Private and commercial			Total[2]	Male drivers	Drivers under 25 years
						Automobiles (incl. taxicabs)	Trucks and buses				
U.S.[3]	49,300	62,870	73,869	90,361	94,177	77,959	14,884	1,752.8	98,496	59.2	(NA)
Ala	686	1,041	1,282	1,663	1,732	1,400	308	25.3	1,690	59.9	(NA)
Alaska	(NA)	(NA)	81	109	108	70	34	4.3	119	58.8	20.2
Ariz	271	415	624	825	863	662	183	17.3	908	59.9	29.3
Ark	477	584	708	914	955	667	277	12.2	948	59.9	(NA)
Calif	4,620	6,189	7,799	9,989	10,347	8,642	1,561	314.8	9,916	58.1	18.4
Colo	564	737	924	1,158	1,201	910	270	24.8	1,123	63.1	28.0
Conn	716	921	1,107	1,415	1,489	1,319	155	21.3	1,766	58.3	17.4
Del	108	154	192	244	256	216	37	3.5	277	56.7	20.8
D.C.	195	197	206	236	242	214	19	2.6	344	59.0	(NA)
Fla	985	1,616	2,367	3,037	3,221	2,799	375	53.7	3,092	59.8	(NA)
Ga	898	1,239	1,512	1,990	2,099	1,697	374	24.0	2,183	59.9	(NA)
Hawaii	138	181	231	310	325	284	35	12.0	362	58.8	(NA)
Idaho	272	338	375	434	446	304	130	20.0	427	61.4	(NA)
Ill	2,651	3,268	3,776	4,437	4,705	4,108	547	81.0	5,597	58.9	21.4
Ind	1,435	1,763	2,046	2,427	2,551	2,063	462	63.6	2,686	59.9	(NA)
Iowa	1,072	1,195	1,325	1,549	1,609	1,273	314	32.6	1,511	57.8	19.7
Kans	853	1,048	1,163	1,369	1,405	1,015	368	28.0	1,355	55.0	22.8
Ky	784	1,032	1,198	1,500	1,575	1,251	305	21.2	1,353	61.6	22.7
La	707	952	1,177	1,442	1,556	1,232	304	18.9	1,537	59.9	(NA)
Maine	276	323	374	424	434	348	80	6.4	505	60.8	(NA)
Md	685	938	1,155	1,481	1,534	1,336	183	21.3	1,639	59.0	22.1
Mass	1,280	1,546	1,803	2,104	2,173	1,939	205	36.4	2,635	60.8	(NA)
Mich	2,433	3,114	3,306	3,991	4,024	3,501	472	82.0	4,306	51.7	23.9
Minn	1,169	1,365	1,592	1,890	1,943	1,573	346	50.0	1,974	57.4	21.8
Miss	484	637	723	921	957	701	240	9.8	887	59.9	(NA)
Mo	1,261	1,490	1,720	2,085	2,221	1,768	430	37.3	2,406	60.0	18.3
Mont	265	331	373	429	439	293	137	13.8	382	57.6	19.8
Nebr	569	662	734	849	870	640	217	16.1	896	56.6	(NA)
Nev	77	124	175	266	279	208	62	9.6	267	58.1	21.2
N.H.	172	212	267	334	334	277	48	7.2	387	60.7	(NA)
N.J.	1,579	2,061	2,401	2,980	3,123	2,778	306	41.4	3,398	58.1	20.0
N. Mex.	238	340	426	525	549	403	133	10.6	512	60.0	(NA)
N.Y.	3,735	4,643	5,067	5,939	6,162	5,485	583	67.1	7,402	61.3	16.6
N.C.	1,056	1,437	1,720	2,156	2,307	1,821	424	26.9	2,340	59.2	24.2
N. Dak	276	309	345	396	406	265	134	7.9	363	59.8	24.4
Ohio	2,795	3,526	4,087	4,935	5,238	4,669	521	93.8	5,500	60.5	19.7
Okla	831	1,026	1,184	1,438	1,496	1,080	395	28.0	1,390	55.6	20.8
Oreg	689	802	919	1,119	1,167	946	200	33.8	1,113	57.4	20.4
Pa	3,010	3,737	4,287	4,968	5,196	4,528	612	87.5	6,102	62.4	19.7
R.I.	251	308	341	406	423	374	44	6.9	447	60.9	(NA)
S.C.	579	782	879	1,094	1,147	938	189	12.5	1,088	60.8	23.4
S. Dak	290	325	354	398	401	280	112	9.4	396	57.8	23.8
Tenn	858	1,102	1,307	1,655	1,757	1,420	311	26.2	1,862	59.9	(NA)
Tex	2,968	3,869	4,457	5,610	5,711	4,450	1,179	74.8	5,414	58.4	20.5
Utah	247	336	417	525	544	418	115	13.9	562	63.2	(NA)
Vt	121	136	152	175	179	138	39	5.0	204	60.8	(NA)
Va	918	1,243	1,426	1,800	1,875	1,572	272	20.2	2,160	59.8	(NA)
Wash	924	1,164	1,377	1,659	1,756	1,384	337	55.9	1,579	58.3	17.8
W. Va.	482	552	601	696	731	580	139	13.5	822	63.6	21.7
Wis	1,201	1,386	1,600	1,839	1,890	1,572	287	40.6	2,141	58.5	20.8
Wyo	145	174	207	225	224	146	72	6.0	223	61.4	(NA)

NA Not available.
[1] Excludes vehicles owned by military services.
[2] Estimated from data reported by States for current and previous years; no allowance made for deaths, emigration, or revocation.
[3] Incomplete data for some States.

SOURCE: Statistical Abstracts of the U. S.—1967 U. S. Dept. of Commerce, Washington, D. C.

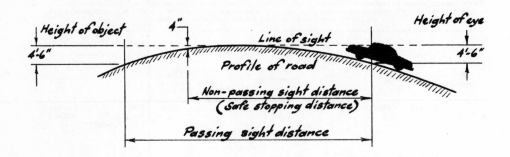

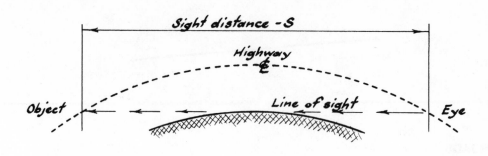

PROFILE VIEW—VERTICAL SIGHT DISTANCE

On three lane highways opposing traffic should be restricted from using center lane in passing zones by pavement markings.

PLAN VIEW—HORIZONTAL SIGHT DISTANCE

radius of curve required s^2

s   sight distance   8m

m   distance from obstruction

location of obstruction or slope in cut, 4.5' above grade.

MINIMUM VERTICAL AND HORIZONTAL SIGHT DISTANCES

speed	DESIGNED PASSING—PROVIDE AS OFTEN AS PRACTICABLE				NON-PASSING
	2 lane highway		3 lane highway		provide at all points on all highways
	desirable	absolute	desirable	absolute	
30 mph	600'	500'			200'
40	1100	900			275
50	1600	1400	1100'	900'	350
60	2300	2100	1500	1300	475
70	3200	2900	2000	1800	600
80					750
90					950
100					1200

AIR AND RAIL TRANSPORTATION

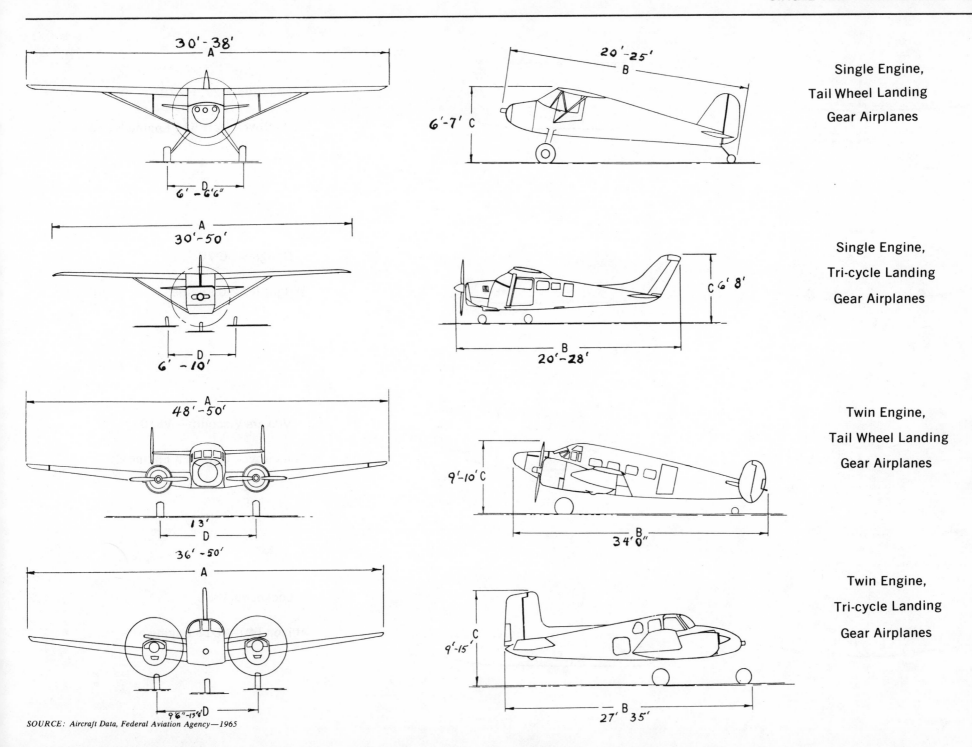

30'-38'
A
20'-25'
B
6'-7' C
6' - 6'6"
D

Single Engine,
Tail Wheel Landing
Gear Airplanes

A
30'-50'
D
6' - 10'
C 6' 8'
B
20'-28'

Single Engine,
Tri-cycle Landing
Gear Airplanes

A
48'-50'
13'
D
9'-10' C
B
34' 0"

Twin Engine,
Tail Wheel Landing
Gear Airplanes

36' - 50'
A
9'6"-13'8" D
9'-15' C
B
27' 35'

Twin Engine,
Tri-cycle Landing
Gear Airplanes

SOURCE: Aircraft Data, Federal Aviation Agency—1965

155

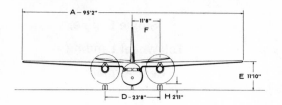

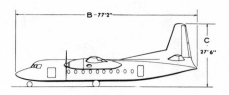

Fairchild F-27, F-27B

Rolls Royce Dart 511 Engine

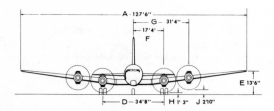

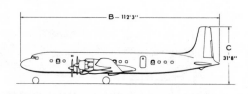

Douglas DC 7C

Wright R3350 Engine

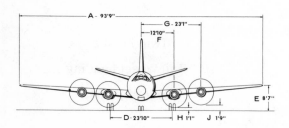

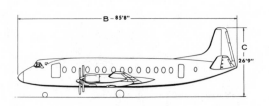

Vickers Viscount—V810

Rolls Royce Dart 525 Engine

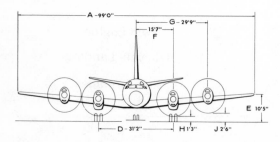

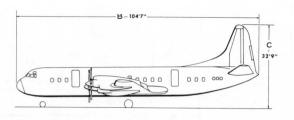

Lockheed 188C

Allison 501—D13 Engine

SOURCE: Aircraft Data, FAA-1965

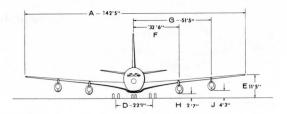

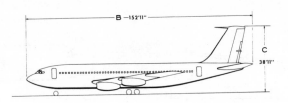

Boeing 707—400

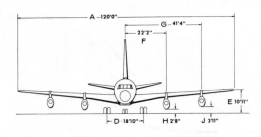

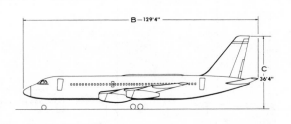

Convair 880
General Electric 805—3 Engine

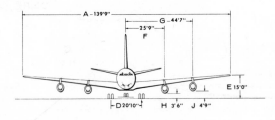

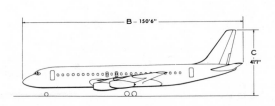

Douglas DC 8
JT3C6 Engine

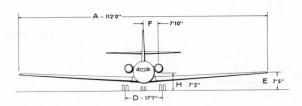

Carvelle SE 210
Rolls Royce Avon 522 Engine

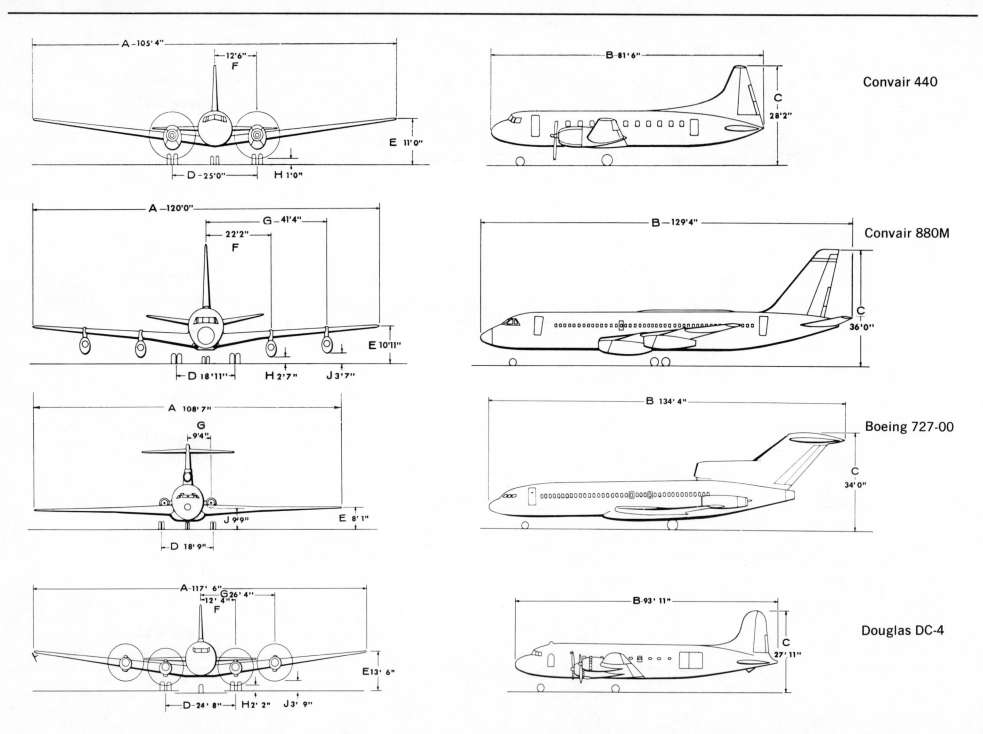

Convair 440

Convair 880M

Boeing 727-00

Douglas DC-4

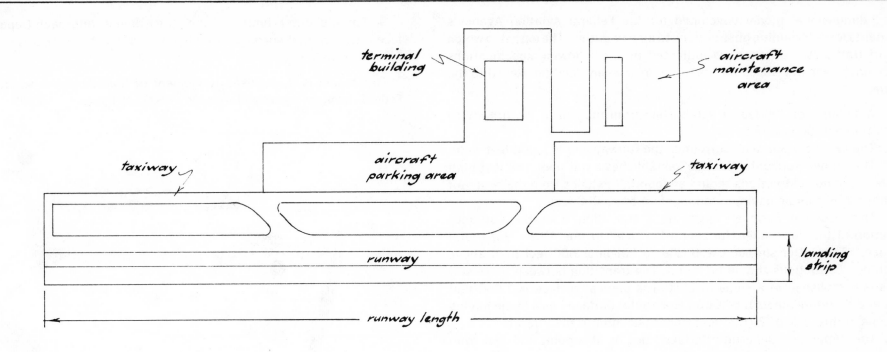

runway length	widths			runway CL to taxiway CL	CL of parallel taxiways	CL of taxiways to aircraft parking area	CL of taxiways to obstacle	runway CL to building line (instruments)	runway CL to building line (non-instr.)
	landing strip	runway	taxiway						
1600–3200	250	75 max.	40 max.	150	100	100	75		250
3201–4200	400	100	50	250	200	175	100	750	500
4201–6000	500	150	75	400	300	250	200	750	750
6001–7500	500	150	75	400	300	250	200	750	750
7501–10,500	500	150	75	400	300	250	200	750	750

CL=CENTER LINE

SOURCE: Airport Design, Federal Aviation Agency

A 3-dimensional model developed for the Federal Aviation Agency's standards for determining obstructions to air navigation. The extent to which airport traffic uses air space is indicated by the following specifications which have been developed for the larger instrument facilities keyed to the Figure:

1. A distance of 200 feet is established from the end of the runway to the "Approach-Departure Surface".

2. The "Primary Surface" surrounds the runway and is 1,000 feet wide.

3. The "Inner Horizontal Surface" establishes a flat floor 150 feet high above which no obstructions should be found. It extends from the center of the airport as a circle having a radius of up to 13,000 feet.

4. The "Conical Surface" exists as a transition from the 150 foot elevation of the flat "Inner Horizontal Surface" to the "Outer Horizontal Surface." This latter surface establishes a flat floor 500 feet high above which no obstructions should be found. The transition between these surfaces is established at a slope of 20:1. The conical surface is 7,000 feet wide and therefore meets the "Outer Horizontal Surface" as a circle having a radius in this case of 20,000 feet from the center of the Airport.

5. The "Approach-Departure Surface" begins at a point 200 feet from the end of the runway and extends straight up from zero elevation to the "Outer Horizontal Surface" at a slope of 50:1. It thus traverses 25,000 feet before reaching the 500 foot floor. The first part of this surface, shown as the darker shaded portion, is known as the "Clear Zone". It reaches an elevation of 50 feet after traversing 2,500 feet from zero point.

6. The "Transitional Surface" extends along the "Approach-Departure Surface" and has a slope of 7:1.

7. The "Outer Horizontal Surface" is a flat floor 500 feet high above which no obstructions should be found. It extends 30,000 feet from the end of the conical surface. Its outer limit is a circle with a radius up to 50,000 feet from the center of the Airport.

8. The outer limits of the "Instrument Approach-Departure Surface" fan out past the "Outer Horizontal Surface" limits, extending over 50,000 feet from the end of the runway. At this distance, the surface is 16,000 feet across.

9. For the outer limits of the "Instrument Approach-Departure Surface", transitional surfaces are also provided with a 7:1 slope. These are 5,000 feet wide each.

This model is a proposed refinement of the somewhat similar existing Federal Aviation Agency standards (T.S.O. N-18).

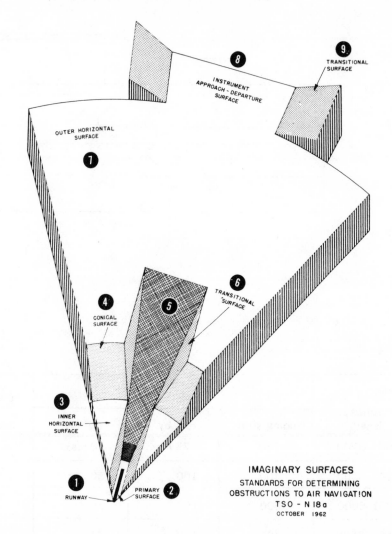

IMAGINARY SURFACES
STANDARDS FOR DETERMINING
OBSTRUCTIONS TO AIR NAVIGATION
TSO - N 18 a
OCTOBER 1962

Reprinted by Permission From "Airspace in Urban Development" by Michael M. Bernard, Copyright 1963,
Urban Land Institute, 1200 18th Street, Wash. D. C.-T. B. No. 46-20p.p.

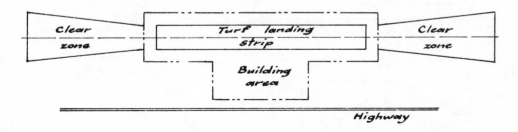

Approximate min. land areas required for small

airports at specified elevations

Elevation of site in feet	Landing strip [1] dimensions in feet			Acreage required [2]	
	Width	Length		Min.	Max.
		Min.	Max.		
Sea level	250	1800	3400	27	43
1000	250	1900	3600	28	45
2000	250	2100	3900	30	48
3000	250	2200	4100	31	51
4000	250	2300	4400	32	53
5000	250	2400	4600	33	55

[1]Landing strip lengths are shown to the nearest 100′ after correcting sea level lengths for elevation.

[2]Based on min. rectangular parcals of land as shown on above sketch. In addition, adequate property interests should be acquired in the 16 acres contained in the clear zones.

SOURCE: Small Airports, Federal Aviation Agency

Future airport requirements should be carefully considered when acquiring land. It is desirable that the area obtained be adequate for development to the size required for the foreseeable future. Where boundaries of present ownership make it necessary to acquire more land than is actually required for the initial development, the portion not needed immediately for the full airport development may be put to other revenue-producing uses until it is needed.

Specific land requirements cannot be given because of the variable conditions that may be encountered, but the accompanying table may be used to estimate the minimum amount of property that will be required. The indicated acreages are based on landing-strip lengths corrected only for elevation, minimum building area, and clear-zone requirements.

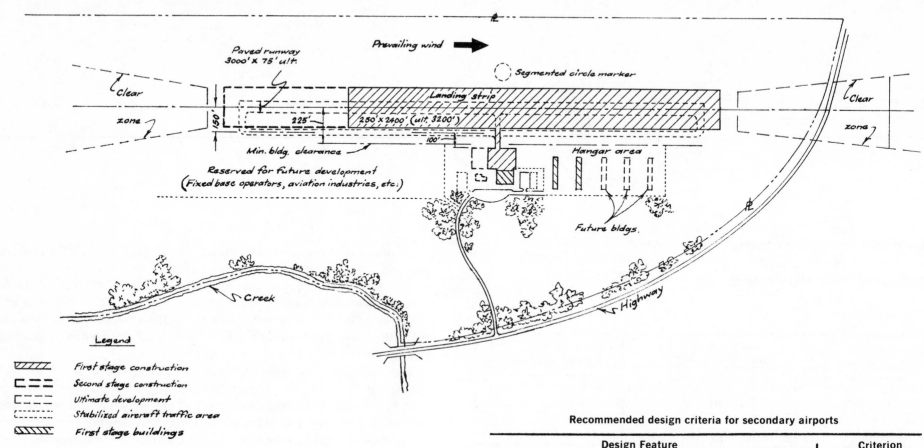

Paved runway
3000' x 75' ult.

Prevailing wind →

Segmented circle marker

Clear zone

Landing strip

Clear zone

150'

225'

250' x 2400' (ult. 3200')

Min. bldg. clearance

100'

Hangar area

Reserved for future development
(Fixed base operators, aviation industries, etc.)

Future bldgs.

Creek

Highway

Legend

⬛	First stage construction
⬜	Second stage construction
⬜	Ultimate development
⬜	Stabilized aircraft traffic area
⬛	First stage buildings

Recommended design criteria for secondary airports

Design Feature	Criterion
Length of landing strip[1]	1,800 3,400 feet.
Width of landing strip	250 feet.
Length of paved runway[1]	1,600 3,200 feet.
Width of paved runway	75 feet.
Width of taxiway	40 feet.
Distance between centerline of runway and centerline of parallel taxiway.	150 feet.
Distance between centerline of taxiway and edge of aircraft parking apron.	100 feet.
Distance between centerline of taxiway and obstruction	75 feet.
Centerline of landing strip or runway to building line	225 feet.
Longitudinal runway or landing strip grade	2% max.
Effective gradient	1½% max.
Transverse runway or landing strip grade	1½ 3%.
Longitudinal taxiway grade	2% max.
Transverse taxiway grade	1½ 3%.

SOURCE: Small Airports, Federal Aviation Agency

[1]Lengths within the dimensions shown should be corrected for airport elevation and gradient.

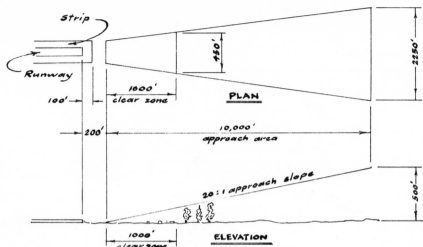

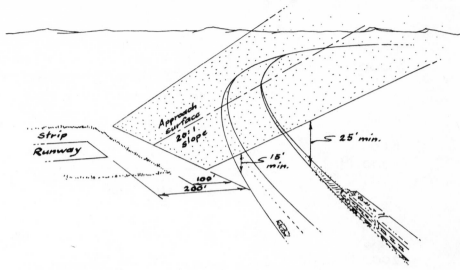

Obstructions to flight in the local area is an important factor that should be considered in choosing a site. They consist of fences, trees, pole lines, buildings, and other natural or manmade objects in the area immediately adjacent to the airport. In some instances, the ground itself may slope upward from the end of the landing strip to such an extent that it constitutes an obstruction to aircraft operation. If obstructions exist around a site on which an airport is to be built, their removal is imperative, though it may involve considerable expense and litigation.

Aircraft when taking off or landing gain or lose altitude very slowly compared to their forward speed. Because of this characteristic, they need space at the ends of the landing strips, known as "approach areas," over which they may safely gain or lose altitude. An approach area begins at a point 200 feet from the end of the runway and extends a distance of 10,000 feet. Being symmetrical about the extended centerline, the width of the approach area increases with distance from the end of the landing strip. An approach area should be free of obstructions that exceed a height of 1 foot above the end of the landing strip for each 20 feet of distance from the end of the strip.

At small airports, the most critical portion of the approach area is the first 1,000 feet. This area, known as the "clear zone," is the innermost portion of the approach area. Its configuration and dimensions are shown in

figure 2. The purchase of land in this zone is recommended. If this cannot be done, sufficient control over the land should be acquired to allow for the removal of existing obstructions and to control the future use of the land and any construction thereon which would interfere with operations at the airport.

The FAA does not regard the clear zone as an "overrun area" or "landing strip extension." Therefore, it is not necessary to grade the area, but obstructions must be removed. Naturally, a level area is preferable, but it is not required. Fences, ditches, and other minor obstacles are permitted. In the same vein, roads and railroads are not objectionable in clear zones providing they comply with the recognized clearance standard (see fig. 3). Clearance does not ordinarily present a problem in the approach area beyond the clear zone.

However, certain clearance restrictions exist for railroads and highways located anywhere in the approach area. At least the minimum clearances as shown in figure 3 are required. The "critical clearance" is the vertical distance between the 20:1 approach surface and the edge of the highway pavement, or the railroad rail nearest the end of the landing strip. This clearance should not be less than 15 feet over highways, or 25 feet over railroads. Regardless of topography, in no case should the end of a landing strip be closer than 100 feet to the nearest edge of a highway or railroad.

SOURCE: Small Airports, Federal Aviation Agency

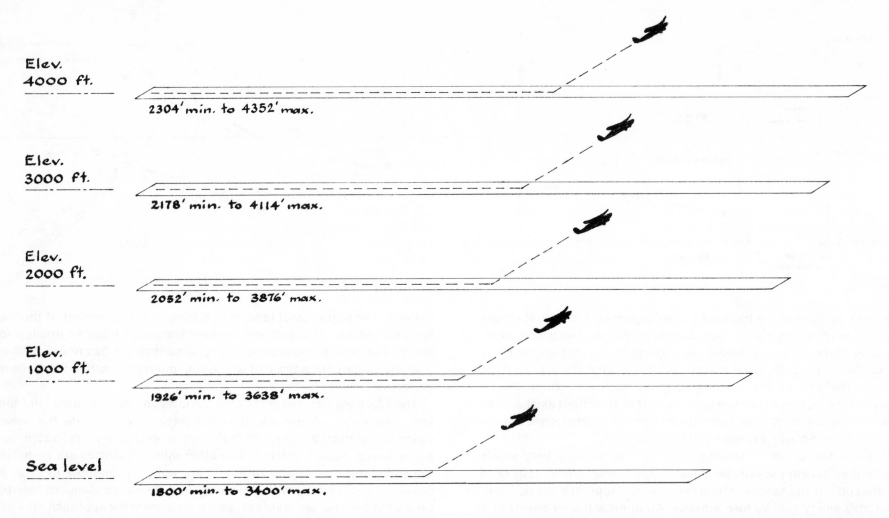

Elev. 4000 ft.

2304' min. to 4352' max.

Elev. 3000 ft.

2178' min. to 4114' max.

Elev. 2000 ft.

2052' min. to 3876' max.

Elev. 1000 ft.

1926' min. to 3638' max.

Sea level

1800' min. to 3400' max.

Small, or secondary, airports are generally designed for personal flying, whether it be for business or pleasure.

The popular kinds of aircraft in use at these airports range from small single-engine trainers of low horsepower to light twin-eigine-type aircraft. In between are the three- and four-passenger single-engine aircraft of medium horsepower. These vary widely in size and performance, affecting the required length of the landing strip. Obviously, a small single-engine aircraft of 1,200 pounds gross weight requires a shorter landing strip than does a multi-engine aircraft of much greater gross weight. For the aircraft that will use secondary airports, landing strips having lengths of 1,800 feet to 3,200 feet at sea level are adequate. If the landing strips are properly designed, these airports will accommodate aircraft having gross weights up to 12,500 pounds.

A major factor affecting the size of the airport is the elevation of the site above sea level. The above illustrates the effect of elevation on the distance required for an aircraft to gain sufficient speed to become airborne. To compensate for this effect, the basic sea-level length should be increased 7 percent for each 1,000 feet that the airport is above sea level.

SOURCE: Small Airports, Federal Aviation Agency

GENERAL. Classification of heliports/helistops is provided to indicate the major differences between kinds of installations for helicopter operations. The differences lie mainly in use, types of helicopters served, and the nature of supporting facilities included on the heliport. Classification is helpful in planning and zoning for heliports and serves to relate the operational factors involved to land use considerations.

a. Use. A heliport/helistop is either a privately operated exclusive use facility, on which the operator has control over the type and number of helicopters which may use it, or it is a publicly owned and operated facility open to any helicopter operator.

b. Size. A heliport/helistop may be any size down to the minimum recommended in this chapter and defined in Chapter 6. The size refers to the dimensions of the landing and takeoff area.

c. Helicopter Types. Helicopter types refer to those in the normal category as defined in FAR Part 27 or those in the transport category as defined in FAR Part 29.

    1. Normal category helicopters are machines 6,000 pounds or less maximum gross weight operated principally in private, business, charter, or commercial flying other than air carrier operations.

    2. Transport category helicopters are single-engine or multi-engine machines of unlimited weight operated in scheduled or nonscheduled passenger service.

d. Supporting Facilities. These refer to passenger and/or cargo facilities, helicopter parking, fueling, and maintenance provisions on the heliport. A helistop has none of these facilities except that it may be a pickup and discharge point for passengers or cargo.

HELIPORT CLASSIFICATION. Heliports are classified in accordance with uses, as follows:

    Class I—Private

    Class II—Public (Small)

    Class III—Public (Large)

1. Private Heliport (Class I). The landing and takeoff area dimensions are selected by the owner and are based on the overall length of the helicopter. Minimum length of the area should be at least 1.5 times the overall length of the helicopter and the width equal to the length. For example, if the largest helicopter to be served has an overall length of 60 feet, the minimum dimensions would be 90 feet by 90 feet (Figure 8).

2. Small Public Heliport (Class II). The landing and takeoff area dimensions should be sufficient to accommodate any of the various models of helicopters in the normal category, the airworthiness requirements of which are defined in FAR Part 27 (formerly CAR 6). These heliports should have a minimum landing and takeoff area length of 2.0 times the overall length of the helicopter and a width of 1.5 times the overall helicopter length (Figure 9).

3. Large Public Heliport (Class III). The landing and takeoff area dimensions should be sufficient to accommodate any model helicopter in the normal and transport categories, the airworthiness requirements of which are defined in FAR Parts 27 and 29 (formerly CARs 6 and 7). These heliports should have a minimum landing and takeoff area length of 2.0 times the overall length of the helicopter and a width of 1.5 times the overall helicopter length (Figure 10).

They are further subclassified in accordance with their available support facilities, as follows:

    Subclass A—Minimum support facilities—no buildings, maintenance or fueling (a helistop).

    Subclass B—Limited support facilities—no maintenance or fueling.

    Subclass C—Complete support facilities.

Note: Any heliport may be either privately or publicly owned or operated. Whether it is private or public does not affect its subclassification.

SOURCE: Heliport Design Guide Federal Aviation Agency-1959

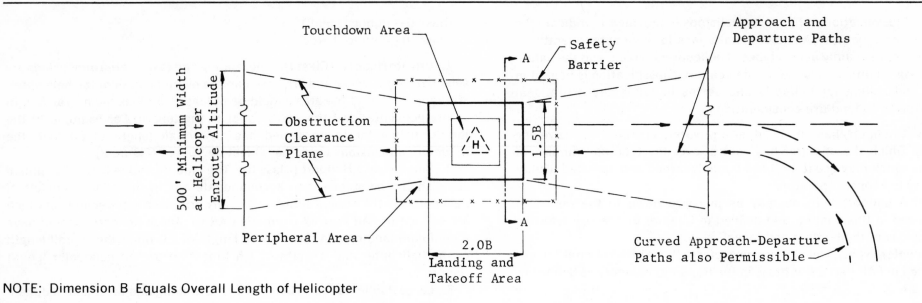

NOTE: Dimension B Equals Overall Length of Helicopter

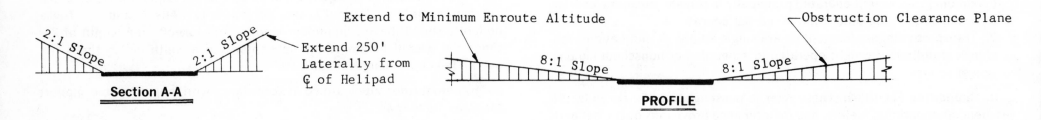

Section A-A

PROFILE

HELIPORT LAYOUT. The size, shape, and appurtenances of heliports are determined by a variety of interrelated factors—principally the nature of the site available, size and performance of the helicopter, and the buildings or other objects in the surrounding area. Although heliports may be square, rectangular, or circular, an irregular-shaped site may be equally functional. Minimum operational safety requirements will not vary from one design to another.

a. Landing and Takeoff Area. Since landing and takeoff areas should provide sufficient space for the helicopter to maneuver, size depends to a large extent on the overall length of the helicopter, i.e., the tip to tip dimension of the rotor system. These dimensions vary considerably according to the type of helicopter.

Heliports at Elevations Less Than 1,000 Feet Above Sea Level. Minimum recommended landing and takeoff area dimensions shown above are applicable to all heliports 1,000 feet above sea level or less.

Heliports at Elevations More Than 1,000 Feet Above Sea Level. For elevations of more than 1,000 feet above sea level, it is recommended that consideration be given to increasing the length of the landing and takeoff area or diameter (if circular) by 15 percent per 1,000 feet of sea level elevation above 1,000 feet or that part thereof, in order to prevent drastic off-loading of non-supercharged helicopters. For example, on a heliport 3,000 feet above sea level, the minimum length would be increased by 30 percent.

SOURCE: Heliport Design Guide, FAA-1959

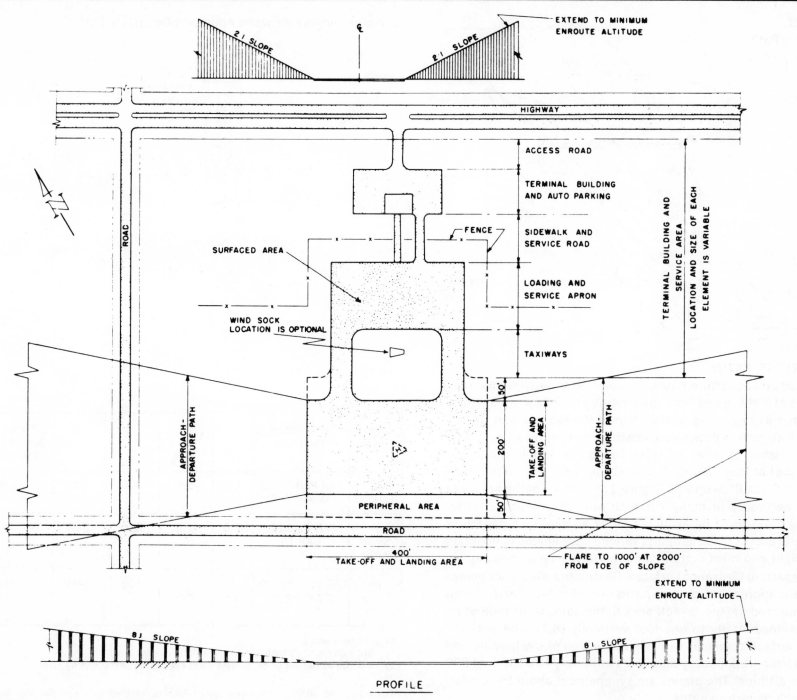

EXTEND TO MINIMUM
ENROUTE ALTITUDE

2:1 SLOPE

2:1 SLOPE

HIGHWAY

ACCESS ROAD

TERMINAL BUILDING
AND AUTO PARKING

FENCE

SIDEWALK AND
SERVICE ROAD

SURFACED AREA

LOADING AND
SERVICE APRON

WIND SOCK
LOCATION IS OPTIONAL

TAXIWAYS

TERMINAL BUILDING AND
SERVICE AREA

LOCATION AND SIZE OF EACH
ELEMENT IS VARIABLE

ROAD

APPROACH-
DEPARTURE PATH

50'

200'

TAKE-OFF AND
LANDING AREA

APPROACH-
DEPARTURE PATH

PERIPHERAL AREA

50'

ROAD

400'
TAKE-OFF AND LANDING AREA

FLARE TO 1000' AT 2000'
FROM TOE OF SLOPE

EXTEND TO MINIMUM
ENROUTE ALTITUDE

8:1 SLOPE

8:1 SLOPE

PROFILE

SOURCE: *Heliport Design Guide, Federal Aviation Agency—1959*

167

Perspective View of
Approach-Departure Path

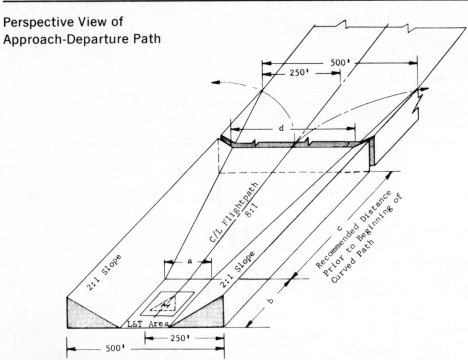

Minimum Angles Between Approach-Departure Paths

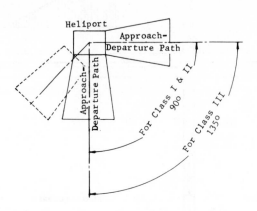

APPROACH-DEPARTURE PATHS

a. General. Approach-departure paths are selected to provide the most advantageous lines of flight to and from the landing and takeoff area. These paths are considered as beginning at the edge of the landing and takeoff area and usually are aligned as directly as possible into the prevailing winds. It is generally necessary to have at least two paths which should be separated by an arc of at least 90 degrees for Class I and Class II heliports and 135 degrees for Class III heliports (Figure 11). Curved paths are quite practical and are necessary in many cases to provide a suitable route. Emergency landing areas must be available along all approach-departure paths for all heliports except those heliports serving multiengine helicopters able to continue flight and meet certain climb performance on one engine.

b. Approach-Departure Clearance Surfaces. Obstruction clearance planes in the direction of the approach-departure paths extend outward and upward from the edge of the landing and takeoff area to the enroute altitude at an angle of eight feet horizontally to one foot vertically (8:1). The width of the sloping plane surface coincides with the dimension of the landing and takeoff area at the heliport boundary and flares uniformly to a width of 500 feet at the enroute altitude. The planes are symmetrical about the center-lines of the approach-departure paths.

SOURCE: Heliport Design Guide, FAA-1959

Heliport Class	FAR Category Helicopter	a	b	c	d	Minimum Angle Between Approach-Departure Paths
I Private	FAR Part 27, 29 (CAR 6 & 7)	1.5	1.5	300'	200'	90°
II Small Public	FAR Part 27 (CAR 6)	1.5	2.0	300'	300'	90°
III Large Public	FAR Part 27, 29 (CAR 6 & 7	* 1.5	* 2.0	400'	300'	135°

Dimensions a and b:
(1) are expressed as multiples of overall helicopter length.
(2) may be increased or decreased upon evaluation of the site by FAA.

*For scheduled airline operations, other factors, related to a specific site would need to be considered.

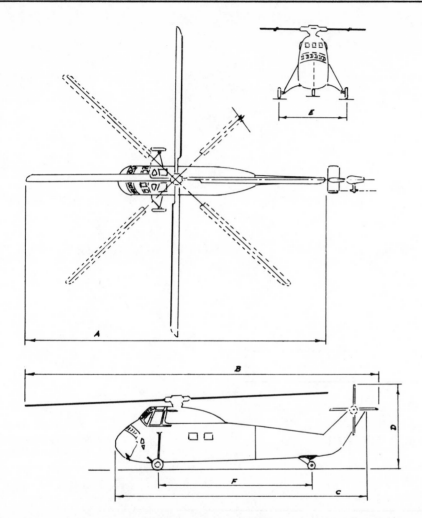

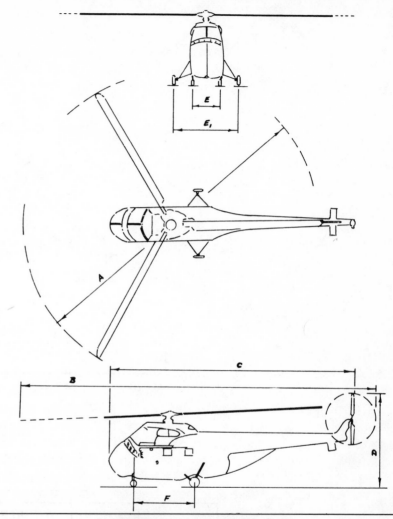

REPRESENTATIVE HELICOPTER DATA										
Company	Model Designation	A Rotor Diam.	B Length O.A.	C Length Fuselage	D Height	E Tread Forward	E₁ Tread Aft	F Wheel Base	Max. Gr. Wt. (1000 Lbs.)	No. of Engs.
Doman	LZ5-2	48'-0"	62'-11"	38'-0"	16'-1"	7'-6"		7'-9"	5.2	1
Kaman	K-600	47'-0"	*47'-0"	25'-2"	15'-7"	6'-11"	8'-4"	8'-2"	7.5	1
Omega	SB-12	39'-0"	47'-5"	38'-6"	13'-0"	3'-9"	11'-9"	10'-0"	4.35	2
Sikorsky	S-55A	53'-0"	62'-3"	42'-2"	15'-3"	4'-8"	11'-0"	10'-6"	7.5	1
Republic	Alouette SE 3130	33'-6"	40'-10"	31'-10"	9'-0"	6'-10"	—	10'-0"	3.3	1
Republic	DJINN SO 1221	36'-0"	29'-3"	17'-3"	8'-6"	6'-2"		9'-0"	1.7	1

*No tail rotor

SOURCE: Heliport Design Guide, FAA—1959

REPRESENTATIVE HELICOPTER DATA									
Company	Model Designation	A Rotor Diam.	B Length O.A.	C Length Fuselage	D Height	E Tread	F Wheel Base	Max. Gr. Wt. (1000 Lbs.)	No. of Engs.
Bell	47-J	37'-2"	43'-5"	32'-5"	9'-4"	7'-6"	9'-7" Skids	2.8	1
Bell	47G-2	35'-2"	41'-5"	30'-5"	9'-5"	7'-6"	10'-1" Skids	2.5	1
Bell	204	44'-0"	53'-0"	42'-8"	11'-3"	8'-4"	10'-10" Skids	7.2	1
Cessna	CH-1	35'-0"	42'-8"	32'-1"	11'-8"	8'-4"	Skids	3.0	1
Hiller	12-C	35'-0"	40'-6"	29'-5"	9'-9"	7'-8"	Skids	2.5	1
Sikorsky	S-56	72'-0"	82'-10"	64'-11"	21'-6"	19'-9"	36'-11"	31.0	2
Sikorsky	S-58	56'-0"	65'-10"	47'-2"	15'-11"	12'-0"	28'-3"	13.0	1
Sikorsky	S-62	53'-0"	62'-3"	44'-7"	16'-0"	11'-0"	17'-10"	7.5	1
(Possible Future Helicopter)		100'-0"	120'-0"	80'-0"	25'-0"	25'-0"	50'-0"	50.0	3 Or More

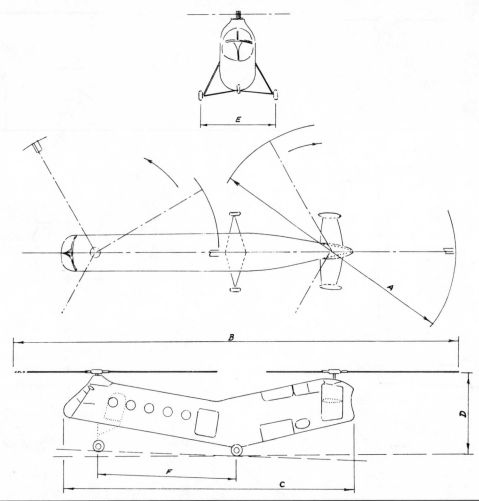

REPRESENTATIVE HELICOPTER DATA									
Company	Model Designation	A Rotor Diam.	B Length O.A.	C Length Fuselage	D Height	E Tread	F Wheel Base	Max. Gr. Wt. (1000 Lbs.)	No. of Engs.
Vertol	42/44	44'-0"	86'-4"	52'-6"	15'-5"	14'-4"	24'-6"	15.0	1
Vertol	107	48'-4"	81'-8"	44'-7"	16'-10"	13'-11"	24'-9"	16.65	2
Vertol	YHC-1B	59'-0"	97'-6"	50'-0"	18'-4"	10'-4"	21'-0"	33.0	2
Kaman/Forey	Rotodyne	104'-0"	*104'-0"	64'-6"	25'-0"	28'-0"	21'-0"	60.0	2**

*No tail rotor
**Plus 4 tip jets

SOURCE: Heliport Design Guide, FAA—1959

COMPARATIVE PLANS OF TRANSPORT SYSTEMS (drawn to the same scale) scale in feet 10 0 50 100 150 200	COMPARATIVE SECTIONS FOR 2 DIRECTIONS scale in feet 10 5 0 10 20 30 40	ECONOMIC DISTANCE BETWEEN STOPS OR STATIONS	PASSENGER OR VEHICLE CAPACITY PER HOUR ONE WAY	AVERAGE SPEED	ECONOMIC RUNNING COST PER CAR OR PASSENGER MILE
OPEN BUS TRAILER (automated robotug tractor)	26' radius	as required	100 v.p.h. 7,500	8 m.p.h.	
CARVEYOR 10 SEAT (non-stop system)		·25 mile	11,000 seated 22,000 seated and standing	·15 m.p.h.	
TELEPHERIQUE GONDOLA CAR (4 seat car)		1 mile or over	500–1,000	6–10 m.p.h.	·5d
PEDESTRIAN CONVEYOR OR MOVING BELT	straight only	100 feet–800 feet	32" belt = 3,000 people 48" belt = 10,000 people	1·5–2 m.p.h.	·025d
MONORAIL (Alweg system)		·5 mile min.	16–20,000	50 m.p.h.	
MONORAIL (Safege system)	100' radius	·5–3 mile / 16 mile	8 coach = 48,000 / 2 coach = 12,000	50 m.p.h. / 75 m.p.h.	·5d–1·5d
TRANSIT EXPRESSWAY (Westinghouse)	150' radius	·5–2 miles	8–20,000	23 m.p.h. (·5 mile stops) 39 m.p.h. (2 mile stops)	
UNDERGROUND RAILWAY (London system)	330' radius	·5–2 mile	40,000	20–30 m.p.h.	28 cents 35·4d per car mile
ARTICULATED 3-CAR TRAM		·25–·5 mile	20,000	20–30 m.p.h.	·56d

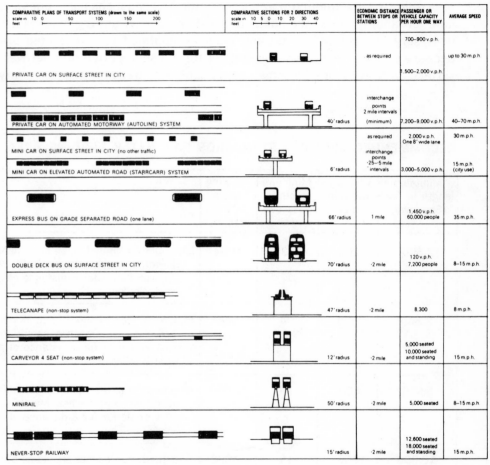

COMPARATIVE PLANS OF TRANSPORT SYSTEMS (drawn to the same scale) scale in feet 10 0 50 100 150 200	COMPARATIVE SECTIONS FOR 2 DIRECTIONS scale in feet 10 5 0 10 20 30 40	ECONOMIC DISTANCE BETWEEN STOPS OR STATIONS	PASSENGER OR VEHICLE CAPACITY PER HOUR ONE WAY	AVERAGE SPEED
PRIVATE CAR ON SURFACE STREET IN CITY		as required	700–900 p.h. / 1,500–2,000 v.p.h.	up to 30 m.p.h.
PRIVATE CAR ON AUTOMATED MOTORWAY (AUTOLINE) SYSTEM	40' radius	interchange points 2 mile intervals (minimum)	7,200–9,000 v.p.h.	40–70 m.p.h.
MINI CAR ON SURFACE STREET IN CITY (no other traffic)		as required	2,000 v.p.h. One 8' wide lane	30 m.p.h.
MINI CAR ON ELEVATED AUTOMATED ROAD (STARRCARR) SYSTEM	6' radius	interchange points ·25–5 mile intervals	3,000–5,000 v.p.h.	15 m.p.h. (city use)
EXPRESS BUS ON GRADE SEPARATED ROAD (one lane)	66' radius	1 mile	1,450 v.p.h. 60,000 people	35 m.p.h.
DOUBLE DECK BUS ON SURFACE STREET IN CITY	70' radius	·2 mile	120 v.p.h. 7,200 people	8–15 m.p.h.
TELECANAPE (non-stop system)	47' radius	·2 mile	8,300	8 m.p.h.
CARVEYOR 4 SEAT (non-stop system)	12' radius	·2 mile	5,000 seated 10,000 seated and standing	15 m.p.h.
MINIRAIL	50' radius	·2 mile	5,000 seated	8–15 m.p.h.
NEVER-STOP RAILWAY	15' radius	·2 mile	12,600 seated 18,000 seated and standing	15 m.p.h.

SOURCE: Brian Richards, New Movements in Cities, Reinhold Publishing Corp. New York 1966

THE WATER-OPERATING AREA

Most natural water areas will provide, without modification, the required dimensions necessary for seaplane operations. Where the available water area is limited, the minimum water-operating area must consist of one water lane for landings and take-offs and a taxi channel. A turning basin will be necessary in cases where turning must be confined to a restricted area because of water depth requirements or for the segregation of other water surface-craft activities. In some cases anchorage areas may be necessary.

RECOMMENDED MINIMUM STANDARDS FOR WATER LANDING AREAS

Minimum length in feet (Sea level)	Minimum width in feet	Minimum depth in feet	Turning basin in feet-diameter	Remarks
2.500	200	3	None	Minimum for limited small float plane operation. Approaches should be 20:1 or flatter for a distance of at least 2 miles.
3,500	300	4	None	Minimum for limited commercial operation. Approaches should be 40:1 or flatter for a distance of at least 2 miles.
5,000	500	10	1,000	Minimum for extensive commercial operation. Approaches should be 40:1 or flatter for a distance of at least 2 miles.
10,000	700	15	2,000	Unlimited. Approaches should be 50:1 or flatter for a distance of at least 2 miles.

The lengths indicated above for glassy water, no wind, sea level conditions at standard temperature of 59° Fahrenheit.

The lengths shown will be increased at the rate of 7 percent for each 1,000 feet of elevation above sea level. This corrected length shall be further increased at the rate of one-half of 1 percent for each degree that the mean temperature of the hottest month of the year, averaged over a period of years, exceeds the standard temperature.

See figure 5 which contains a chart entitled "Effect of Elevation and Temperature on Water-Lane Lengths."

SOURCE: Seaplane Facilities, Civil Aeronautics Administration, U. S. Dept. of Commerce, Wash., D. C.—1950

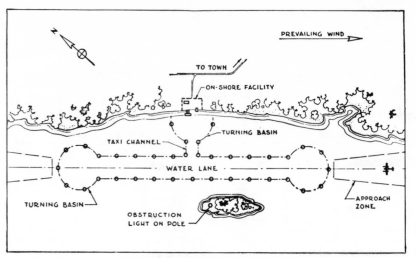

GENERAL OPERATING AREA

APPROACH ZONES

For seaplane operations the ideal approach zone is one which permits unobstructed approaches over water at a ratio of 40 : 1 or flatter, with ample clearance on either side of the approach zone center line. The width of the zone should increase from the ends of the water lanes so that at a distance of one mile from the end of the water lane, the zone is approximately the width of the water lane plus 1,000 feet.

Under favorable temperature conditions a water-borne aircraft will leave the water and fly level for approximately four (4) seconds and a distance of about 400 feet before starting to climb. The rate of climb after this four-second period is about 20 : 1. This ratio allows for a very limited margin of safety and requires maximum aircraft and engine performance at full load. Where commercial operations are anticipated, it is recommended that the approach angle should be 40 : 1 or flatter.

The approach zones should be over water, wherever possible, thereby permitting a reasonably safe landing in the event of power failure during initial climb or landing approach. Furthermore, for obvious safety reasons, climbs and approaches should not be made over populated areas, beaches and similar shore developments. Apart from the all-important safety factors involved, such maneuvers can create ill will and antagonism on the part of local inhabitants and boating interests. Where a suitable water area exists and the shore and surrounding development prohibits straight-away approach zones, it may be possible to establish operations in which an over-water climbing turn or let-down procedure is used.

TYPICAL LAYOUT OF ON-SHORE AND SHORE-LINE DEVELOPMENT

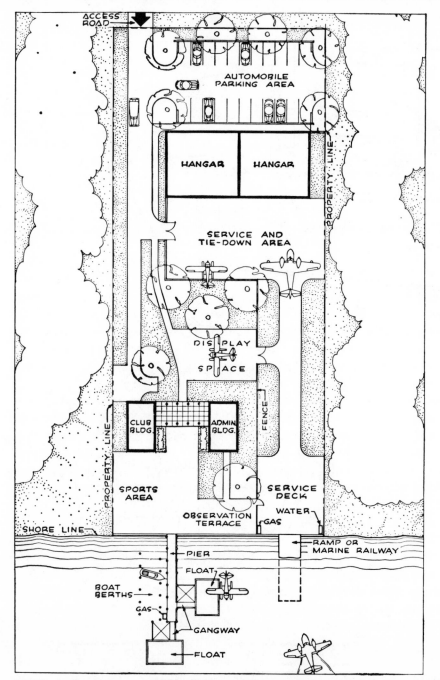

SOURCE: Seaplane Facilities, Civil Aeronautics Administration, U. S. Dept. of Commerce, Wash., D. C.—1950

No site for the on-shore development should be given serious consideration until it is known that adequate room is available for all of the space-taking elements required. Determination of size will require a knowledge of: (1) How many planes will need hangars or tie-down space; (2) how many car parking spaces will be necessary; (3) how many patrons will use the facility; (4) whether a small office will suffice or whether an administration building with facilities for eating, refreshments, and other nonaviation activities is required; (5) how much outdoor common space, such as for lawns, walks, terrace, etc., is needed. Answers to numbers 1 and 2 can be fairly accurately measured while 3, 4, and 5 will depend upon local conditions varying from a very simple installation, in remote recreation areas, to large installations in metropolitan areas. Minimum unit requirements are as follows:

MINIMUM UNIT REQUIREMENTS FOR A SINGLE ON-SHORE FACILITY

Item	Facility	Area in Square Feet
1 plane	Hangar or tie-down space	3,000
1 car	Parking space	250
Office	Small building	80
Common outdoor space	Walks, lawn, or open space	20 percent of above total

To compute the number of square feet for a given facility, multiples of the above criteria may be used. For example, a facility basing 15 aircraft in the water and 6 on land would need a maximum of 21 car-parking spaces (one for each plane) during maximum use period, plus one for each employee; i.e., approximately 25 cars or 6,250 square feet of area. Hangar or tie-down space for 6 planes would occupy 18,000 square feet. One small office building with food counter would require another 400 square feet. Finally, the common outdoor use space would occupy about 4,930 square feet (this figure representing 20 percent of the sum of the other areas). Accordingly, the total area would amount to about 29,580 square feet or about seven-tenths of an acre.

In addition to being adequate in size, the shore facility should be located reasonably close to the water-operating area to eliminate long taxiing operations.

The availability of utilities such as electricity, water, telephone and sewage should be investigated. The basic installation may not require all utilities, but water and sanitary facilities of some sort should be provided for at all locations. In remote rural areas, established water lines and sewerage facilities will be out of the question. If such is the case, well water and chemical toilet units are feasible. State or local sanitary codes must be respected when it is planned to install water and sanitary facilities of this nature.

The most desirable sites have a moderately sloping shore-line and a water depth suitable to permit aircraft taxiing operations as close to the shore-line as possible. Excessive fluctuations in water level are not desirable since this condition requires expensive shore-line installations. Care should be taken to determine whether the water level off-shore will permit aircraft operations when the water level is low.

In all cases, the area for a seaplane facility should be sufficient in extent to form a complete unit without any interior private holdings and with good boundary alignment for complete land utilization and protection. It may also be desirable in some cases to secure a liberal set-back from the highway in order to protect the project and adjacent property from noise and glare and to provide room for widening any highway paralleling the property line. If sufficient land is available, a greenbelt all around the project will enhance the desirability of a seaplane facility in a neighborhood area.

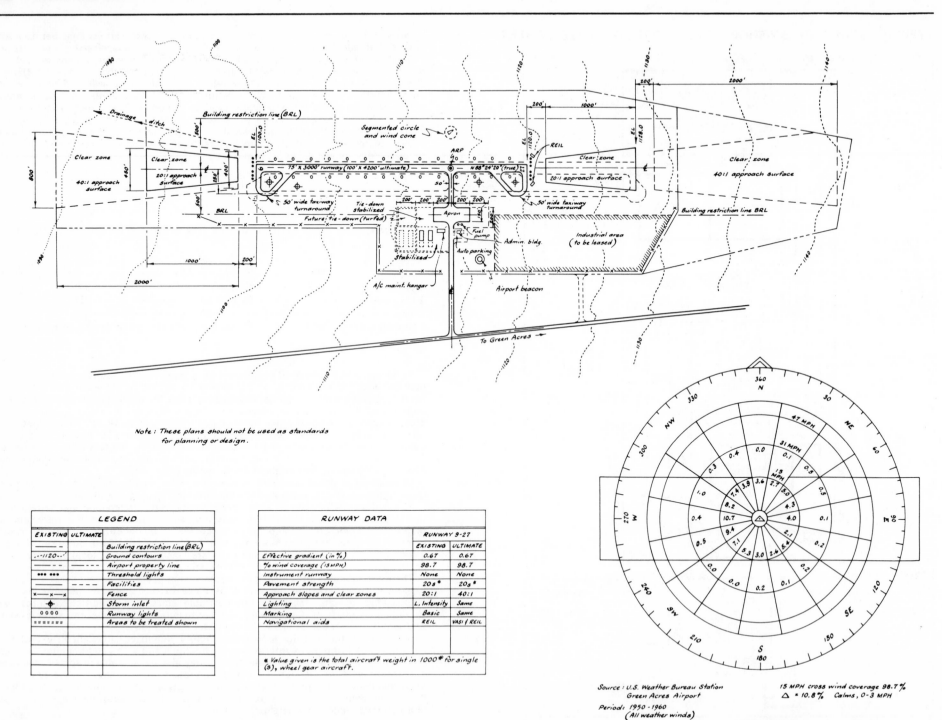

Note: These plans should not be used as standards for planning or design.

LEGEND		
EXISTING	ULTIMATE	
———	-	Building restriction line (BRL)
·-·-1120·-·'		Ground contours
———	- - - -	Airport property line
••• •••		Threshold lights
———	- - -	Facilities
x—x—x		Fence
◆		Storm inlet
0000		Runway lights
=======		Areas to be treated shown

RUNWAY DATA		
	RUNWAY 9-27	
	EXISTING	ULTIMATE
Effective gradient (in %)	0.67	0.67
% wind coverage (15 MPH)	98.7	98.7
Instrument runway	None	None
Pavement strength	20s*	20s*
Approach slopes and clear zones	20:1	40:1
Lighting	L. Intensity	Same
Marking	Basic	Same
Navigational aids	REIL	VASI & REIL

* Value given is the total aircraft weight in 1000# for single (3), wheel gear aircraft.

Source: U.S. Weather Bureau Station
Green Acres Airport

Period: 1950-1960
(All weather winds)

15 MPH cross wind coverage 98.7%
△ = 10.8%   Calms, 0-3 MPH

WIND ROSE

SOURCE: *Preparation of Airport Layout Plans, Federal Aviation Agency—1965*

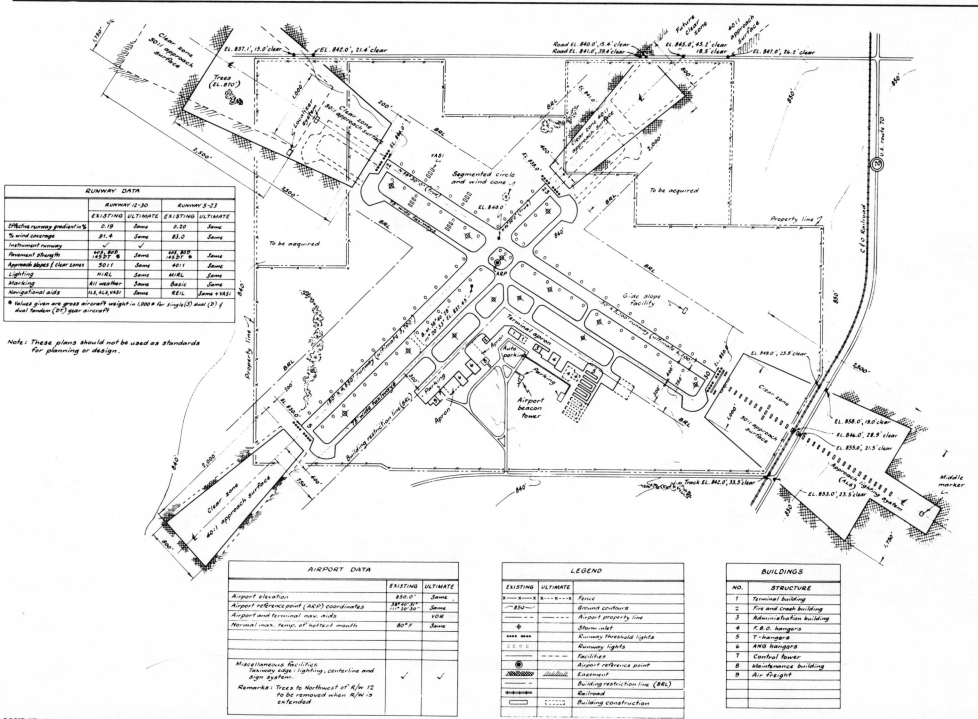

RUNWAY DATA				
	RUNWAY 12-30		RUNWAY 5-23	
	EXISTING	ULTIMATE	EXISTING	ULTIMATE
Effective runway gradient in %	0.19	Same	0.20	Same
% wind coverage	91.4	Same	83.0	Same
Instrument runway	✓		✓	
Pavement strength	60S, 80D 145 DT *	Same	60S, 80D 145 DT *	Same
Approach slopes & clear zones	50:1	Same	40:1	Same
Lighting	HIRL	Same	MIRL	Same
Marking	All weather	Same	Basic	Same
Navigational aids	ILS, ALS, VASI	Same	REIL	Same + VASI

* Values given are gross aircraft weight in 1,000 # for single (S) dual (D) & dual tandem (DT) gear aircraft

Note: These plans should not be used as standards for planning or design.

AIRPORT DATA			
		EXISTING	ULTIMATE
Airport elevation		850.0'	Same
Airport reference point (ARP) coordinates		38°40'31" 111°20'30"	Same
Airport and terminal nav. aids			VOR
Normal max. temp. of hottest month		80° F	Same
Miscellaneous facilities			
Taxiway edge lighting, centerline and sign system.		✓	✓
Remarks: Trees to Northwest of R/w 12 to be removed when R/w is extended			

LEGEND		
EXISTING	ULTIMATE	
x—x—x	x---x---x	Fence
~850~		Ground contours
– – –	– – – –	Airport property line
⊕		Storm inlet
•••• ••••		Runway threshold lights
o o o o		Runway lights
	– – –	Facilities
⊙		Airport reference point
▨▨▨		Easement
—		Building restriction line (BRL)
+++++		Railroad
▭▭▭	⋯⋯	Building construction

BUILDINGS	
NO.	STRUCTURE
1	Terminal building
2	Fire and crash building
3	Administration building
4	F. B. O. hangars
5	T-hangars
6	ANG hangars
7	Control tower
8	Maintenance building
9	Air freight

SOURCE: Preparation of Airport Layout Plan-, Federal Aviation Agency—1965

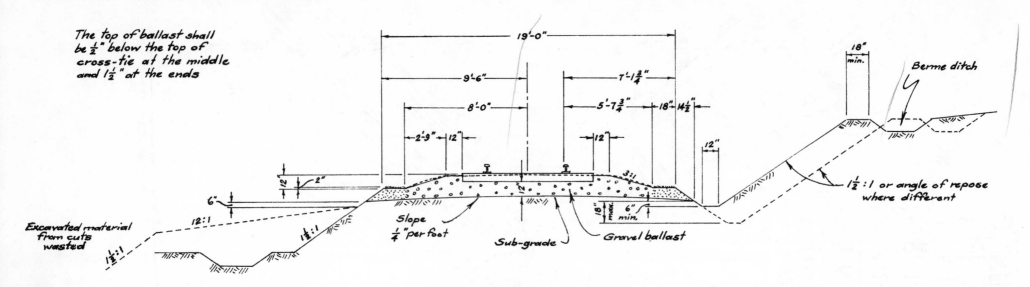

The top of ballast shall be ½" below the top of cross-tie at the middle and 1½" at the ends

Single main track on tangent

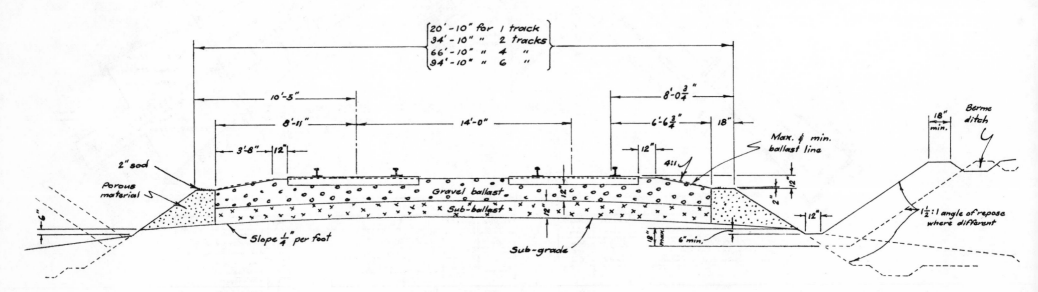

Double main track on tangent

SOURCE: Adopted from Railway Engineering and Maintenance, Cyclopedia—1922

EDUCATIONAL FACILITIES

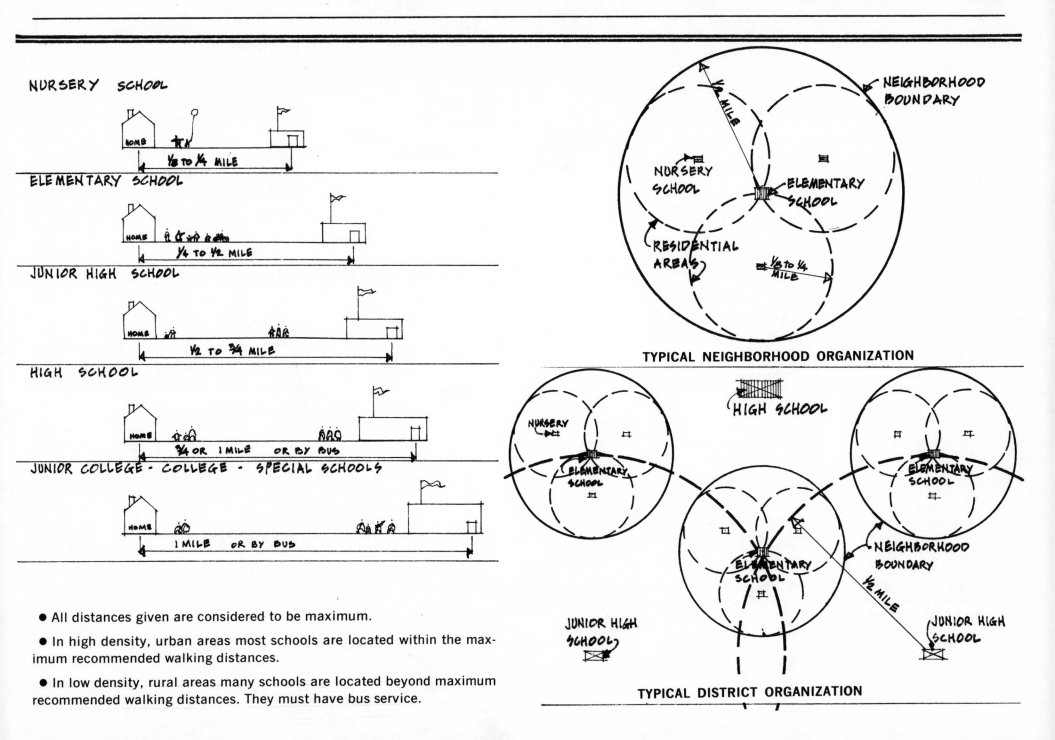

NURSERY SCHOOL

HOME 1/8 TO 1/4 MILE

ELEMENTARY SCHOOL

HOME 1/4 TO 1/2 MILE

JUNIOR HIGH SCHOOL

HOME 1/2 TO 3/4 MILE

HIGH SCHOOL

HOME 3/4 OR 1 MILE OR BY BUS

JUNIOR COLLEGE · COLLEGE · SPECIAL SCHOOLS

HOME 1 MILE OR BY BUS

NEIGHBORHOOD BOUNDARY

NURSERY SCHOOL

ELEMENTARY SCHOOL

RESIDENTIAL AREAS

1/8 TO 1/4 MILE

1/2 MILE

TYPICAL NEIGHBORHOOD ORGANIZATION

HIGH SCHOOL

NURSERY

ELEMENTARY SCHOOL

ELEMENTARY SCHOOL

ELEMENTARY SCHOOL

NEIGHBORHOOD BOUNDARY

1/2 MILE

JUNIOR HIGH SCHOOL

JUNIOR HIGH SCHOOL

TYPICAL DISTRICT ORGANIZATION

● All distances given are considered to be maximum.

● In high density, urban areas most schools are located within the maximum recommended walking distances.

● In low density, rural areas many schools are located beyond maximum recommended walking distances. They must have bus service.

Assumed Family Size	3.5 persons	Area Required	4 classes—4000 SF
			6 classes—6000 SF
			8 classes—8000 SF
Assumed Population Characteristics	60 children of Nursery School age per 1000 persons or 275–300 families		
		Accessory Facilities	Playlot or children's play area with equipment. Play area should be completely fenced in from other activities
Number of Children of Nursery School Age Per Family	.20 children		
Age of Children Served	2½ to 5 years old	Radius of Area Served	1–2 blocks—desirable
			⅛ mile—maximum
Size of Nursery School	Minimum—4 classes (60 children)		
	Average—6 classes (90 children)	Design Features	Nursery School should be accessible by footpath from dwelling units without crossing any streets. If street must be crossed it should be minor street
	Maximum—8 classes (120 children)		
Population Served	4 classes—1000 persons 275–300 families		
	6 classes—1500 persons 425–450 families	General Location	Near an Elementary School or Community Center
	8 classes—2000 persons 550–600 families	Accessory Parking	1 space for each 2 classes

These figures will vary for most areas. They are based on a full cross-section of the population. Population figures should be checked for local age distribution and birth trends for any specific location.

Assumed Family Size	3.5 persons		Area Required	Minimum school—7–8 acres Average school—12–14 acres Maximum school—16–18 acres
Assumed Population Characteristics	175 children of Elementary School age per 1000 persons or 275–300 families		Accessory Facilities	Playground completely equipped for a wide range of activities Playground area should be completely screened from street
Number of Children of Elementary School Age Per Family	.54 children			
			Radius of Area Served	¼ miles—desirable ½ mile—maximum
Age of Children Served	5 thru 11 years			
Size of Elementary School	Minimum—250 pupils Average—800 pupils Maximum—1200 pupils		Design Features	Elementary School should be accessible by footpath from dwelling units without crossing any streets. If street must be crossed it should be a minor street
Size of Typical Class	30–32 pupils			
			General Location	Near center of residential area, near or adjacent to other community facilities
Population Served	Minimum school—1500 persons Average school—5000 persons Maximum school—7000 persons		Accessory Parking	One space per class plus 3 spaces

These figures will vary for most areas. They are based on a full cross-section of the population. Population figures should be checked for local age distribution and birth trends for any specific location.

9-4 JUNIOR HIGH SCHOOL
GENERAL REQUIREMENTS

Assumed Family Size	3.5 persons
Assumed Population Characteristics	75 children of Junior High School age per 1000 persons 275–300 families
Number of Children of Jr. High School Age Per Family	.22 children
Age of Children Served	12 to 14 years
Size of Junior High School	Minimum school—800 pupils Average school—1200 pupils Maximum school—1600 pupils
Size of Typical Class	30–32 pupils
Population Served	Minimum school—10,000 persons 2,750–3,000 families Average school—16,000 persons 4,500–5,000 families Maximum school—20,000 persons 5,800–6,000 families

Area Required	Minimum school—18–20 acres Average school—24–26 acres Maximum school—30–32 acres
Accessory Facilities	Playfield completely equipped for a wide range of game activities
Radius of Area Served	½ mile—desirable ¾ miles—maximum
Design Features	School should be away from major arterial streets; pedestrian walkways from other areas should be provided
General Location	Located near concentration of dwelling units or near center of residential area
Accessory Parking	One space per classroom plus six spaces

These figures will vary for most areas. They are based on a full cross-section of the population. Population figures should be checked for local age distribution and birth trends for any specific location.

Assumed Family Size	3.5 persons	Area Required	Minimum—32–34 acres Average—40–42 acres Maximum—48–50 acres
Assumed Population Characteristics	75 children of High School age per 1000 persons or 275 to 300 families		
Number of Children of High School Age Per Family	.22 children	Accessory Facilities	Playfield completely equipped for a wide range of game activities
Age of Children Served	15–18 years	Radius of Area Served	¾ mile—desirable 1 mile—maximum
Size of High School	Minimum—1000 pupils Average—1800 pupils Maximum—2600 pupils	Design Features	School should be located adjacent to a park area. School should be adequately screened from noise or objectionable uses
Size of Typical Class	30–35 pupils		
Population Served	Minimum—14,000 persons 3,800–4,000 families Average—24,000 persons 6,800–7,000 families Maximum—34,000 persons 9,800–10,000 families	General Location	School should be centrally located for easy access. Proximity to other community facilities is advantageous
		Accessory Parking	1 space per classroom plus 16 spaces

These figures will vary for most areas. They are based on a full cross-section of the population. Population figures should be checked for local age distribution and birth trends for any specific location.

DIMENSIONS FOR GAME AREAS[1]

Type of game	Elementary	Upper grades	High school	Area size (square feet)
1	2	3	4	5
Basketball	40′ x 60′	42′ x 74′	50′ x 84′	5,000
Volleyball	25′ x 50′	25′ x 50′	30′ x 60′	2,800
Badminton			20′ x 44′	1,800
Paddle tennis			20′ x 44′	1,800
Deck tennis			18′ x 40′	1,800
Tennis		36′ x 78′	36′ x 78′	7,200
Ice hockey			85′ x 200′	17,000
Field hockey			180′ x 300′	54,000
Horseshoes		10′ x 40′	10′ x 50′	1,000
Shuffleboard			6′ x 52′	648
Lawn bowling			14′ x 110′	7,800
Tetherball	10′ circle	12′ circle	12′ circle	....
Croquet	38′ x 60′	38′ x 60′	38′ x 60′	2,275
Handball	18′ x 26′	18′ x 26′	20′ x 34′	1,280
Baseball			350′ x 350′	122,500
Archery		50′ x 150′	50′ x 300′	20,000
Softball (12″ ball)[2]	150′ x 150′	200′ x 200′	250′ x 250′	62,500
Football—with 440-yard track—220-yard straightaway			300′ x 600′	180,000
Touch football		120′ x 300′	160′ x 360′	68,400
6-Man football			120′ x 300′	49,000
Soccer			165′ x 300′	57,600

[1] Athletic Institute, Inc. *Planning Facilities for Health, Physical Education, and Recreation.*
The Institute, 209 South State St., Chicago 4, Ill. 1956. p. 26.
[2] Dimensions vary with size of ball used.

SOURCE: School Sites—Selection, Development, and Utilization, U. S. Dept. of Health, Education, and Welfare, Office of Education

EDUCATIONAL ATTAINMENT OF POPULATION: 1950 1985

Although more than 7 percent of the population over age 25 have less than five years of schooling, the level of education is rising. Half of those 18 years of age or older are high school graduates, compared with less than 37 percent in 1950; and among those age 22 and over, about 10 percent are college graduates (compared with some 6 percent in 1950). Moreover, it is projected that by 1985, nearly 60 percent of those age 25 and older will have completed some high school work; nearly 30 percent, one or more years of college.

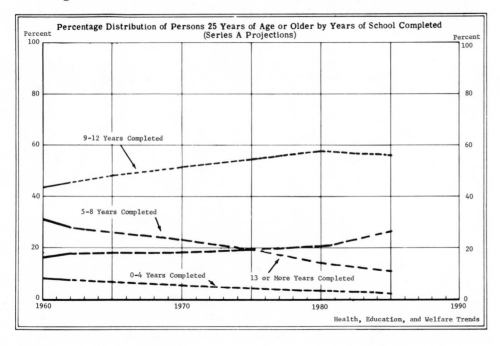

Percentage Distribution of Persons 25 Years of Age or Older by Years of School Completed (Series A Projections)

Health, Education, and Welfare Trends

Year [1]	Graduates [2]				Years of school completed by persons 25 years old and over [3]								
	High School		College			Millions of persons				Percent			
	Mil-lions	Percent of population 18+ years	Mil-lions	Percent of population 22+ years	Popu-lation 25+ years	No school through elementary 0-4	5-8	High school 9-12	Col-lege 13+	No school through elementary 0-4	5-8	High school 9-12	Col-lege 13+
Both sexes													
1950...	38.3	36.6	6.0	6.3	87.5	9.8	32.6	33.3	11.9	11.1	37.2	38.1	13.6
1960 [4]...	51.6	44.6	8.1	7.6	99.4	8.3	31.2	43.6	16.4	8.3	31.4	43.8	16.5
1962 [5]...	57.4	48.1	9.-	9.0	100.7	7.8	28.4	46.2	18.2	7.8	28.3	45.9	18.1
1970(A).	-	-	-	-	110.0	6.4	26.0	57.3	20.4	5.8	23.6	52.1	18.5
(B).	70.3	52.2	10.8	9.0	110.0	6.4	26.5	57.1	20.0	5.8	24.1	51.9	18.2
1985(A)					139.1	3.6	13.9	78.5	37.6	2.6	14.3	56.7	27.0
(B)					139.1	3.9	19.8	78.6	36.8	2.8	14.2	56.5	26.5
Males													
1950...	17.6	34.0	3.4	7.2	42.6	5.2	16.4	14.9	6.1	12.3	38.4	35.0	14.3
1960 [4]...	24.0	42.6	4.8	9.3	47.9	4.5	15.5	19.1	8.8	9.4	32.4	39.9	18.3
1962 [5]...	26.7	46.1	5.9	11.2	48.3	4.2	13.9	20.3	9.8	8.7	28.9	42.1	20.3
1970(A).	-	-	-	-	52.6	3.3	12.8	25.0	11.4	6.4	24.3	47.6	21.7
(B).	32.5	-	6.5	-	52.6	3.4	13.0	25.1	11.1	6.4	24.7	47.7	21.2
1985(A)					66.2	1.9	9.3	33.6	21.3	28.7	14.0	50.8	32.1
(B)					66.2	2.1	9.7	33.4	21.0	31.7	14.7	50.5	31.7
Females													
1950...	20.7	39.0	2.6	5.4	44.9	4.5	16.2	18.4	5.7	10.1	36.1	41.0	12.8
1960 [4]...	27.6	46.5	3.3	6.0	51.5	3.8	15.7	24.4	7.6	7.4	30.4	47.5	14.8
1962 [5]...	30.7	50.1	3.8	6.9	52.4	3.6	14.5	25.9	8.4	6.9	27.7	49.5	16.0
1970(A).	-	-	-	-	57.5	3.0	13.2	32.3	9.0	5.3	22.9	56.2	15.6
(B).	37.8	-	4.3	-	57.5	3.0	13.5	32.1	8.9	5.3	23.5	55.8	15.4
1985(A)					72.9	1.7	9.6	45.3	16.3	23.3	13.2	62.1	22.4
(B)					72.9	1.8	10.1	45.2	15.8	24.7	13.9	62.0	21.7

SOURCE: U.S. Department of Commerce, Bureau of the Census; Series P-20, No. 91, "Projections of Educational Attainment in the United States: 1969 to 1985," April 14, 1965 includes assumptions, methodology, and definitions. Current Population Report, Series P-25, No. 187 supplied basic July 1 population projections. Series II, assuming continuation of fertility at the 1955-57 level, gradually declining mortality, and net annual immigration of 300,000 persons. A cohort technique of applying projected percentage distributions by attainment for five-year age groups to projected numbers of males and females in those respective age groups determined the educational experience at each future date of each age-sex group which had already completed its formal education. The probable future educational attainment of persons yet to complete their schooling was based on different assumptions regarding continuation of past trends and present levels. The projected percentage distributions by educational attainment were then applied to projections of the population at each date to obtain the numbers of persons expected to attain various levels of education. 1 Spring of Year. Excludes Alaska and Hawaii except for 1960 and 1962 data on years of school completed. 2 Persons who have completed four or more years. 3 Data pertain to "regular" day or night schooling applicable towards a diploma or degree. 4 Data on years of school completed, including 400,000 persons in Alaska and Hawaii, are from U.S. Census of Population, 1960: General Social and Economic Characteristics. . . . U.S. Summary, PC (1) 1C. 5 Data for 1962 (Current Population Reports, Series P-20, No. 121) are not strictly comparable with those from the 1960 census or earlier surveys because of differences in sample design, in the training of enumerators, and in the weighting of survey results.

SOURCE: Trends-1965 U.S. Dept of Health, Education, and Welfare, Wash. D. C.

NEIGHBORHOOD AND COMMUNITY FACILITIES

NEIGHBORHOOD COMMUNITY FACILITIES AS A WHOLE

GROUPING

The facilities should, if possible, be grouped together in the direction of the major traffic flow from the development area to the outside, accessible by direct pedestrian and automobile routes. Such grouping will encourage the use of all facilities.

The existence of a physical center of the neighborhood stimulates the growth of community relationships and the acceptance of community responsibilities by the residents.

As most community facilities require comparatively flat land, topography will, to some extent, govern their grouping and location. Special situations may occur in which such grouping will not be advisable, especially where existing facilities must be taken into account.

Within the group, the various community facilities should be physically separated from each other to prevent conflict of circulation. It is especially important that pedestrian access to the school be separate from all vehicular access to other facilities.

TOTAL LAND REQUIREMENTS

For many neighborhood planning purposes, it is desirable to know community facility land requirements as a whole. Therefore, is a summation of these requirements. It should be noted that this table combines recommended and assumed areas; the values given are therefore not to be considered mandatory standards.

USE OF EXISTING FACILITIES

Before final decisions are made in regard to the provision of neighborhood community facilities, the area should be examined for available existing facilities. Special care must be taken to check the capacity as well as the location of such facilities. There may be city-wide or district facilities that can also be used by the neighborhood and that will in reality be so used if they provide good service and are readily accessible.

The possibility of using these facilities should be investigated if any of them exist within acceptable distance from the development.

LAND AREA OF ALL NEIGHBORHOOD COMMUNITY FACILITIES
Component Uses and Aggregate Area, by Type of Development and Population of Neighborhood [a]

	NEIGHBORHOOD POPULATION				
TYPE OF DEVELOPMENT	1,000 persons 275 families	2,000 persons 550 families	3,000 persons 825 families	4,000 persons 1,100 families	5,000 persons 1,375 families
ONE- OR TWO-FAMILY DEVELOPMENT [b]					
Area in Component Uses					
1) Acres in school site.............	1.20	1.20	1.50	1.80	2.20
2) Acres in playground.............	2.75	3.25	4.00	5.00	6.00
3) Acres in park.................	1.50	2.00	2.50	3.00	3.50
4) Acres in shopping center.........	.80	1.20	2.20	2.60	3.00
5) Acres in general community facilities [c].................	.38	.76	1.20	1.50	1.90
Aggregate Area					
6) Acres: total.................	6.63	8.41	11.40	13.90	16.60
7) Acres per 1,000 persons.........	6.63	4.20	3.80	3.47	3.32
8) Square feet per family..........	1,050	670	600	550	530
MULTI-FAMILY DEVELOPMENT [d]					
Area in Component Uses					
1) Acres in school site.............	1.20	1.20	1.50	1.80	2.20
2) Acres in playground.............	2.75	3.25	4.00	5.00	6.00
3) Acres in park.................	2.00	3.00	4.00	5.00	6.00
4) Acres in shopping center.........	.80	1.20	2.20	2.60	3.00
5) Acres in general community facilities [c].................	.38	.76	1.20	1.50	1.90
Aggregate Area					
6) Acres: total.................	7.13	9.41	12.90	15.90	19.10
7) Acres per 1,000 persons.........	7.13	4.70	4.30	3.97	3.82
8) Square feet per family..........	1,130	745	680	630	610

a This table combines the recommended or assumed values
b With privite lot area of less than ¼ acre per family (for private lots of ¼ acre or more, park area may be omitted).
c Allowance for indoor social and cultural facilities (church, assembly hall, etc.) or separate health center, nursery school, etc.
d Or other development predominantly without private yards.

SOURCE: *Planning the Neighborhood by the American Public Health Association, Committee on the Hygiene of Housing, Public Administration Service, Chicago, Ill. 1960*

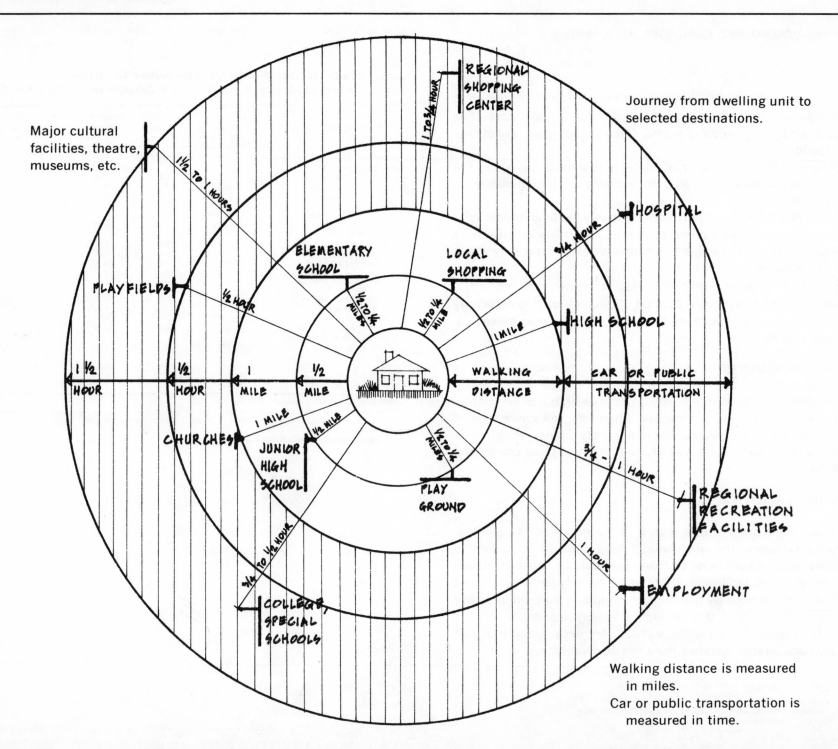

Journey from dwelling unit to selected destinations.

Major cultural facilities, theatre, museums, etc.

REGIONAL SHOPPING CENTER

1 TO 3/4 HOUR

1 1/2 TO 1 HOURS

HOSPITAL

3/4 HOUR

ELEMENTARY SCHOOL

LOCAL SHOPPING

PLAYFIELDS

1/2 HOUR

1/2 TO 1/4 MILES

1/2 TO 1/4 MILE

1 MILE

HIGH SCHOOL

1 1/2 HOUR   1/2 HOUR   1 MILE   1/2 MILE   WALKING DISTANCE   CAR OR PUBLIC TRANSPORTATION

1 MILE

1/2 MILE

1/4 TO 1/4 MILES

CHURCHES

JUNIOR HIGH SCHOOL

PLAY GROUND

3/4 — 1 HOUR

REGIONAL RECREATION FACILITIES

3/4 TO 1/2 HOUR

1 HOUR

EMPLOYMENT

COLLEGE, SPECIAL SCHOOLS

Walking distance is measured in miles.
Car or public transportation is measured in time.

The size of a neighborhood is expressed in two ways: the population and the geographic area. The upper and lower limits for population are set by the capacity of the elementary school. The maximum extent of the area is fixed mainly by walking distance to school and other community facilities. Since density is the ration of population to area, two of these variables will determine the third. Therefore, population or area within the above limits will depend on desirable densities. The Table indicates neighborhood areas based on maximum neighborhood densities for different dwelling types.

EFFECT OF ACCESSIBILITY STANDARDS ON NEIGHBORHOOD AREA

Assuming a fairly central location of the school and other community facilities, an area of 126 acres will be equivalent to ¼-mile radius of accessibility. An area of 500 acres will correspond to ½-mile radius.

Within these geographic limits of accessibility the area of the neighborhood will depend on densities and dwelling types in relation to the population housed.

A 5,000-person neighborhood can range from 44 acres for a 13-story building development to 265 acres for a single-family detached house development. Calculations of required acreage indicated that all neighborhoods of 5,000 persons or less, developed predominantly with row or multi-family structures, will contain less than 126 acres, the area equivalent to ¼-mile radius of accessibility. Developments composed of detached or semidetached houses will contain less than 500 acres, the area equivalent to ½-mile radius of accessibility, and will in general fall below 222 acres, equivalent to ⅓-mile radius.

It appears, therefore, that the desirable standard of ¼-mile radius is practicable for all except neighborhoods of detached or semidetached one-family houses. The distance from the farthest house to the school and other community facilities need seldom exceed ⅓ mile even in low density developments.

EFFECT OF SCHOOL CAPACITY ON NEIGHBORHOOD POPULATION AND AREA

For a school with only one classroom per grade, neighborhood areas will range from 16 to 110 acres. Even at the low density of 5 families per acre, the area will not exceed ¼-mile radius. At high densities the service areas will be so small as to be economically inefficient. A school with two classrooms per grade, which is supported by about 4,300 persons, can serve an area with ¼-mile radius for moderate to high densities (11 to 35 families per acre) and the neighborhood will not exceed 240 acres, equivalent to slightly more than ⅓-mile radius, even at low densities.

It appears, therefore, that a 4,000-to 5,000-person neighborhood offers certain advantages as a planning unit. In the first place, it makes for efficient use of land since, as outlined in previous sections, population concentrations above these figures may require duplication of some community facilities. Second, the 4,000-to 5,000-person neighborhood supports a school of the size recommended by many educational authorities. Third, the

SOURCE: *Planning the Neighborhood, by the American Public Health Association, Committee on the Hygiene of Housing, Public Administration Service, Chicago, Ill. 1960*

NEIGHBORHOOD AREA DERIVED FROM NEIGHBORHOOD DENSITY ALLOWANCES
Acres in All Neighborhood Uses, by Type of Dwelling and Population of Neighborhood

DWELLING TYPE	NEIGHBORHOOD POPULATION				
	1,000 persons 275 families	2,000 persons 550 families	3,000 persons 825 families	4,000 persons 1,100 families	5,000 persons 1,375 families
ONE-OR TWO-FAMILY DWELLINGS	Acres in All Neighborhood Uses				
1-family detached	57	108	162	213	265 Within ¼–½ mile radius
1-family semidetached *or* 2-family detached	40	75	111	149	183
1-family attached (row) *or* 2-family semidetached	28	49	73	95	116
MULTI-FAMILY DWELLINGS					
2-story	22	38	55	71	88 Less than ¼-mile radius
3-story	18	29	43	56	69
6-story	14	22	32	41	50
9-story	13	21	30	38	46
13-story	13	19	28	36	44

geographic area will not exceed the desirable ¼-mile radius of accessibility, except for low densities, in which case the farthest dwellings will only be slightly more than ⅓-mile distant from the school.

Among additional considerations which may modity neighborhood sizes based on school capacity, accessibility of community facilities and densities, the following should be noted in particular.

SUITABLE SIZE FOR RESIDENTS' PARTICIPATION

No scientific data exist as to the neighborhood size most suitable for resident participation in neighborhood size most suitable for resident participation in neighborhood activities and for the creation of a sense of neighborhood living. However, the general consensus, based on evaluation of existing neighborhood developments and small towns, indicates that many more than 5,000 persons is too large for a single neighborhood under normal circumstances.

This fact in no way precludes the development of appropriate housing areas for a large population. It merely implies that in those cases, consideration should be given to the possibility of dividing such areas into several neighborhoods, just as it may be advisable to incorporate a number of smaller developments into a single neighborhood.

SUITABLE AREA FOR ADMINISTRATION

Administrative practices of local government may considerably affect the size of the neighborhood area. Neighborhoods at high densities of 30 families of more per acre, supporting a small elementary school (1 classroom per grade), may be contained in less than 20 acres, and still meet density and population requirements. However, municipal funds for schools, playgrounds, etc. are limited. Multiplication of such facilities within a small area is apt to overburden municipal finances and thereby affect the adequacy of the facilities. It is, therefore, considered unlikely that neighborhood units of less than 30 acres will in the long run be considered desirable by city officials, except for redevelopment projects in extremely high density areas.

GENERAL SITE REQUIREMENTS

☐ EASILY ACCESSIBLE

☐ PREFERABLY ON MAIN THOROUGHFARE

☐ LOCATED IN A SUBSHOPPING AREA

☐ LOCATED NEAR A NEIGHBORHOOD CENTER. EASE OF PARKING IS ADVANTAGE-OUS, BUT NOT SO IMPORTANT AS TO JUSTIFY AN OTHERWISE UNDESIRABLE LOCATION. A PARK—OFTEN SUGGESTED—USUALLY HAS LITTLE TO RECOMMEND IT

☐ A MINIMUM OF 20 YEARS EXPANSION OF SERVICE & COMMUNITY GROWTH SHOULD BE POSSIBLE

TYPES AND CHARACTERISTICS

Type	Area Served	Population Served	Miscellaneous
CENTRAL or MAIN	Whole City or Municipality	No Limit & Varies	Should be within a block or two of main business & shopping area & convenient to main traffic & transportation arteries.
BRANCH	1 to 1½ miles	Minimum Is from 25,000 to 55,000 People	Should be easily accessible. These requirement are for cities of 100,000 people or more.
SUB-BRANCH	Detached Areas & Smaller Cities	Varies	Frequently not open every day or housed in a library-owned building. Can be in community buildings or schools or rented quarters.

THE MINIMUM BOOK STOCK OF ANY LIBRARY, AS AN INDEPENDENT UNIT, SHOULD BE 6,000 VOLUMES REGARDLESS OF POPULATION SERVED.

POPULATION OF LIBRARY AREA		Volumes	Up to
Minimum	Maximum	per Capita	Volumes
6,000	10,000	3.0	25,000
10,000	35,000	2.5	70,000
35,000	100,000	2.0	175,000
100,000	200,000	1.75	300,000
200,000	1,000,000	1.5	1,000,000
Over 1,000,000		1.0	

CHURCH SERVING ONE NEIGHBORHOOD ONLY

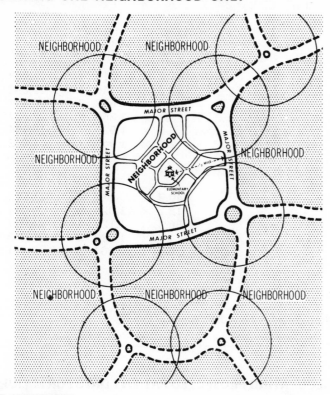

LOCATION OF CHURCHES SERVING MORE THAN ONE NEIGHBORHOOD

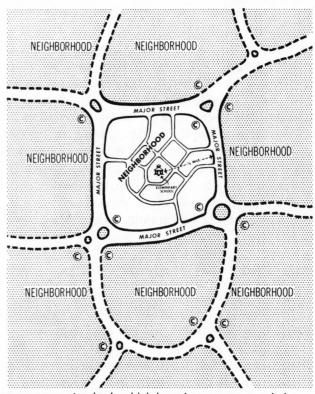

MEMBERSHIP STANDARDS

C. A. Perry estimated that a population of 5,000 persons could probably support three churches of about 1,500 persons each. The Conference on Church Extension suggested one Protestant church for each 1,500 to 2,500 persons. It should be noted that on the national basis about 60 per cent of the population may be expected to affiliate with a local church. In the western region this percentage is considerably lower. Thus, on the average, a population of 1,500 might be expected to produce a church of 900 constituents, disregarding the churching of some people outside of the neighborhood, and internal heterogeneity of the population which may cut the degree of affiliation to one specific church.

Many urban churchmen believe that a church of about 500 members is the optimum size of a neighborhood institution, while a downtown church, to support a diversified staff and program, may need 1,500 or 2,000 or even more.

AREA-REQUIREMENTS

There is no common uniform agreement as to the adequate size of a church site. Certainly the size of the site will depend upon the size of the church which is being projected, and the scope of the program. If an outdoor recreational program is desired, that will increase the size appreciably. If a parochial school is to be included, this will mean another appreciable increase in site needs. In most cases, landscaping and off-street parking should be provided for.

SOURCE: Robert C. Hoover & Everett L. Perry, Church and City Planning, Bureau of Research and Survey, National Council of the Churches of Christ in the U. S. A.

1 The following are some standards which have been recommended.

Source	Acres Recommended for Church Site
1. Conference on Church Extension Standards based on:[a] (below)	
0–400 membership	1 acre
400–800 membership	2 acres
800–1,200 membership	3 acres
1,200 or more members	4 acres
2. Presbyterian Board of Missions[b]	3 acres (on the average)
3. Urban Land Institute[c]	3–5 acres (Preferably near a shopping center)
4. Van Osdal[d]	5–6 acres (for a 600 seat church with 150 parking spaces)
	8 acres (For a Catholic church with a parochial school)

[a] Sanderson, Ross W., condensed report, conference on church extension, 1953, N.Y. National Council of Churches.
[b] Perry, Everett L., Selections of a Church Site, The City Church, September, 1953.
[c] Urban Land Institute, Community Builders Handbook, 1954, p. 89.
[d] Van Osdal, N. K., Jr. "The Church and the Planned Community," The City Church, May, 1952.

ILLUSTRATIVE NEED CALCULATION

Calculating general hospital bed needs is a basic tool in matching area-wide resources to needs.

The following contain an illustrative calculation of bed need for a hypothetical planning region with a target-year population of about 250,000. The example makes use of assumed figures which in actual practice would be obtained from health departments, hospitals, and related medical facilities. While an attempt has been made to use realistic figures in the illustration, one should not assume that the need figures derived in the example will apply to any actual planning region with a quarter-million population.

The example illustrates one method of calculating need. For didactic purposes it carries out the calculations in considerable detail. In working out bed needs for an actual planning region, more or less detail can be used depending on the availability and quality of statistics pertaining to the particular area.

STEP I—CALCULATING TOTAL PROJECTED PATIENT DAYS

The initial step in projecting the number of short-term, general hospital beds needed in the target year is a calculation of the expected total annual number of patient days. This is equal to the sum of projected patient days for each of the population's age and sex groupings. The number of projected patient days for each age and sex group may be derived by substituting the appropriate data in the following equation.

```
Projected population        Current patient days        Projected patient days
in thousands for        ×   per thousand            =   in the target year
the target year             population
```

The figures on population and use rate are given in the example. In actual practice, these statistics would have to be obtained from local sources.

Calculating Total Projected Patient Days

	Projected population in thousands for target year	Present patient days per thousand population	Projected patient days in target year	Totals
A. Under 15	41.9 ×	315. 1 =	13,203	
B. 15–24	16.2 ×	745. 8 =	12,082	
C. 25–44	32.7 ×	698. 7 =	22,847	
D. 45–64	23.8 ×	1,366. 7 =	32,527	
E. 65–74	5.6 ×	1,920. 4 =	10,754	
F. +	2.5 ×	1,945. 1 =	4,863	
G. Total projected patient days for males		=		96,276
Females:				
H. Under 15	40.9 ×	274. 2 =	11,215	
I. 15–24	18.7 ×	1,029. 6 =	19,254	
J. 25–44	36.5 ×	1,125. 4 =	41,077	
K. 45–64	24.7 ×	1.022. 2 =	25,248	
L. 65–74	6.3 ×	1,504. 9 =	9,481	
M. 75+	3.2 ×	1,924. 1 =	6,157	
N. Total projected patient days for females		=		112,432
O. Total projected patient days (line G+line N)		=		208,708

STEP II—CALCULATING PROJECTED PATIENT DAYS FOR MAJOR CLINICAL SERVICES

The number of projected patient days for medical and surgical, pediatric, and obstetrical patients can now be calculated. Projected obstetrical and pediatric days are calculated individually from known data and subtracted from total projected patient days (line "O", Step I) to obtain the projected number of patient days from medical and surgical cases.

1. Calculating Projected Obstetrical Patient Days

```
Projected obstetrical   =   Average length of   ×   Projected number
patient days                stay per delivery       of deliveries
```

A. Projected number of females 15–44, in thousands (Step I, line I+line J.) = 55.2

B. Current deliveries per 1,000 females 15–44 (Obstained from Health Departmnts or calculated from other available data.) .... = 95.6

C. Projected annual number of deliveries (Step II, line A × line B.) .... = 5,277.0

D. Current number of hospital days per delivery (Data obtained either from Health Departments, or directly from hospitals. Use figures pertaining to local facilities only.) .... = 4.5

E. Projected obstetrical patient days (Step II, line C × line D.) .... = 23,747.0

2. Calculating Projected Pediatric Patient Days

Projected pediatric patient days	=	Projected patient days for males under 15 (Step I, line A)	+	Projected patient days for females under 15 (Step I, line H)

F. Projected pediatric patient days = 13,203 + 11,215 .... = 24.418

3. Calculating Projected Medical and Surgical Patient Days

Projected medical and surgical patient days	=	Total projected patient days (Step I, line O)	—	Sum of Projected obstetrical and pediatric patient days (Step II, line E plus line F)

G. Projected medical and surgical patient days = 208,708 − 48,165 .... = 160,543

SOURCE: *Procedures for Areawide Health Facility Planning, U. S. Dept. of Health, Education and Welfare, Public Health Service Publication No. 930-B-3—1963*

STEP III—CALCULATING PROJECTED AVERAGE DAILY CENSUS

The following equation can be used to calculate projected average daily census:

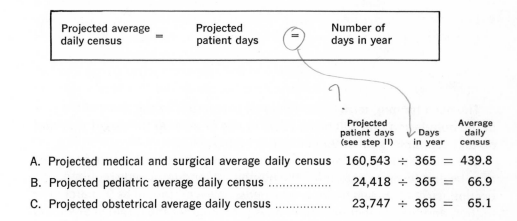

		Projected patient days (see step II)	Days in year	Average daily census
A.	Projected medical and surgical average daily census	160,543 ÷	365 =	439.8
B.	Projected pediatric average daily census	24,418 ÷	365 =	66.9
C.	Projected obstetrical average daily census	23,747 ÷	365 =	65.1

STEP IV—CALCULATING PROJECTED BED NEED

Assume that the planning agency has recommended the following occupancy goal:

	Present occupancy
Medical and surgical beds	85
Pediatric beds	75
Obstetrical beds	75

The equation below will then yield the number of beds needed.

Projected bed need	=	Average daily census	÷	Occupancy goal

		Projected average daily census (see step III)	Occupancy goal	Number of beds needed
A.	Medical and surgical	439.8 ÷	.85 =	517
B.	Pediatric	66.9 ÷	.75 =	89
C.	Obstetrical	65.1 ÷	.75 =	87

D. Total short-term, general beds needed in the planning region .... = 693

The need for long-term beds should be calculated on the basis of the size of the population that will be 65 years of age or older in the target year and on an occupancy goal of 95 percent or higher.

The same basic equation used for calculating short-term, acute bed need may be employed to determine the number of long-term beds required. The occupancy goal chosen for long-term beds, however, should be 95 percent or higher, and the number of patient days projected for the target year should be determined on the basis of the population 65 years of age and older.

Because of the prolonged length of stay associated with chronic illness, long-term facilities, unlike general hospitals, are not characterized by wide day-to-day fluctuations in occupancy. As a result, average occupancy in nursing homes and other long-term facilities is usually rather high. In addition, the need for long-term facilities is particularly related to the older segments of the population, since the vast preponderance of chronic illness occurs in the older age groups.

Wide variations occur from State to State and within States with respect to the proportion of the total population presented by the aged. Therefore, figures used in calculating the projected number of long-term patient days should be based solely on population data relating to the aged population in the particular planning region.

STEP V—CALCULATING BASIC LONG-TERM BED NEEDS

The ratio of persons receiving care in existing long-term facilities to the population 65 years of age and older should be determined as an initial step in calculating long-term bed needs. The magnitude of the present institutional population can usually be found in health department and / or welfare department statistics.

To continue the example, assume that appropriate data have shown that the present patient population of long-term care facilities represents 5 percent of the 65-and-over age group. While the calculation shown below is based on the continuation of present patterns of service, planning officials should recognize that possible changes in the financing of care may bring about substantial changes in the demand for long-term beds.

1. Determining the Long-Term Average Daily Census

	Projected population 65 and over (see step I)	Long-term patients ÷ population 65 and over	Average daily census
A. Long-term average daily census .... =	17,600	× 0.05	= 880

2. Determining the Number of Long-Term Beds Needed

	Long-term average daily census	Desirable occupancy rate	Long-term beds needed
B. Long-term beds needed .... =	880	÷ 0.95	= 926

SOURCE: *Procedures for Areawide Health Facility Planning, U. S. Dept. of Health, Education and Welfare, Public Health Service Publication No. 930-B-3—1963*

The Grading Schedule is a means of classifying municipalities with reference to their fire defenses and physical conditions. From a study of pertinent conditions and performance records extending over many years, certain standards have been developed; these are set forth in the Schedule, and the various features of fire defense in the municipality under consideration are compared with them. For each deviation from these standards, deficiency points are assigned, the number depending upon the importance of the item and the degree of deviation. The natural and structural features that increase the general hazard, and the lack or inadequacy of laws or of their enforcement for the control of unsatisfactory conditions, are graded in the same way. The total number of deficiency points charged against the municipality determines its relative classification. The word "municipality" is used in a broad sense to include cities, towns, villages, or other municipal organizations.

The Table shows the various features considered, as well as the relative value and maximum number of deficiency points allocated to each.

RELATIVE GRADING OF MUNICIPALITIES IN FIRE DEFENSES AND PHYSICAL CONDITIONS

Points of Deficiency	Relative Class of Municipality
0– 500	First
501–1,000	Second
1,001–1,500	Third
1,501–2,000	Fourth
2,501–2,500	Fifth
2,501–3,000	Sixth
3,001–3,500	Seventh
3,501–4,000	Eighth
4,001–4,500	Ninth#
More than 4,500	Tenth*

A ninth-class municipality is one (a) receiving 4001 to 4500 points of deficiency, or (b) receiving less than 4001 points but having no recognized wather supply.

* A tenth-class municipality is one (a) receiving more than 4500 points of deficiency, or (b) without a recognized water supply and having a fire department grading tenth-class, or (c) with a water supply and no fire department, or (d) with no fire protection.

RELATIVE VALUES AND MAXIMUM DEFICIENCY POINTS

Feature	Per Cent	Points
Water Supply	34	1,700
Fire Department	30	1,500
Fire Alarm	11	550
Fire Prevention	7	350
Building Department	4	200
Structural Conditions	14	700
	100	5,000

SOURCE: *Standard Schedule for Grading Cities and Towns of the U. S., National Board of Fire Underwriters—1956 New York, Chicago, San Francisco.*

Fire stations are major capital improvements and will be in use for many years. Therefore, their locations should be selected with care so as to result in the best fire protection possible, considering both life hazard and value of buildings and contents.

Many points should be considered when choosing the location so that the company or companies to be housed in the new station will provide good coverage of the area to be protected and quick response to alarms of fire or other emergency calls.

The type of area to be protected, that is, business, industrial, warehouse, institutional, residential, or a combination of them, is an important factor

Stations should be near extensive industrial or business districts and near districts where there is a high life hazard, even though this often appears to be out of line with a plan of uniform distribution.

Sufficient stations should be provided so that no point in a high value district will be more than 1 mile travel distance from an engine company or 1¼ miles travel distance from a ladder company except that for districts requiring a fire flow of 9000 gpm or more, these distances should be ¾ mile and 1 mile respectively, and in districts requiring a fire flow less than 4500 gpm these distances may be 1½ miles and 2 miles respectively. Distribution should also provide for ready concentration of companies to multiple alarm fires in any high value district, and in areas where the life hazard is severe, without stripping other sections of protection in case of a second fire.

The majority of building fires occur in and around the older portions of most cities where congestion is greater, values higher, and buildings lack those structural features essential to protect life and to restrict the spread of fire. Therefore there should be no general elimination of stations or companies, nor wider spacing in these portions of most cities. Exceptions are where a station is in an area no longer of high value, is so situated that company runs are all in one direction, or the effective response has been reduced by limited access highways or other construction; in these instances, relocation would be desirable.

In average residential districts, response distances may be increased up to 2 miles for engine companies and 3 miles for ladder companies or companies providing adequate ladder service. However, for closely built residential districts requiring more than 2000 gpm fire flow or having buildings 3 or more stories in height, including tenement houses, apartments, or hotels, the distances should be reduced to 1½ and 2 miles respectively. Where the life hazard is above normal, it may be necessary to further reduce these distances to 1 and 1¼ miles, respectively.

Topographical features of a city also affect station location and the total number required. A city divided into two or more portions by rivers, bluffs, mountains, and similar natural barriers, with few means for companies to respond from one portion to another, requires additional stations to provide proper protection. The same is true when there are man-made barriers, such as railroad tracks, limited access highways, and canals; the possibility of delay in response because of railroad crossings at grade, drawbridges, and heavy traffic must be considered. A hillside location is not satisfactory, nor is one at the bottom of the hill when many responses must be made up grade. Where heavily traveled streets enter into the problem, a station may be located on a parallel street or a cross street with the traffic lights at nearby intersections arranged for control from the station in order to permit response across or onto the heavily traveled street; locating a station directly on such a street is ordinarily not desirable. One-way streets pose another problem which may be handled by traffic lights controlled from the station.

Remote sections of a city, separated from the major portion by intervening municipalities, will generally require at least one station, unless the area is very small.

When stations are to be built in outlying areas, it should be remembered that a location too close to the city limits reduces the response area, thereby decreasing efficiency. However, when locating an outlying station and the possibility of the city annexing additional territory exists, the total area requiring protection in the future should be considered.

Many cities have been faced with the problem of providing protection in newly annexed areas. When an area to be annexed is large and well populated, it is possible that at least one additional company and station will be needed to provide proper protection for this area alone. Plans for protecting such areas should be made well in advance of the date of annexation.

A site at an intersection is good as it permits response in more than two directions. Stations should be set well back from the curb line, especially where the street is narrow. The lot should be of ample size so as to provide parking facilities for the men, and adequate space for holding company drills.

Proposed locations of fire stations may be submitted to the office of the local insurance inspection board or to the American Insurance Association (formerly the National Board of Fire Underwriters) for comment. Such requests should be directed to the organization which made the last municipal fire protection survey in the municipality concerned.

SOURCE: *Special Interest Bulletin No. 176, National Board of Fire Underwriters—1963*

GENERAL REQUIREMENTS

Where it is necessary to develop an entirely new water supply system for a suburban area, the "Standard Schedule for Grading Cities and Towns of the United States With Reference to Their Fire Defenses and Physical Conditions" (1) should be used as a guide in providing adequate fire protection.

The required fire flow for the principal business district in the average municipality is obtained by the use of the formula:

$$G = 1{,}020\sqrt{P}\,(1 - 0.01\sqrt{P}),$$

where G is the required fire flow in gallons per minute and P is the population in thousands. The flow may be increased or decreased in accordance with structural conditions and degree of congestion. In many new suburban areas, the fire flow indicated by the formula will be reduced because there are a number of small scattered business districts instead of a single large one. Where buildings, such as super-markets, have excessive area, the fire flow indicated by the formula (or perhaps even more) will be needed because of the large amount of combustible material that may be under one roof. Where suburbs contain industrial, institutional, or other sections that require fire flows in excess of that necessary for the principal business district, the highest required fire flow should govern the design. Fire flows of 1,000 gpm should be available for 4 hr, the duration increasing with larger fire flows up to a maximum of 10 hr for 2,500 gpm or more.

REQUIRED FIRE FLOW

Population	Required Fire flow for Average City		Duration, hours	Population	Required Fire flow for Average City		Duration, hours
	gpm	mgd			gpm	mgd	
1,000	1,000	1.44	4	22,000	4,500	6.48	10
1,500	1,250	1.80	5	27,000	5,000	7.20	10
2,000	1,500	2.16	6	33,000	5,500	7.92	10
3,000	1,750	2.52	7	40,000	6,000	8.64	10
4,000	2,000	2.88	8	55,000	7,000	10.08	10
5,000	2,250	3.24	9	75,000	8,000	11.52	10
6,000	2,500	3.60	10	95,000	9,000	12.96	10
10,000	3,000	4.32	10	120,000	10,000	14.40	10
13,000	3,500	5.04	10	150,000	11,000	15.84	10
17,000	4,000	5.76	10	200,000	12,000	17.28	10

Over 200,000 population, 12,000 gpm, with 2,000 to 8,000 gpm additional for a second fire, for a 10-hour duration.

SOURCE: *Standard Schedule for Grading Cities and Towns of the U. S., National Board of Fire Underwriters—1956 New York, Chicago, San Francisco*

The required fire flow for residential districts consisting of small-area, one-family dwellings one or two stories in height varies from 500 to 2,000 gpm for 2—4 hr, depending on the degree of exposure between buildings.

In order to provide an adequate supply, the system should be capable of delivering the maximum fire flow required for the specified duration with consumption at the maximum daily rate. To meet this requirement the capacity of the supply works can be made equal to the maximum daily consumption rate and sufficient storage can be provided on the distribution system to deliver the required fire flow.

RESERVE CAPACITY

It is obvious that some reserve capacity should be available in the supply works. Those dependent on pumps should be capable of delivering the required fire flow for the specified time during a 5-day period with consumption at the maximum daily rate and any two pumps out of service.

SOURCE: *Kenneth J. Carl, Engr., Fire Protection, Journal American Water Works Association, Vol. 47, No. 10—1955*

LAND AREA PER FAMILY FOR NEIGHBORHOODS OF VARIOUS SIZES
Basic Allowance, in Square Feet, by Type of Dwelling and Population of Neighborhood [a]

DWELLING TYPE	NEIGHBORHOOD POPULATION				
	1,000 persons 275 families	2,000 persons 550 families	3,000 persons 825 families	4,000 persons 1,100 families	5,000 persons 1,375 families
	Square Feet per Family				
ONE- OR TWO-FAMILY DWELLINGS					
1-family detached..................	9,060	8,600	8,520	8,460	8,440
1-family semidetached or 2-family detached	6,460	6,000	5,920	5,860	5,840
1-family attached (row) or 2-family semidetached	4,360	3,900	3,820	3,760	3,740
MULTI-FAMILY DWELLINGS					
2-story....................	3,425	2,960	2,885	2,825	2,795
3-story....................	2,825	2,360	2,285	2,225	2,195
6-story....................	2,210	1,745	1,670	1,610	1,580
9-story....................	2,095	1,630	1,555	1,495	1,465
13-story...................	2,030	1,565	1,490	1,430	1,400

[a] Calculated, with street allowances added.

LAND AREA PER FAMILY FOR NEIGHBORHOOD OF 5,000 PERSONS (1,375 FAMILIES) [a]
Illustrative Calculation of Basic Allowances, in Square Feet, by Type of Dwelling [b]

DWELLING TYPE	LAND AREA IN SQUARE FEET PER FAMILY AND PER CENT OF TOTAL									
	Net Residential		Streets Serving Dwellings[d]		Community Facilities		Streets Serving Com. Fac.		TOTAL	
ONE- OR TWO-FAMILY DWELLINGS										
1-family detached............	6,000	71%	1,800	22%	530	6%	110	1%	8,440	100%
1-family semidetached or 2-family detached	4,000	68	1,200	21	530	9	110	2	5,840	100
1-family attached (row) or 2-family semidetached	2,400	64	700	19	530	14	110	3	3,740	100
MULTI-FAMILY DWELLINGS										
2-story....................	1,465	53	600	21	610	22	120	4	2,795	100
3-story....................	985	45	480	21	610	28	120	6	2,195	100
6-story....................	570	36	280	18	610	39	120	7	1,580	100
9-story....................	515	35	220	15	610	42	120	8	1,465	100
13-story...................	450	32	220	15	610	44	120	9	1,400	100

[a] Assumed: average family size 3.6 persons.
[b] Organization of this and later tables by dewelling types does not imply that a neighborhood should consist of one dwelling type alone
[d] Will vary locally with volume of traffic, street widths, parking scheme, etc.
Allowance is approximately 20 per cent of area of community facilities.

SOURCE: *Planning the Neighborhood*, by the American Public Health Association, Committee on the Hygiene of Housing, Public Administration Service, Chicago, Ill. 1960

NEIGHBORHOOD DENSITY: PERSONS PER ACRE [a]
Basic Allowance, by Type of Dwelling and Population of Neighborhood

DWELLING TYPE	NEIGHBORHOOD POPULATION				
	1,000 persons 275 families	2,000 persons 550 families	3,000 persons 825 families	4,000 persons 1,100 families	5,000 persons 1,375 families
	Persons per Acre				
ONE- OR TWO-FAMILY DWELLINGS					
1-family detached..................	17	18	18	18	19
1-family semidetached or 2-family detached	24	26	27	27	27
1-family attached (row) or 2-family semidetached	36	40	41	42	42
MULTI-FAMILY DWELLINGS					
2-story....................	46	53	54	56	56
3-story....................	56	66	69	71	72
6-story....................	71	90	94	98	99
9-story....................	75	96	101	105	107
13-story...................	77	100	105	110	112

[a] Calculated, assuming average family size of 3.6 persons.

NEIGHBORHOOD DENSITY: FAMILIES PER ACRE
Basic Allowance, by Type of Dwelling and Population of Neighborhood

DWELLING TYPE	NEIGHBORHOOD POPULATION				
	1,000 persons 275 families	2,000 persons 550 families	3,000 persons 825 families	4,000 persons 1,100 families	5,000 persons 1,375 families
	Families per Acre				
ONE OR TWO-FAMILY DWELLINGS.......					
1-family detached	4.8	5.1	5.1	5.1	5.2
1-family semidetached or 2-family detached	6.8	7.3	7.4	7.4	7.5
1-family attached (row) or 2-family semidetached	10.0	11.2	11.4	11.6	11.7
MULTI-FAMILY DWELLINGS					
2-story....................	12.7	14.7	15.1	15.5	15.6
3-story....................	15.5	18.5	19.1	19.6	19.9
6-story....................	19.7	25.0	26.1	27.1	27.6
9-story....................	20.8	26.8	28.0	29.2	29.8
13-story...................	21.5	27.8	29.2	30.5	31.2

USE OF DENSITIES IN DESIGN AND LEGAL CONTROL

The fact that neighborhood density figures are based on a combination of all neighborhood land makes them a valuable tool in planning and housing. They are used early in the planning process to set the broad limits of total population in relation to the size of the site. They provide a method for expressing total land and population ratios for the purpose of preliminary cost estimates. They make it possible to calculate the various possible combinations of dwelling types desired to make up a neighborhood.

Neighborhood densities, in addition to their use in planning individual neighborhoods, offer a tool for the city in setting over-all patterns for population density. By control of over-all densities through zoning, master plans, etc., the local government can and should keep all densities within the limits necessary to health and amenity, and should establish a density pattern to obtain the most efficient population distribution, not only from the point of view of the neighborhood but of the city as a whole. The adequacy of city-wide utility systems, transit, education, recreation and other municipal services is affected by the density pattern, which, if unplanned, may cause serious spot over-loading.

PARKS AND RECREATION

A. Standards for Recreational Activities

Type of Recreational Activity	Space Requirements for Activity Per Population	Ideal Size of Space Required for Activity	Recreational Area Wherein Activity May Be Located
Active Recreation			
1. Children's Play Area (with equipment)	0.5 acre/1,000 pop.	1 acre	Playgrounds-Neighborhood Parks Community Parks, School Paygrounds
2. Field Play Areas for Young Children	1.5 acres/1,000 pop.	3 acres	Playgrounds-Neighborhood Parks Community Parks
3. Older Children-Adult Field Sports Activities	1.5 acres/1,000 pop.	15 acres	Playfield-Community Park District Park
4. Tennis-Outdoor Basketball Other Court Sports	1.0 acres/5,000 pop.	2 acres	Playfield-Community Park
5. Swimming	1 outdoor pool/25,000	Competition size plus wading pool 2 acres	Playfield-Community Park
6. Major Boating Activities	100 acres/50,000	100 acres and over	District Park-Regional Park or Reservation
7. Hiking-Camping-Horseback Riding-Nature Study	10 acres/1,000 pop.	500–1,000 acres	Large District Park-Regional Park
8. Golfing	1–18 hole course per 50,000 pop.	120 acres	Community Park-District Park
Passive Recreation			
1. Picnicking	4 acres/1,000 pop.	varies	All parks
2. Passive Water Sports Fishing-Rowing-Canoeing	1 Lake or Lagoon per 25,000 pop.	20 acre water area	Community Park Special Regional Reservations
3. Zoos, Arboretums, Botanical Gardens	1 acre/1,000 pop.	100 acres	Large District Park or Special Facility
Other			
1. Parking at Recreational Areas	1 acre/1,000 pop.	varies	Playfields, Community, District & Regional Parks
2. Indoor Recreation Centers	1 acre/10,000 pop.	1–2 acres	Community Parks
3. Outdoor Theaters, Band Shells	1 acre/25,000 pop.	5 acres	District Parks

B. Standards for Recreation Areas

Type of Area	Acres Per 1000 Population	Size of Site		Radius of Area Served
		Ideal	Minimum	
Playgrounds	1.5	4 acres	2 acres	0.5 miles
Neighborhood Parks	2.0	10	5	0.5
Playfields	1.5	15	10	1.5
Community Parks	3.5	100	40	2.0
District Parks	2.0	200	100	3.0
Regional Parks and Reservations	15.0	500–1,000	varies	10.0

SOURCE: George Nez, Standards for New Urban Development—The Denver Background, Reprinted by Permission of Urban Land, Vol 20, No 5 Urban Land Institute, 1200 18th Street, N.W., Wash. D.C.

The term "park" is frequently used generically and applied to many different kinds of areas. Most of the States use a number of classifications based upon considerations such as character, use, custom, and statutory requirements. These vary from State to State, and more than 60 classifications are currently in use. And there are extensive public areas reserved for purposes other than recreation which also offer recreation opportunities in addition to the use for which they were primarily intended.

NATIONAL

Established areas administered by agencies of the Federal Government, and potential areas of national significance, have been classified in accordance with the following definitions:

National Parks.—Spacious land areas essentially of primitive or wilderness character which contain scenery and natural wonders so outstanding in quality that their preservation intact has been provided for by their having been designated and set aside by the Federal Government to be preserved unimpaired for the benefit, enjoyment, and inspiration of the people.

National Monuments.—Nationally significant landmarks, structures, objects, or areas of scientific or prehistoric interest so designated by the Federal Government for preservation and public use.

National Recreation Areas.—Spacious areas selected, developed, managed, and conserved to provide broad public recreation opportunities which can best be provided by the Federal Government or where there is a Federal responsibility to conserve and develop recreation opportunities.

National Seashores.—Natural coastal areas set aside for the preservation and public recreation use of their nationally significant scenic, scientific, historic, or recreation values, or a combination of such values. (The term "national lakeshores" has been used recently to designate similar types of proposed areas on the Great Lakes, and "national rivers" has been suggested in proposals to preserve free-flowing streams.)

National Parkways.—Federally owned elongated parks featuring roads designated for pleasure travel, and embracing scenic, recreational, or historic features of national significance. Access from adjoining properties is limited and commercial traffic is not permitted. National parkways have sufficient merit and character to make them a national attraction and not merely a means of travel from one region to another. National parkways can be established only by acts of Congress.

National Historic Sites.—Historic sites, buildings, or objects so designated in recognition of their national significance.

National Memorials.—Structures or areas designated to commemorate ideas, events, or personages of national significance.

National Battlefields.—Battlefields of national significance preserved in part, or in entirety, for the inspiration and benefit of the people.

National Wildlife Refuges.—Areas administered by the Bureau of Sport Fisheries and Wildlife, designated for the protection and propagation of game animals, birds, and fish, within which certain outdoor recreation facilities and activities are permitted as long as they do not interfere with the primary purposes of the refuges.

National Forests.—Federal lands administered by the Forest Service, U. S. Department of Agriculture, under a multiple-use policy for outdoor recreation, range, timber, watershed, and wildlife and fish purposes.

STATE AND LOCAL

In formulating recommendations to establish and potential State, local, quasi-public, and private areas, they should be classified in accordance with the definitions that follow. These are based on definitions adopted by the Board of Directors of the National Conference on State Parks.

Parks.—Relatively spacious areas of outstanding scenic and wilderness character, oftentimes containing also significant historical, archeological, ecological, geological, and other scientific values, preserved as nearly as possible in their original or natural condition and providing opportunity for appropriate types of recreation where such will not destroy or impair the features and values to be preserved. Commercial exploitation of resources is usually prohibited.

Monuments and Historic Sites.—Areas, usually limited in size, established primarily to preserve objects of historic and scientific interest, and places commemorating important persons or historic events. The facilities usually provided are those required for the safety and comfort of the visiting public, such as access, parking, water sanitation, interpretive devices, and sometimes facilities for picnicking and other recreation facilities.

Recreation Areas.—Areas selected and developed primarily to provide nonurban outdoor recreation opportunities to meet other than purely local needs but having the best available scenic quality. Hunting and some other recreation activities not usually associated with parks may be permitted. Commercial exploitation of resources is usually prohibited.

Waysides.—Relatively small areas along highways selected for their scenic or historical significance and providing opportunity for the traveler to relax, enjoy a scenic view, read a historical marker, or have a picnic lunch.

In addition to the preceding definitions adopted by the National Conference on State Parks, other types of areas are defined as follows:

Wilderness.—Areas to preserve primeval environment and devoted primarily to such wilderness types of educational and recreational uses as are consistent with the maintenance of the natural character of the area.

Nature Preserves.—Areas, often limited in size, established for the purpose of preserving distinctive natural communities of plants and animals for their scientific and esthetic interest.

Beaches.—Areas with frontage on the oceans, lakes, and streams designed primarily to provide swimming, boating, fishing, and other waterfront activities. Other coastal areas acquired primarily for the scenic and scientific values are included in the classification "parks."

Parkways.—Elongated or "ribbon" parks featuring a motor road for noncommercial traffic, connecting parks, monuments, beaches, and recreation areas or otherwise affording an opportunity for pleasant and safe driving. Access and roadside developments are controlled. As an adjunct to the motor road, appropriate facilities such as turnouts, picnic areas, and other recreation developments are frequently provided where space permits.

Scenic Roads.—Generally, rural highways, existing or proposed, located in areas having such highly scenic or cultural values that their further development for emphasis on safe and pleasant recreation motoring is justified, including facilities for interpretation of cultural features, for picnicking and camping and development of other recreation potentialities for the roadside.

Trails.—Extended and usually continuous strips of land or water established independently of other routes of travel and dedicated, through ownership or easement, to recreational travel, including hiking, bicycling, horseback riding, or canoeing.

Free-Flowing Streams.—Streams or portions of streams that are still unmodified by the works of man or that, in spite of such modification, retain natural scenic qualities and -recreation opportunities. There must be provision for adequate protection against undesirable streamside developments, and for the preservation through public control of the existing character and quality of the adjacent landscape.

Forests.—Areas established and managed primarily for timber production and watershed protection. Recreation is an increasingly important use.

SOURCE: Parks—U. S. Dept of Parks, Wash. D. C.

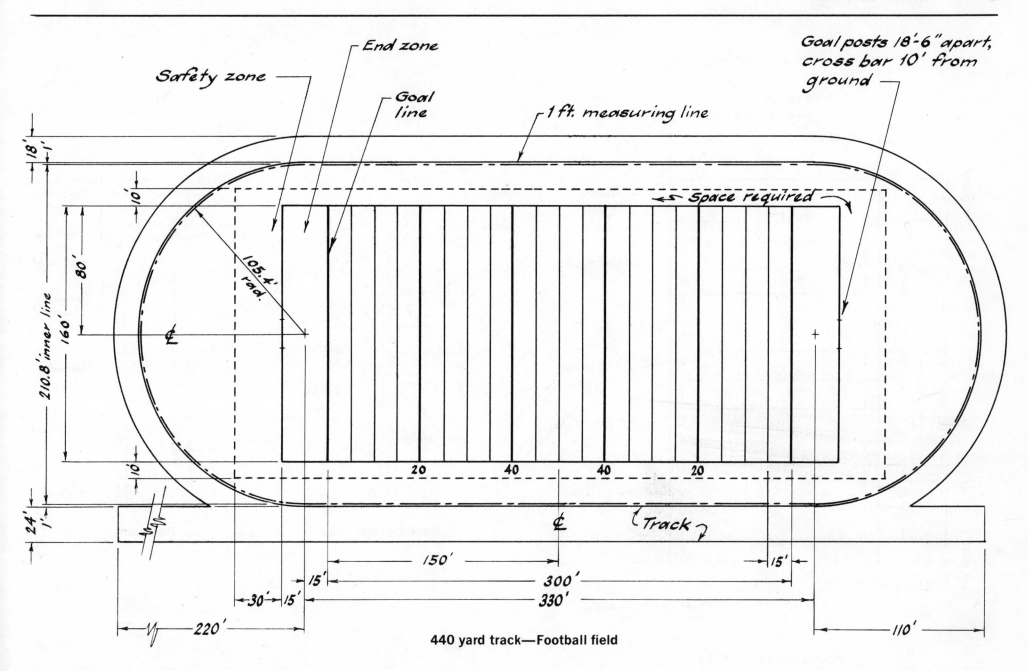

440 yard track—Football field

Football Field provide one per 20,000 persons usually combined with a soccer or athletic field or a secondary school

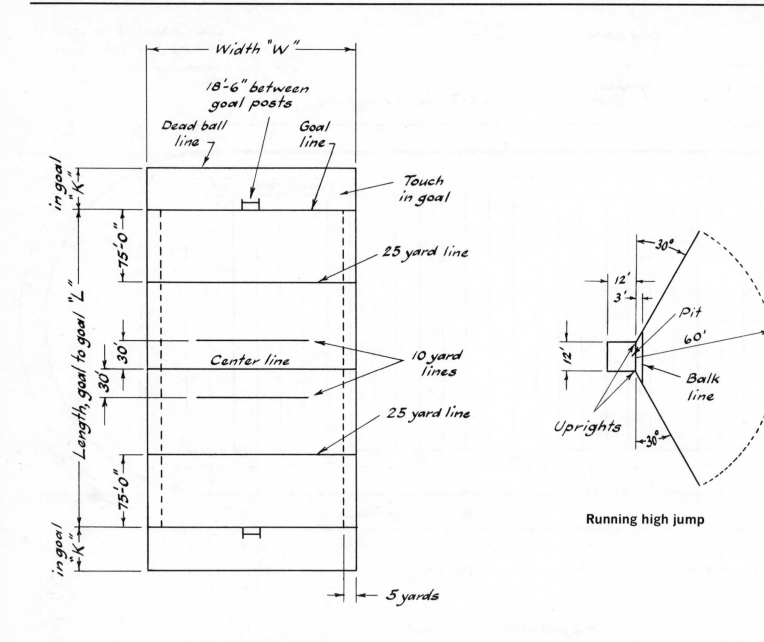

Rugby football (R.F.U.)

Running high jump

Pole vault

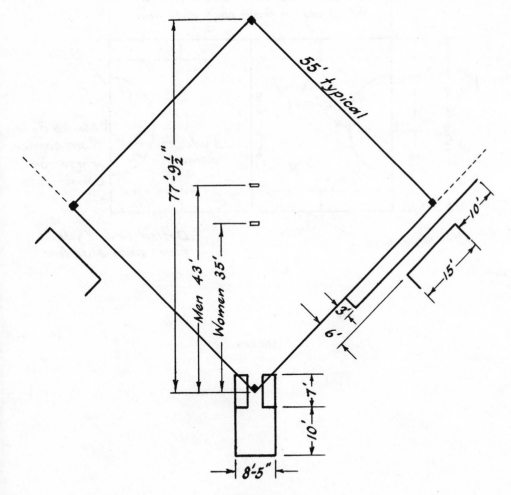

Recommended batting
radius 200 ft. from home
plate using a 12 inch ball

55' typical

77'-9½"

Men 43'

Women 35'

15'

3'

6'

10'

10'

7'

8'-5"

Regulation field
Softball

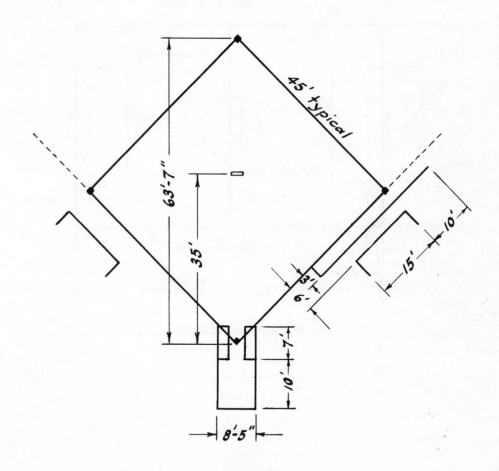

Recommended batting
radius 150 ft. from home
plate using a 12 inch ball

45' typical

63'-7"

35'

15'

10'

3'

6'

7'

10'

8'-5"

For younger boys and girls
Softball

Softball Field provide one per 3,000 persons usually a neighborhood facility

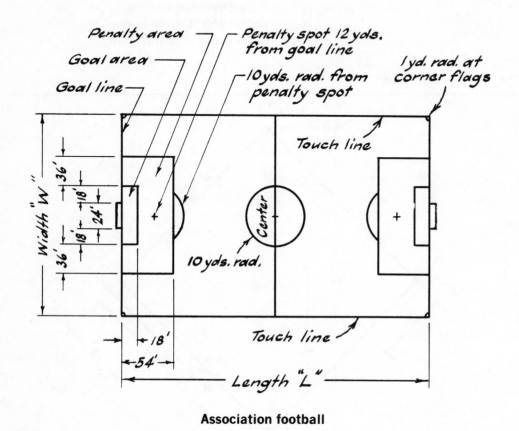

Penalty area

Goal area

Goal line

Penalty spot 12 yds. from goal line

10 yds. rad. from penalty spot

1 yd. rad. at corner flags

Touch line

Width "W"

36'

18'

24'

18'

36'

10 yds. rad.

Center

18'

54'

Touch line

Length "L"

Association football

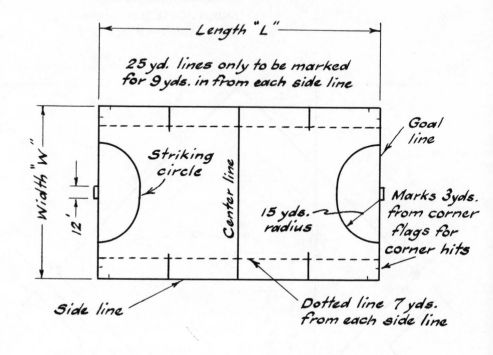

Length "L"

25 yd. lines only to be marked for 9 yds. in from each side line

Width "W"

12'

Striking circle

Center line

15 yds. radius

Goal line

Marks 3 yds. from corner flags for corner hits

Side line

Dotted line 7 yds. from each side line

Hockey

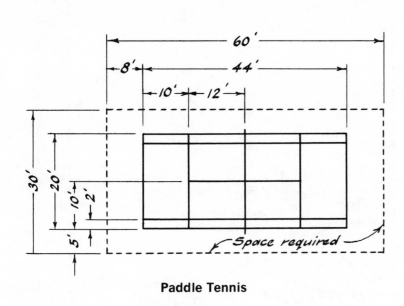

Paddle Tennis

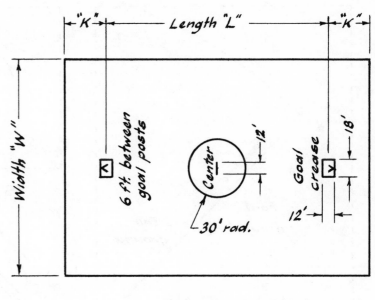

Lacrosse

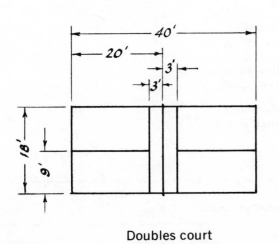

Doubles court

Deck Tennis

Lacrosse (Box or Field)	provide one per 20,000 persons	generally located in community park

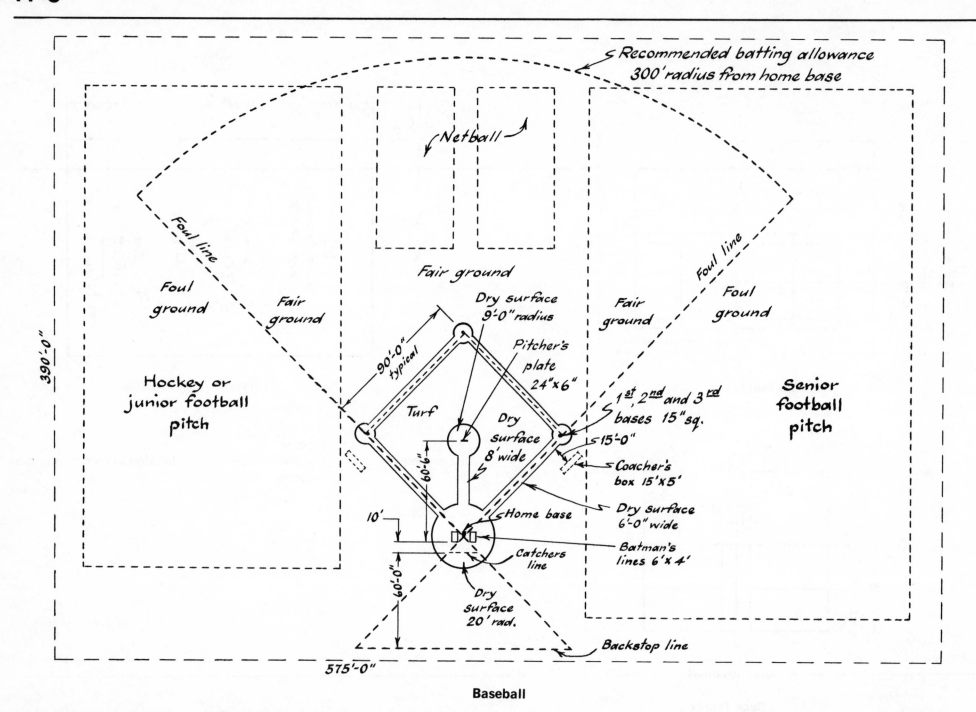

Recommended batting allowance
300' radius from home base

Netball

Fair ground

Foul line

Foul ground

Fair ground

Fair ground

Foul line

Foul ground

Dry surface
9'-0" radius

Pitcher's
plate
24" x 6"

90'-0"
typical

Hockey or
junior football
pitch

Turf

Dry
surface
8' wide

1st, 2nd and 3rd
bases 15" sq.

Senior
football
pitch

15'-0"

60'-6"

Coacher's
box 15' x 5'

Dry surface
6'-0" wide

10'

Home base

Batman's
lines 6' x 4'

Catchers
line

390'-0"

60'-0"

Dry
surface
20' rad.

Backstop line

575'-0"

Baseball

Baseball Field provide one per 5,000 persons usually a neighborhood facility

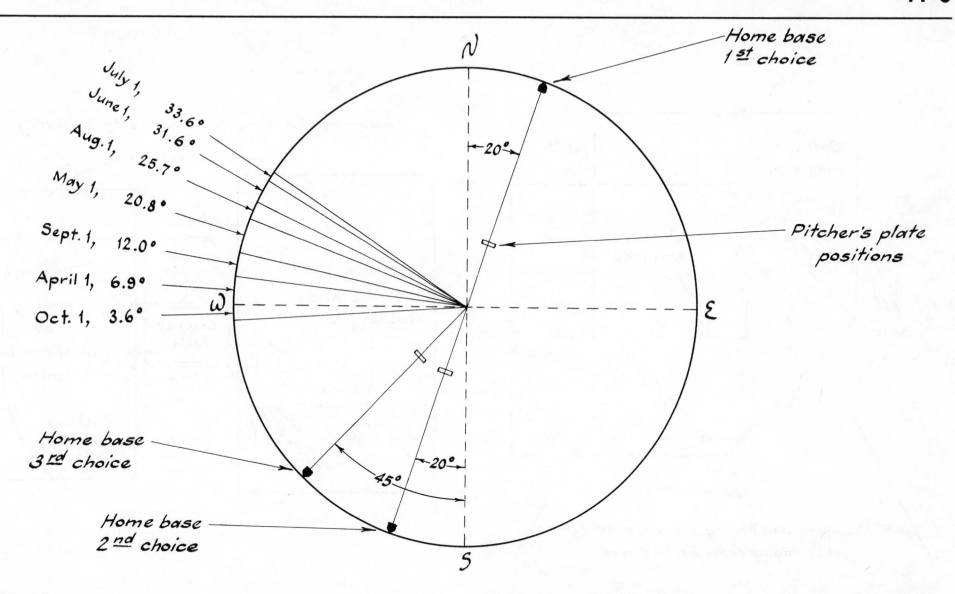

ORIENTATION

To ensure minimum nuisance from the sun when sighting balls in mid-air it is desirable that the principal line of play of any game should be away from the direction of the setting sun.

So far as team games are concerned the advantage of good orientation should always be weighed against the effects of surface gradients where, for economic or other reasons, these have to be accepted of greater severity than is normally advisable. Quite apart from the effect on the run of the ball the physical strain of play increases in proportion to the gradient. It is therefore recommended that where the surface gradient exceeds 1 in 40, the main direction of play should be transverse to the inclination irrespective of the demands of good orientation.

Where high buildings, trees or surrounding hills effectively screen the sun at low altitude, some latitude in the interpretation of orientation requirements is permissible, particularly if a more satisfactory layout results.

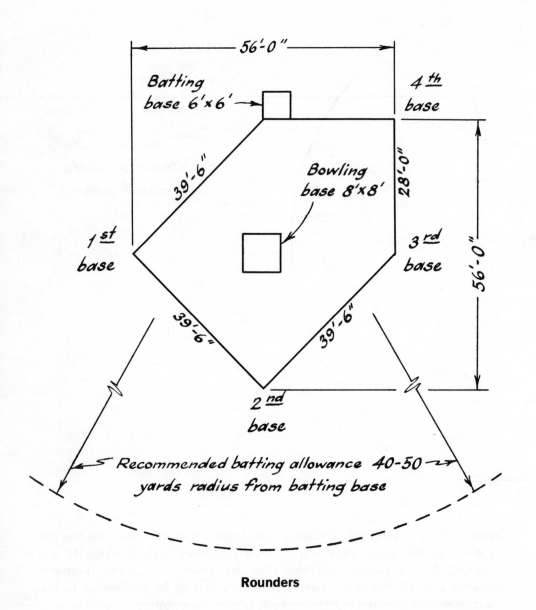

Rounders

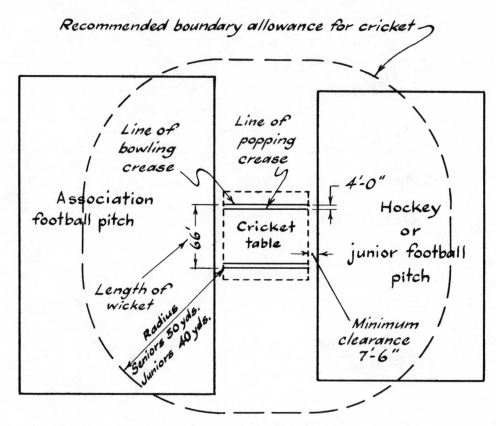

Cricket

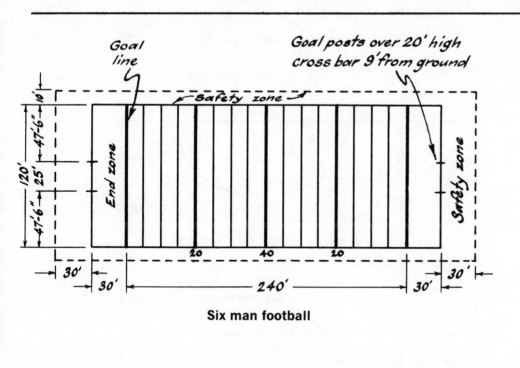

Six man football

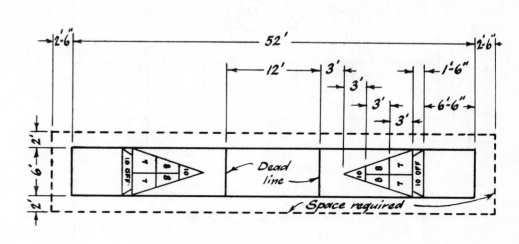

Shuffle board

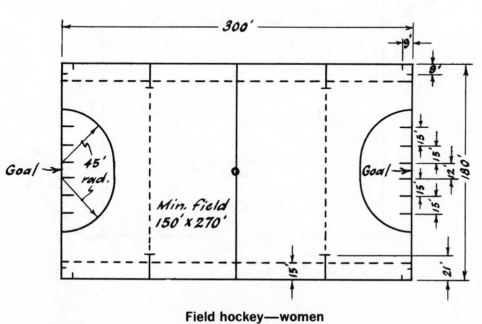

Field hockey—women

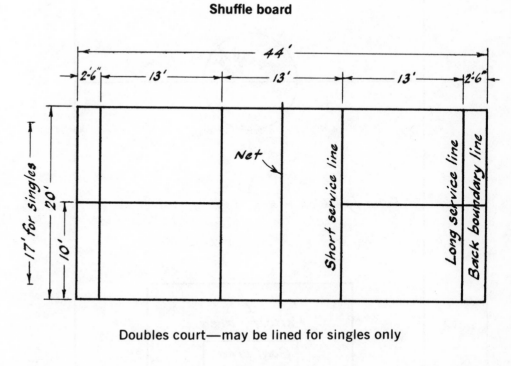

Doubles court—may be lined for singles only

Badminton

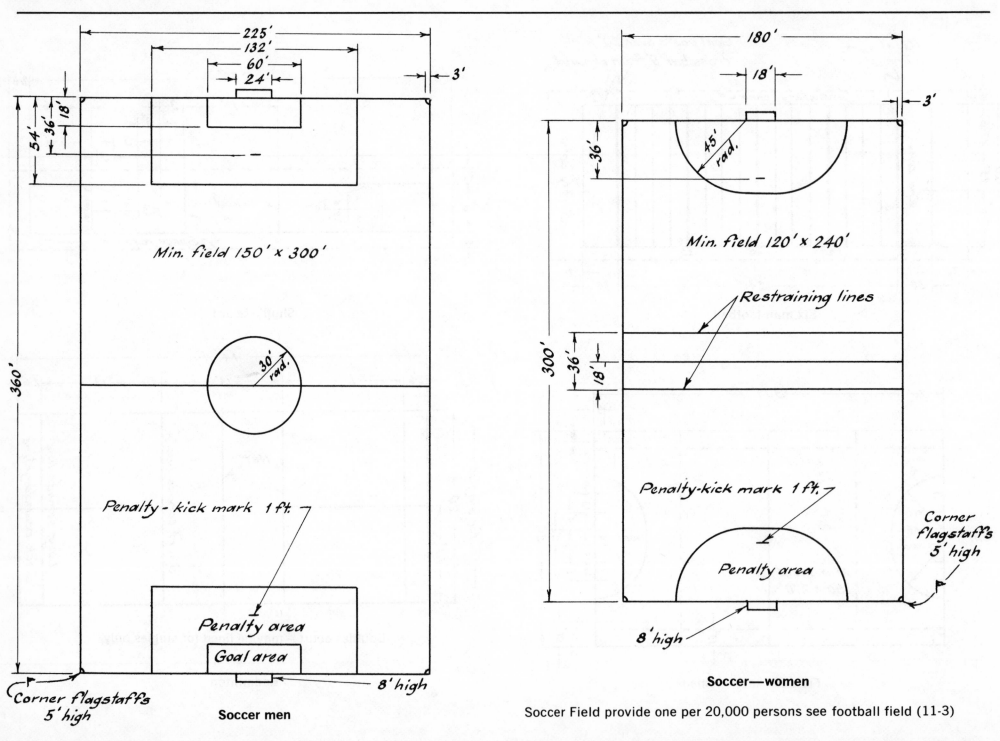

225'
132'
60'
24'
3'
18'
36'
54'
Min. field 150' x 300'
30' rad.
360'
Penalty - kick mark 1 ft.
Penalty area
Goal area
8' high
Corner flagstaffs 5' high

Soccer men

180'
18'
3'
36'
45' rad.
Min. field 120' x 240'
Restraining lines
300'
36'
18'
Penalty-kick mark 1 ft.
Penalty area
Corner flagstaffs 5' high
8' high

Soccer—women

Soccer Field provide one per 20,000 persons see football field (11-3)

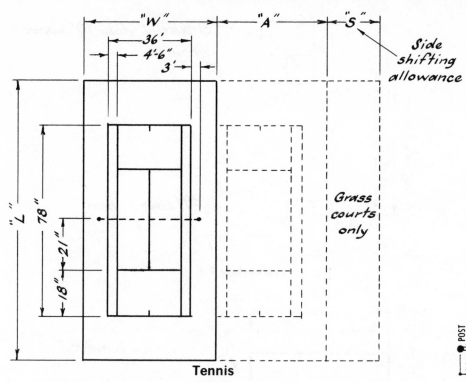

Tennis

Double

Single

For economy of construction and convenience of use and maintenance, tennis courts should be grouped together as a block. It is preferable for courts to be sited side by side rather than end on. The former arrangement is not only better for the players but is not so costly as less surfacing and intermediate stop netting are required. Odd shaped areas between the courts and the boundary should, if possible, be avoided as they increase the difficulties of maintenance and seldom serve any useful purpose.

Where levelling is necessary, due allowance must be made for banks or retaining walls.

A shelter with front open and provided with seats is desirable.

Type of Court	Overall Length "L"	Overall width of first court "W"	Additional width for each further court "A"	Side shifting allowance (grass courts only) "S"
	Feet	Feet	Feet	Feet
HARD				
Tournament	120–130	60–65	48–50½	—
Public Schools	114	56	46	—
High School	114	56	46	—
GRASS				
Tournament	120	60	48	24
Public Schools	110	56	46	23
High School	110	56	46	23

Tennis Courts one location per 5,000 persons usually combined with some other facility

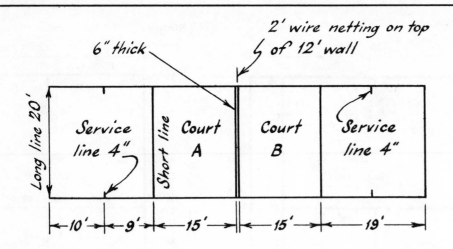

Handball

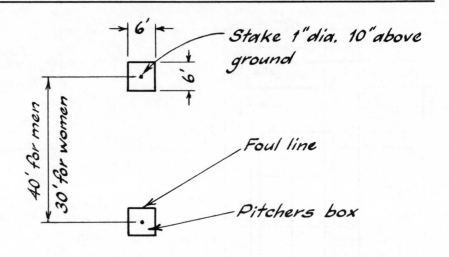

Horseshoe Pit

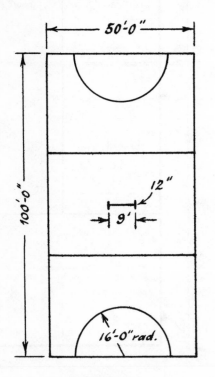

Dimensions are 100' x 50' and the marginal clearance should not be less than 5' all round. Where sited side by side the margin between pitches should be increased to 10'.

Netball

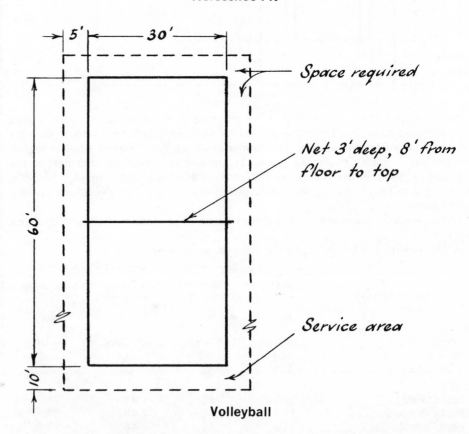

Volleyball

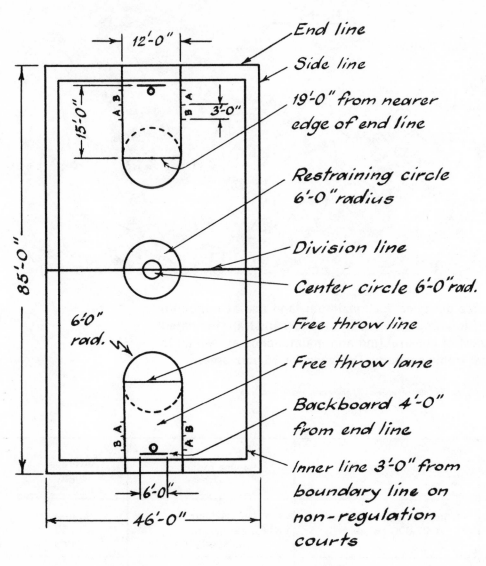

End line

Side line

19'-0" from nearer edge of end line

Restraining circle 6'-0" radius

Division line

Center circle 6'-0" rad.

Free throw line

Free throw lane

Backboard 4'-0" from end line

Inner line 3'-0" from boundary line on non-regulation courts

Basketball

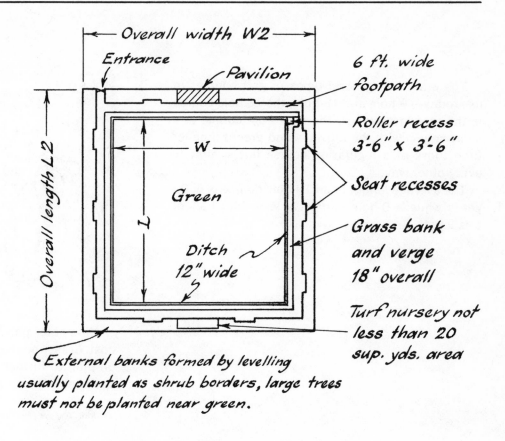

Overall width W2

Entrance

Pavilion

6 ft. wide footpath

Roller recess 3'-6" x 3'-6"

Seat recesses

Green

W

L

Ditch 12" wide

Grass bank and verge 18" overall

Turf nursery not less than 20 sup. yds. area

External banks formed by levelling usually planted as shrub borders, large trees must not be planted near green.

Flat rink Bowling Green

RECOMMENDED DIMENSIONS

Rinks	Green width "W"		Green length "L"	Overall width "W2"		Overall length "L2"
	Ft.	ins.	Feet	Ft.	ins.	Feet
2	52	6	126	86	6	160
3	73	6	126	107	6	160
4	94	6	126	128	6	160
5	115	6	126	149	6	160
6	126	0	126	160	0	160

There are two general types of golf courses in use today—9-hole and 18-hole, the 18 hole course is the standard layout, the nine hole course is a short course with the fairways and greens smaller than those of a regulation course but similar in every other way.

The average length of an 18-hole course is 6500 yards while a 9-hole course is less than half of this length.

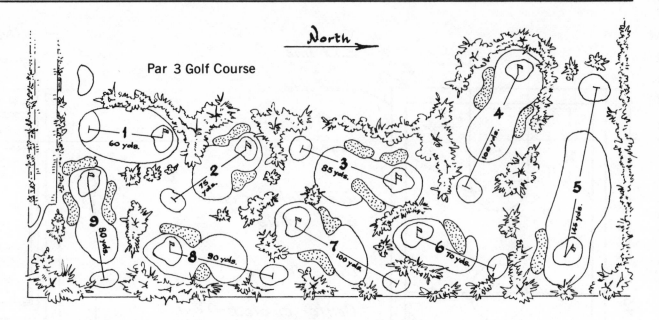

North

Par 3 Golf Course

Nine-hole, par 3 course designed for maximum land use at minimum cost. Grassy bunkers and hollows can be substituted for sand traps indicated on plan to further cut cost of construction and maintenance as well as to speed up play for greater traffic capacity. Designed for 15 acre area.

SOURCE: Golf Operators Handbook, edited by Ben Chlevin, National Golf Foundation, Inc.,—1956, p. 86

	Minimum area required	Maximum area required	No. of parking spaces	Population served	Service radius	Average length
9-hole course	60 acres	80 acres	100 cars	1 hole per 3000 persons or 27,000 persons	½–¾ hour by car or public transportation	Approx. 2250 yards
18-hole course	120 acres	160 acres	200 cars	1 hole per 1500 persons or 25,000 persons	1 hour max. by car or public transportation	6500 yards

ROQUE COURT

Stake

6'-0"

4'-3"

2'-4"

Arches

Double arch

1'-6"

14'-3"

25'-4"

12'-8"

51'-6"

60'-0"

5'-9"

9'-3"

9'-3"

5'-9"

15'-9"

6'-0"

6'-0"

13'-4"

2'-4"

2'-3"

Stake

4'-3"

4'-3"

21'-6"

4'-3"

30'-0"

CROQUET COURT

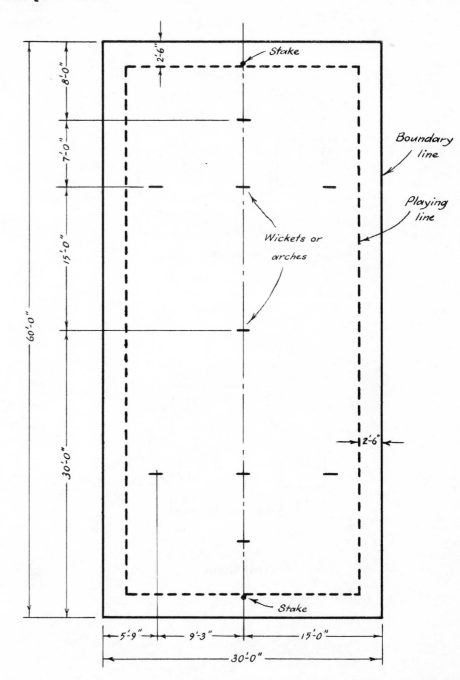

Stake

2'-6"

8'-0"

7'-0"

Boundary line

Playing line

15'-0"

Wickets or arches

60'-0"

30'-0"

2'-6"

Stake

5'-9"

9'-3"

15'-0"

30'-0"

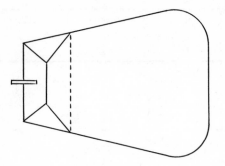

Fan shape

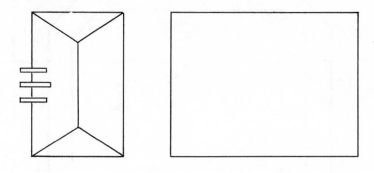

Multiple pool

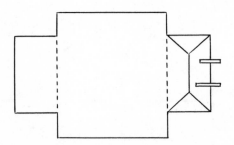

Cross shape

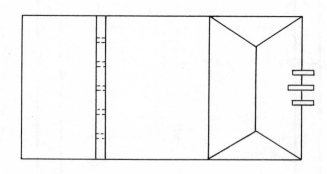

Multiple pool—causeway type

SOURCE: Trends in Swimming Pool Design, Elgin Softener Corp., Elgin, Ill.

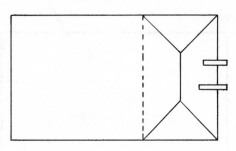

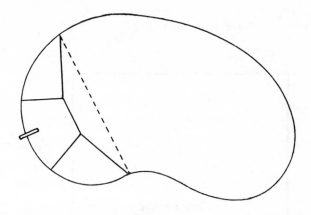

Rectangular hopper-bottom

Free form

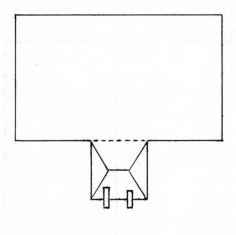

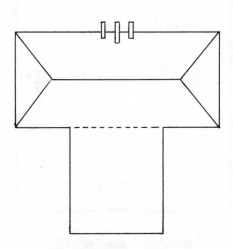

Tee shape

Tee shape (variation)

SOURCE: Trends in Swimming Pool Design, Elgin Softener Corp., Elgin, Ill.

4-WALL HANDBALL COURT

Front wall elev. 23'-0"

Side wall
elev. 23'-0"

Service line

1'-6"

5'-0"

46'-0"

Lines 1½" wide

This line extends
5'-0" high on side
walls

23'-0"

Door

Back wall elev. 10'-0"

23'-0"

SQUASH COURT

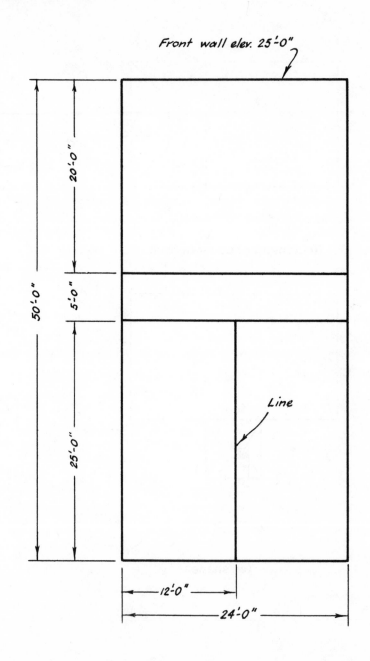

Front wall elev. 25'-0"

20'-0"

5'-0"

50'-0"

25'-0"

Line

12'-0"

24'-0"

RECOMMENDED SURFACINGS FOR RECREATION AREAS, RELATED TO DENSITY

Kind of area	Low and moderate density areas (Singles, twins, row houses, and flats)	High density areas (apartments)
General recreation area ..	Turf, natural soil	Bituminous concrete and sandclay, natural soil.
Special play areas: Child service play yards Game courts	80% turf, 20% concrete .... Bituminous concrete, portland cement concrete, sand-clay, turf.	80% turf, 20% concrete. Bituminous concrete, portland cement concrete, sand-clay, cork asphalt.
Under playground apparatus	Lightloam, sand, tanbark, saw-dust, shavings, turf.	Light loam, sand, tanbark, sawdust, shavings.
Crafts and story-telling	Any hard surfacing or turf	Any hard surface or turf.
Outdoor parties, dances, roller skating, etc.	Any smooth, hard surfacing	Any smooth, hard surfacing.
Local play areas: For small children	Principally turf or natural earth, and smooth hard paving.	Principally a smooth hard paving and some turf or natural earth.
For all age groups	Turf, bituminous concrete, portland cement, concrete.	Bituminous concrete, cork asphalt, portland cement concrete.
Sitting areas	Bituminous concrete, portland cement concrete, brick, precast concrete slabs, flagstones.	

ADVANTAGES AND DISADVANTAGES OF VARIOUS SURFACINGS FOR RECREATION AREAS

Surfacing Type	Advantages	Disadvantages
Turf	Soft surface, ideal for many play purposes. Low first cost.	Cannot be used in wet weather. Difficult to maintain.
Natural soil	Low first cost. Soft surface	Muddy in wet weather, dusty in dry weather.
Gravel	Low first cost. Pleasing appearance	Child throw it about to such extent that it is unsuitable for any use as surfacing in housing developmens.
Sand-clay and clay-gravel	Low cost when suitable material available. Reasonably soft surface.	Difficult to get properly proportioned mixture.
Brick (on sand cushion) ..	Attractive appearance	Initial cost relatively high.
Stone paving blocks (on sand cushion or natural soil).	Low cost when salvaged from old pavements. Satisfactory appearance. Durability.	Surface too rough for play use.
Precast concrete slabs (on sand or natural soil).	Year-round utility. Satisfactory appearance.	Maintenance cost relatively high.
Flagstones (on sand or natural soil).	Year-round utility. Pleasing appearance. Durability.	
Bituminous concrete.	Good surface for most play purposes when properly specified and laid. Not so hard on feet as portland cement concrete. Year round utility.	Rough and abrasive unless properly specified and constructed. (Competent inspection essential for good workmanship.) Hot for bare feet. May become soft. Unattractive in large areas.
Cork asphalt.	Resiliency. Excellent surface for many play purposes. Year-round utility. Satisfactory appearance.	Comparatively high cost. (Competent inspection essential to good workmanship). Softens in very hot weather.
Portland cement concrete	Year-round utility. Minimum maintenance expense. Good surface for wheel toys, roller skating and some court games.	Lacks resiliency. Initial cost relatively high. Large areas require expansion joints. Whiteness and glare of large areas unattractive.

SOURCE: Adapted from Public Housing Design, National Housing Agency, Federal Public Housing Agency—1946

Before applying these standards, municipalities should adapt them according to local factors and interests. Throughout this section:

- a region will contain about 60,000 people
- a community will contain about 25,000 people
- a neighbourhood will contain about 5,000 people

Facility	Standard	Remarks
Arboretum	one per region	develop according to interest
Arena		
Artificial ice area —Indoor	one per 20,000	one in each municipality should have seating capacity for league games; the rest should be for recreation purposes
Artificial ice area —Outdoor	can be built in place of indoor facility	may serve as a summer play area
Natural ice —Outdoor	one per 5,000	used only where normal weather conditions allow two or three months of use
Athletic Field	one per 20,000	in a community park or combined with secondary school
Beach Areas	each municipality should develop all potential beach areas	now considered an essential recreation area
Botanical Gardens	one per region	best when linked to an educational institution

Facility	Standard	Remarks
Library	one per 20,000	additional branches added as required; should include a bookmobile service for suburban and rural areas
Marina	one per suitable watercraft area	size according to need and potential
Museum	one per region	may differ in emphasis—i.e. science, historical, etc.; should grow with the population
Nature & Hiking Trails	as many as possible	develop according to interest; usually in a regional park
Outdoor Theatre	one per region; seat between 1,000 & 10,000	a natural amphitheatre or large structure to accommodate drama, music and films; developed according to interest; interest may require small intimate theatres in neighbourhood parks
Picnic Areas	one acre for each 3,000 to 5,000	usually in regional park or conservation area; enhanced by water frontage or view

SOURCE: *Standards and Definition of Terms, Community Programs Division, Ontario Dept. of Education, Toronto, Canada*

Facility	Standard	Remarks
Camping Areas Day Camp—	to accommodate a minimum of 100 children; at least one location for each 25,000	an isolated area; often found in a conservation or regional park; maximum capacity per unit or for one director is 120 children
Family—	one acre per 5,000	for family or short term camping; located in regional park or conservation area
Resident—	one per 40,000; should serve at least 100 persons	often provided by private agencies
Centres Civic—	one per 100,000	could include some or all of the other centres
Community—	one per 25,000	a multi-purpose building; should be part of secondary school or located in a community park
Fishing Area	one per region	controlled and stocked for public use
Golf Courses Regulation—	18 holes for 50,000	minimum of 120 to 180 acres
Pools Major Indoor—	one per 50,000	should include competitive and spectator facilities
Outdoor-Indoor—	one per 20,000; to accommodate 2½ to 3% of population at one time; min. capacity of 200 per pool using 27 sq. ft. per swimmer	should be located in community or in conjunction with secondary school. These should be built wherever possible in place of outdoor pools
Outdoor—	one per 10,000	deck size twice the size of the water surface; often built as part of a multi-purpose unit in a community park; the second one not considered until after 25,000 is reached

Facility	Standard	Remarks
Pools Spray—	one per 5,000	must be on paved surface with ample drainage
Training—	one per 5,000	requires no diving area
Riding Trails	one per region	can be developed in a regional park or conservation area
Sanctuaries (Bird or Animal)	one per region	should contain shelter and feeding facilities
Skiing Snow—	one per region	developed according to suitability of area; should contain shelter, tow, jumps, snow making machine; could be part of golf course or nature trail. Include beginners, intermediate, advanced & family slopes
Water—	one per region	safe, controlled water area
Stadium or Bowl	one per 100,000	a major multi-purpose sports field with flood lighting, dressing rooms, wash rooms, food concessions and parking for professional or highly organized team sports
Track & Field	one per 20,000	usually part of an athletic field, secondary school or sports stadium; each secondary school should have practice areas
Zoo or Zoological Gardens	one well developed unit for each 250,000 to 500,000 people	should start with 50,000 people and grow with population

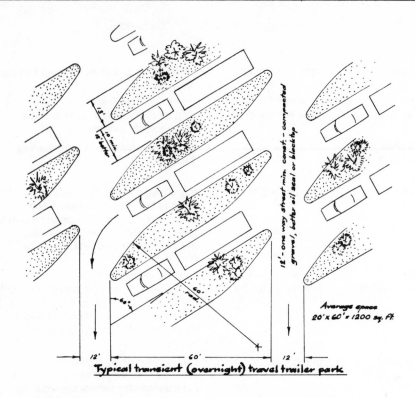

Typical transient (overnight) travel trailer park

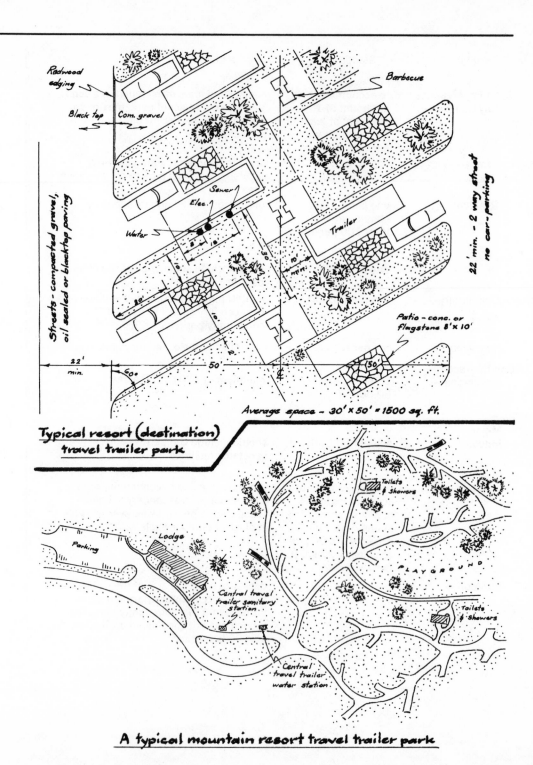

Typical resort (destination) travel trailer park

A typical mountain resort travel trailer park

RECOMMENDED FACILITIES

For Overnight Parks

1. Absolute Minimum: Central travel trailer sanitary & water stations & toilets.
2. Fair: Individual electrical outlets, central travel trailer sanitary & water stations, and toilets.
3. Good: Individual electrical outlets, central travel trailer sanitary & water stations, toilets and showers.
4. Better: Individual electrical & water outlets, several individual sewer connections, one or more central travel trailer sanitary station, toilets, showers and coin-operated laundry.
5. Best: Individual electrical water & sewer connections, toilets & showers, coin-operated laundry and picnic tables.

For Destination Parks

1. Absolute Minimum: Back-in parking, individual electrical outlets, central travel trailer sanitary & water stations, and toilets & showers.
2. Fair: Back-in parking, individual electrical & water connections, central travel trailer sanitary station, toilets & showers.
3. Good: Drive-through parking, individual electrical & water connections, central travel trailer sanitary station, toilets, showers, coin-operated laundry, and picnic tables.
4. Better: Drive-through parking, individual electrical & water connections, central travel trailer sanitary station, toilets, showers, coin-operated laundry, picnic tables and grocery.
5. Best: Drive-through parking, individual electrical, water & sewer connections, toilets, showers, coin-operated laundry, picnic tables, grocery. Also barbecue, bottled gas, travel trailer parts for sale, plus bait & other fishing and sport accessories. Recreation building and swimming pool may be on a "pay as you go" basis.

SOURCE: *Environmental Health Practice in Recreational Areas, Public Health Service, U. S. Dept of Health, Education, and Welfare, Wash. D. C.*

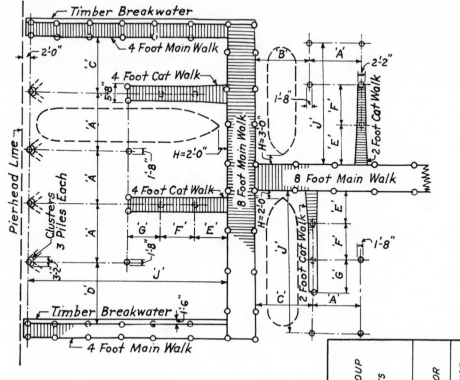

TYPICAL PLEASURE BOAT BASIN

DIMENSION DIAGRAM

FOR

SLIPS AND CAT WALKS

PLATE NO. 2

NOTE: Use this diagram in conjunction with Table I to determine widths of slips, lengths of cat walks and locations for stern anchor piles. Fixed dimensions shown are considered as sufficient for construction purposes.

TABLE 1

DIMENSIONS FOR SLIPS AND CATWALKS

NOTE: Use this tabulation in conjunction with Plate No. 2 to obtain widths of slips, lengths of Catwalks and locations of stern anchor piles. This Tabulation is based upon the use of Traveler Irons.

LENGTH GROUP FOR YACHTS	BEAM TO BE PROVIDED FOR	MIN. CLEARANCE FOR BEAM	MIN. CLEAR WIDTH OF SLIP	ALLOWANCE FOR HALF ANCHOR PILE	ALLOWANCE FOR HALF OF CATWALK	GROSS SLIP WIDTH TYPE "A"	GROSS SLIP WIDTH TYPE "B"	GROSS SLIP WIDTH TYPE "C"	GROSS SLIP WIDTH TYPE "D"	USABLE WIDTH OF CATWALK	1ST CATWALK SPAN LENGTH "E"	2ND CATWALK SPAN LENGTH "F"	3RD CATWALK SPAN LENGTH "G"	TOTAL LENGTH OF CATWALK	DISTANCE "J" TO ANCHOR PILE
20' to 25'	7'-6"	3'-0"	10'-6"	10"	1'-1"	12'-5"	12'-2"	12'-5"	—	2'-0"	10'-0"	8'-0"	—	18'-0"	28'-0"
	8'-6"	3'-0"	11'-6"	10"	1'-1"	13'-5"	13'-2"	13'-5"	—	2'-0"	10'-0"	8'-0"	—	18'-0"	28'-0"
25' to 30'	7'-6"	3'-0"	10'-6"	10"	1'-1"	12'-5"	12'-2"	12'-5"	—	2'-0"	10'-0"	10'-0"	—	20'-0"	33'-0"
	9'-6"	3'-0"	12'-6"	10"	1'-1"	14'-5"	14'-2"	14'-5"	—	2'-0"	10'-0"	10'-0"	—	20'-0"	33'-0"
30' to 35'	8'-6"	3'-0"	11'-6"	10"	1'-1"	13'-5"	13'-2"	13'-5"	—	2'-0"	12'-0"	10'-0"	—	22'-0"	38'-0"
	11'-6"	3'-0"	14'-6"	10"	1'-1"	16'-5"	16'-2"	16'-5"	—	2'-0"	12'-0"	10'-0"	—	22'-0"	38'-0"
35' to 40'	9'-6"	3'-6"	13'-0"	10"	1'-1"	14'-11"	14'-8"	14'-11"	—	2'-0"	12'-0"	12'-0"	—	24'-0"	42'-0"
	12'-0"	3'-6"	15'-6"	10"	1'-1"	17'-5"	17'-2"	17'-5"	—	2'-0"	12'-0"	12'-0"	—	24'-0"	42'-0"
40' to 45'	9'-6"	4'-0"	13'-6"	10"	1'-1"	15'-5"	15'-2"	15'-5"	—	2'-0"	14'-0"	12'-0"	—	26'-0"	47'-0"
	12'-6"	4'-0"	16'-6"	10"	1'-1"	18'-5"	18'-2"	18'-5"	—	2'-0"	14'-0"	12'-0"	—	26'-0"	47'-0"
45' to 50'	10'-6"	4'-0"	14'-6"	10"	1'-1"	16'-5"	16'-2"	16'-5"	—	2'-0"	9'-0"	9'-0"	10'-0"	28'-0"	52'-0"
	13'-6"	4'-0"	17'-6"	10"	1'-1"	19'-5"	19'-2"	19'-5"	—	2'-0"	9'-0"	9'-0"	10'-0"	28'-0"	52'-0"
50' to 60'	11'-6"	5'-0"	16'-6"	1'-7"	1'-1"	19'-2"	18'-11"	18'-5"	—	2'-0"	11'-0"	11'-0"	12'-0"	34'-0"	61'-0"
	14'-6"	5'-0"	19'-6"	1'-7"	1'-1"	22'-2"	21'-11"	21'-5"	—	2'-0"	11'-0"	11'-0"	12'-0"	34'-0"	61'-0"
60' to 70'	12'-6"	5'-0"	17'-6"	1'-7"	2'-10"	21'-11"	19'-11"	21'-2"	—	4'-0"	11'-0"	11'-0"	12'-0"	34'-0"	72'-0"
	14'-6"	5'-0"	19'-6"	1'-7"	2'-10"	23'-11"	21'-11"	23'-2"	—	4'-0"	11'-0"	11'-0"	12'-0"	34'-0"	72'-0"
	16'-0"	5'-0"	21'-0"	1'-7"	2'-10"	25'-5"	23'-5"	24'-8"	—	4'-0"	11'-0"	11'-0"	12'-0"	34'-0"	72'-0"
70' to 80'	13'-0"	5'-0"	18'-0"	1'-7"	2'-10"	22'-5"	20'-5"	21'-8"	—	4'-0"	11'-0"	11'-0"	12'-0"	34'-0"	82'-0"
	16'-6"	5'-0"	21'-6"	1'-7"	2'-10"	25'-11"	24'-11"	26'-2"	24'-7"	4'-0"	11'-0"	11'-0"	12'-0"	34'-0"	82'-0"

SOURCE: Marinas, The National Association of Engine and Boat Manufacturers, Inc., New York, NY—1947

COMMERCIAL DEVELOPMENT

Population Served	Floor Area Required (Sales Area)	Customer Parking Area 2:1 Ratio	Circulation, Service, and Planting Areas 25%	Total Sq. Feet	Total Acres Required	Sq. Ft. Per Family (Gross)	Maximum Walking Distance
800 Familes 2500 Persons	20 SF/Family = 16,000 SF	32,000 SF	12,000 SF	60,000 SF	1.4 Acres	75	¼ Mile
1600 Families 5000 Persons	18 SF/Family = 28,800 SF	57,600 SF	36,400 SF	172,800 SF	4.0 Acres	100	½ Mile

FOOD MARKET — Should include specialty foods and delicatessen goods

BAKERY SHOP — May be included in food market

DRUGSTORE — Should include lunch counter and soda fountain

STATIONERY STORE — Including reading matter, tobacco and vanity goods

RESTAURANT — Including table service and take-out orders

BARBER SHOP — Including shoeshine service

BEAUTY PARLOR — May be combined with barber shop

LAUNDRY AND DRY CLEANING STORE — Combined service, including a laundromat

HARDWARE — Should include household goods

SERVICE STATION — Including filling station, minor repairs, and auto accessories

Population Served	Floor Area Required (Sales Area)	Customer Parking Area 3:1 Ratio	Circulation, Service, and Planting Area 25%	Total Sq. Ft.	Total Acres Required	Sq. Ft. Per Family (Gross)	Maximum Distance
12,000–13,000 Families 40,000 Persons	25 SF/Family = 100,000 SF	300,000 SF	100,000 SF	500,000 SF	10–12 Acres	38–42 SF	1 Mile Walk 15-Minute Drive
30,000–32,000 Families 100,000 Persons	20 SF/Family = 200,000 SF	600,000 SF	200,000 SF	1,000,000 SF	20–24 Acres	32–36 SF	1½ Miles Walk 30-Minute Drive

The community shopping center, designed to serve a larger number of families than the neighborhood shopping center, will contain the basic types of services and facilities required by the neighborhood.

The leading tenant of the community shopping center is the variety or junior department store. In addition, the center should have a florist, milliner, radio and T.V. repairs, children's shoes, gifts, candy, lingerie, liquor, women's apparel, restaurant, book store, children's wear and toys haberdashery, athletic goods shops.

A movie theatre may also be included.

A bank and post office should be included as a public service, if they are not available elsewhere in the neighborhood. They do not pay well, any more than service stores do, but often in a shopping center it is more important to have a balanced variety of stores, than a group of 100% pullers.

In order to make this truly a community center it may also be advisable to include offices for doctor and other professional men. However, it is generally considered among developers that office workers usurp a great deal of parking space all day without drawing sufficient trade to compensate for this. Offices are generally put on the second floor of one of the store buildings, or in a separate building which may be used as a buffer between the stores and the surrounding residences.

Population Served	Floor Area Required (Sales Area)	Customer Parking Area 4:1 Ratio	Circulation, Service, and Planting Area 25%	Total Sq. Ft.	Total Acres Required	Sq. Ft. Per Family (Gross)	Maximum Distance
30,000–32,000 Families 100,000 Persons	20 SF/Family = 200,000 SF	800,000 SF	250,000 SF	1,250,000 SF	30–36 Acres	38–42 SF	One-Mile Walk 30-Minute Drive
75,000–80,000 Families 250,000 Persons	20 SF/Family = 500,000 SF	2,000,000 SF	600,000 SF	3,100,000 SF	50 or more Acres	35–40 SF	1½-Mile Walk 60-Minute Drive

The regional shopping center is much larger than either the neighborhood or community shopping centers. It is a suburban equivalent of the existing downtown shopping center. It will contain, in addition to all the stores normally found in the neighborhood and community centers, at least one major department store. Most planners advocate two department stores, in order to gain the stimulating effect of competition backed up by a wide selection of women's apparel stores. The larger the concentration of such stores, the more business each will do. In a center of limited size it may be advisable to increase the number of these stores at the expense of a more rounded selection such as would normally be advocated. The regional center will provide a wide choice of fashion shopping goods, also home furnishings and household equipment of all types. Women will find here an ample selection. They will spend time making a choice, shopping around, comparing prices, value. The parking turnover will therefore be lower than in either of the other two types of center. Many women will come from comparatively far, though not very often, to do their shopping here.

Such a large center as this, covering an area from 30 to 50 acres, must be placed in a thickly settled suburban area, and be easily accessible by a number of major highways.

COMMERCIAL FACILITIES

A. Shopping Centers**

	Neighborhood Center*	Community Center*	Regional Center*
1. Major function	Sale of convenience goods and personal services	Some functions of the Neighborhood Center plus sale of shopping goods (wearing apparel, appliances, etc.)	Some functions of Community Center plus sale of general merchandise, apparel, furniture, etc.
2. Leading tenants	Super market and drugstore	Variety store and small dept. store	One or more large, major dept. stores
3. Location	Intersection of collector streets a/c secondary roads	Intersections of major roads and/or expressways	Intersections of expressways and/or freeways
4. Radius of service area	½ mile	2 miles	4 miles
5. Min. population to support center	4,000	35,000	150,000
6. Site area (gross land area)	4-8 acres	10–30 acres	40–100 acres and over
7. Desirable maximum size of center as percentage of total area served	1.25% (1 acre/1,000 pop.)	1.00% (0.75 acres/1,000 pop.)	0.50% (0.67 acres/1,000 pop.)
8. Ranges of Gross Floor Area	30,000–75,000 sq. ft.	100,000–250,000 sq. ft.	400,000–1,000,000 sq. ft.
9. Number of stores and shops	5–20	15–40	40–80
10. Parking requirements***	Parking ratio: 4 to 1 (Parking area is four times gross floor area of building; 400 sq. ft. per parking space) 200–600 spaces	1,000–3,000 spaces	4,000 spaces and over

* "A group of commerical establishments, planned, developed, owened, and managed as a unit, with off-street parking provided on the property (in direct ratio to the building area), and related in size (gross floor area) and type of shops to the trade area that the unit serves—generally in an outlying or suburban territory." Definition of the Community Builders Council, ULI.

** The Community Builders Council, ULI offers the following indicators for types and sizes in Shopping Centers (see Community Builders Handbook, Executive Edition, 1960, page 217).

Average Gross Leasable Area	50,000 sq. ft.	150,000 sq. ft.	400,000 sq. ft.
Ranges in GLA	30,000–100,000 sq. ft.	100,000–300,000 sq. ft.	300,000 to over 1,000,000 sq. ft.
Usual Minimum Site Area	4 acres	10 acres	30 acres
Minimum Support	7,500 to 40,000 people	40,000 to 150,000 people	100,000 or more people

*** The CBC recommends a parking ratio of 3 sq. ft. of parking area to 1 square foot of gross floor area be used for planning calculations only. For operations the parking index is more realistic (see Community Builders Handbook, Executive Edition, 1960, pages 300–305).

SOURCE: George Nez, Standards for New Urban Development—The Denver Background, Reprinted by Permission of Urban Land, Vol 20, No 5 Urban Land Institute, 1200 18th Street, N. W., Wash. D. C.

Four density classifications have been selected for the first variable. These are:

  a. Less than 1 d.u. per gross acre (average: 0.5 d.u./acre)
  b. Between 1 and 2.9 d.u. per gross acre (average: 2.0 d.u./acre)
  c. Between 3.0 and 4.9 d.u. per gross acre (average: 3.5 d.u./acre)
  d. Between 5 and 15 d.u. per gross acre (average: 8.0 d.u./acre)

Three distance classifications have been selected for the second variable:

  a. **FRINGE DEVELOPMENT:** development that is contiguous to, and an extension of, an established urban area.

  b. **SEMI-INDEPENDENT DEVELOPMENT:** non-contiguous development some distance from an urban area, but able to be served with public utilities through major extensions of utilities available in central city.

  c. **INDEPENDENT DEVELOPMENT:** Outlying development with own public utilities and some economic base, but within the regional pattern of a large central city.

EFFECTS OF DISTANCE AND DENSITY ON CHARACTERISTICS OF SHOPPING CENTERS

I. DISTANCE FROM A LARGE URBAN AREA	NEIGHBORHOOD SHOPPING CENTER	COMMUNITY SHOPPING CENTER	DISTRICT OR SUB-REGIONAL SHOPPING CENTERS
1. Fringe Development	Characteristics and space requirements unaffected.	Not required for poulations of less than 20,000 unless distance from existing centers is sufficient (over 1½ miles) to warrant the construction of a new community center in anticipation of continuing fringe growth.	Not normally required.
2. Semi-Independent Outlying Development	Characteristics and space requirements unaffected.	Center required capable of serving at least 35,000 persons with service radius of 1½–2 miles. Second center considered when population exceeds 40,000.	District center should be considered if total population potential for the area surrounding the development exceeds 101,000. Second center considered for population of 200,000 or over.
3. Independent Outlying Development	Characteristics and space requirements unaffected.	Center required in practically every case. Standard requirements apply.	Shopping centers, district-wide sub-regional, should be considered for developments with population potential of over 50,000.
II. VARYING DENSITY			
1. Less than 1 d.u. per acre	Larger than standard centers: greater service radius, more parking spaces required.	Standard size and space requirements; smaller percentage of total area; greater service radius (3–4 miles).	Not required.
2. 1-2.9 d.u. per acre	Considerably larger than standard centers, but to lesser degree than the case above.	Standard size and space requirements; greater service radius (2–3 miles).	Marginal conditions for establishment of district center; dependent upon adjacent land uses.
3. 3-4.9 d.u. per acre	Standard requirements.	Standard requirements.	Standard requirements.
4. 5-15 d.u. per acre	Larger than standard center (4–5 percent of total area); less than standard parking requirements. In this density neighborhood shopping centers generally display characteristics of community shopping centers.	Function of community centers served by the larger neighborhood shopping centers.	District centers larger than the standard center: serves populations of 200,000–3,00,000, with radius of 2–3 miles. Standard parking requirements.

Through the entire site planning procedure the architect must remain aware of the architectural expression of the center toward surrounding streets, toward the parking lots and toward pedestrian areas. Site planning must also be directed toward gaining impressive vistas, a well-composed silhouette and well-proportioned spaces between the structures.

Although the schematics on these pages attempt to illustrate the procedure of site planning, they do not aim to give precise information as to the size of each land usage category but rather to illustrate, in a general way, the size of the main planning elements in relation to each other and to show to what degree the planner can adapt a project to the size of the site.

ASSUMPTIONS FOR 3 SCHEMATICS

The schematics are based on the assumption of a regional center with a gross building area (BA) of about 600,000 square feet, of which 500,000 square feet are rental area (RA). Of this rental area a department store occupies 200,000 square feet. The Transportation Area (TA) is shown to be approximately three times the rental area. (Transportation area is understood to be that portion of the site which is necessary for parking, internal traffic roads, bus stations, pick-up stations, taxi stands.) The pedestrian area (SP) is assumed to be slightly less than the rental area on the ground. It consists of malls, courts, sidewalks along the parking side of the stores, and walkways in the parking area. The buffer areas (BUA) surround the parking area.

Case A shows the site needed if all structures are one-story high, without basement, and if all parking is on one level. (SA = BA + SP + TA + BUA). For such an arrangement, a site of approximately 66 acres is necessary.

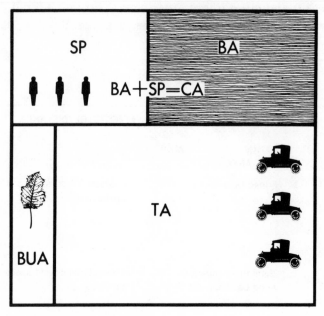

SA = BA + SP + TA + BUA
    BA = Building Area
    SP = Space between Structures
    BA + SP = CA (Shopping Core Area)
    TA = Transportation Area
    BUA = Buffer Area
TA consists of PA (Parking Area)
               MA (Traffic Movement Area)
               PT (Public Transportation Area)
    Assumptions: CA is 1,100,000 sq. ft.
                 TA is RA × 3 (RA is Rental Area)
                     or 1,500,000 sq. ft.*
                 BUA is 250,000 sq. ft.
                 SA (Site Area) is 2,850,000 sq. ft.
                     or approximately 66 acres.

*Alternate method for figuring TA:
500,000 sq. ft. (RA) × 7 cars per 1,000 sq. ft. =
3500 cars × 400 sq. ft. per car = 1,400,000 sq. ft.

SOURCE: Shopping Towns USA, Victor Gruen and Larry Smith, Reinhold Publishing Corp., New York 1965

Case B shows an arrangement in which the department store consists of basement, first floor and second floor. All other stores have basements and first floors. It is assumed that the largest portion of the service area is taken up by service roads. The building arrangement described above has been used in many shopping centers (Northland, Eastland, etc.). For such a building arrangement a site of approximately 55 acres is necessary. (SA = BAG + SP + TA + BUA).

Case C assumes again that one-level parking will prevail but that merchandising generally will be on three levels (similar to Southdale.) Thus all stores would utilize basement, first floor and second floor, while the department store would be arranged on four levels, having a third floor. In this arrangement 48 acres are needed. (SA = BAG + SPG + TA + BUA).

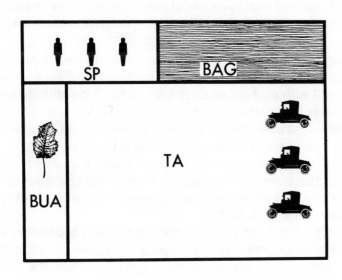

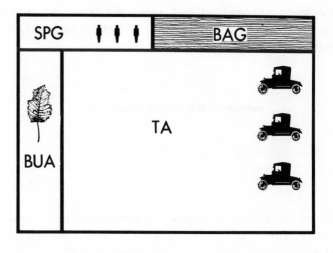

SA = BAG (Building Ground Area) + SP + TA + BUA

    Assumptions: BAG = Department Store + Other Rental + Non-rental Area

$$\frac{3}{}\quad\quad\frac{2}{}$$

On the basis of previous assumption, this results in 66,000 sq. ft. + 200,000 sq. ft. + 50,000 sq. ft. or 316,000 sq. ft.

SP	=	270,000 sq. ft.
TA	=	1,500,000 sq. ft.
BUA	=	250,000 sq. ft.
SA	=	2,336,000 sq. ft.

or approximately 55 acres.

SOURCE: *Shopping Towns USA, Victor Gruen and Larry Smith, Reinhold Publishing Corp., New York*

SA = BAC + SPG + TA + BUA

    Assumptions: BGA = Department Store + Other Rental Area

$$\frac{4}{}\quad\quad\frac{3}{}$$

+ Non-rental Area on Ground Level

On the basis of the earlier assumptions, this is expressed in figures as follows:

BAG = 50,000 + 100,000 + 33,000 sq. ft.

        or   183,000 sq. ft.

SPG	=	150,000 sq. ft.
TA	=	1,500,000 sq. ft.
BUA	=	250,000 sq. ft.
SA	=	2,083,000 sq. ft.

or approximately 48 acres.

━━━━━━━━━━━━━━━━━━━━━━━━━━━

A row of stores along the highway.

■ SHOPS

├─┤ PARKING

Case Study A. The center is comprised of a row of stores, 2,000 feet along the highway. The shopper parks at the curb in front of a store, walks into the store, transacts his business, walks out again, is likely to enter his car and drive off. In this case pedestrian traffic of the second type, shopping traffic, is limited.

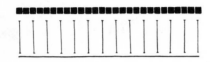

Stores moved back from the highway permit parking in front.

Case Study B. The 2,000-foot-long row of stores is moved back from the highway sufficiently to permit parking in front. Sidewalks, or even covered walkways, encourage foot traffic along the store fronts. This is obviously vastly superior to the first case, as the driver may be converted into a pedestrian some distance away from the entrance door to a specific store, and thus a certain amount of shopping traffic will be created. However, this shopping traffic will still be limited. A distance of 2,000 feet between the extreme ends of the store strip is not conducive to inter-shopping. Having made one purchase the shopper will in many cases return to the car and drive to the store that is next on his list. Besides the disadvantage of the distance between retail units, the sidewalk, which immediately adjoins a parking lot which in turn immediately adjoins a highway, does not represent an attractive walking environment. Even if two powerful magnets, let us say a department store and a junior department store, were to be located at the extreme ends of the 2,000-foot-long shopping strip, the amount of foot traffic generated in the area between them which would require passing intervening stores, would be limited and only a few merchants would benefit.

SOURCE: Shopping Towns USA, Victor Gruen and Larry Smith, Reinhold Publishing Corp., New York

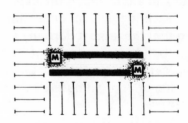

The strip is divided into two rows of stores, opposite each other, along a pedestrian mall with parking on each side. A magnet is placed at each end.

Case Study C. The 2,000-foot store-strip is divided into two halves, creating two 1,000-foot-long strips arranged opposite each other along a pedestrian mall with parking on each side. In this case shopping traffic will be much greater for several reasons:

1. A highly desirable pedestrian area shielded from the noise, smells, confusion and dangers of automobile traffic is created.

2. The two main magnets will be only 1,000 feet apart if placed at extreme ends; therefore the likelihood of interchanging shopping traffic will be much greater and stores located between the two magnets will profit from participation in that traffic.

If, on the other hand, only one main magnet exists and that is located on an extreme end of the mall, then shopping traffic will be reduced because of lack of interchange. Stores furthest removed from the magnet will participate only to a very slight degree in the traffic generated by the main magnet.

Mall center with only one magnet.

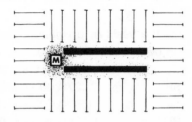

Case Study D. This is a mall arrangement as in Case Study C, but because there is only one main magnet, it is moved to a center position on one side of the mall. Shopping traffic will be improved if compared with Case Study C.

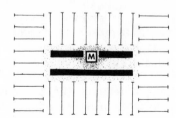

Mall center with magnet centrally placed.

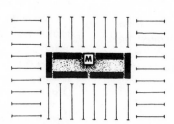

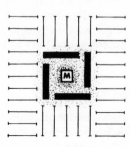

The cluster type arrangement.

■ SHOPS

├──┤ PARKING

Ⓜ MAGNET

░ FOOT TRAFFIC

Case Study E. The major tenant is placed in the center of a cluster arrangement. Nearly all stores thus become neighbors of the most powerful shopping-traffic puller. In contrast to previously discussed cases where all retail units were exposed to parking traffic and shopping traffic, this arrangement exposes the main tenant to shopping traffic only. Because of the superior pulling power of a major department store, this results in no detriment to its business but offers the opportunity of guiding shopping traffic from parking areas along the frontage of other stores toward the center of the cluster.

SOURCE: *Shopping Towns USA, Victor Gruen and Larry Smith, Reinhold Publishing Corp., New York*

Case Study F. This case exemplifies what we will call the introverted center. All store fronts are turned toward the inside of the building cluster. The structures turn their backs to the parking areas and the surrounding roads. Shopping centers following planning principles of this type diminish or completely exclude the possibility of entering individual stores from the parking lot. Shopping traffic is, by plan, funneled through a limited number of entrance arcades into pedestrian areas. Thus density of shopping traffic may be markedly increased and the opportunity to plan its direction and flow increased.

The space for parking customers' cars is a basic requirement in shopping center site planning and development. The layout of the parking space must assist in making the center serve its prime function—that of an attractive and profitable market place. In providing the indispensable parking, the only questions are how much area to provide and how best to arrange the car spaces. The parking spaces so provided are an essential auxiliary to the commercial use and not a commercial use in itself.

1. How Much Parking

From the site area standpoint, parking takes up more area than all other physical features of the shopping center combined. The parking for each project must be given careful consideration.

The number of parking spaces needed for a shopping center depends upon factors affecting the parking demand. These are:

Size and type of center

Composition of the tenancy

Location in relation to customer traffic from public transportation

Character and income level of the trade area

Amount of walk-in trade generated from nearby areas

Local parking habits; rate of turnover in the parking spaces; peak loads encountered

Size and shape of the property

Cost of the land and maintenance costs.

By taking the above factors into consideration, the parking area can be gauged in relation to the need. See the recommended standard that follows.

Two terms are used to describe parking in its relationship to the shopping center structure: the parking ratio and the parking index.

(a) Parking Ratio

Parking ratio is a relationship between the **area** devoted to parking and the **area** devoted to building. This ratio is best expressed in terms of gross floor area.

For **planning purposes** and for **estimating adequacy** of site area, the parking ratio is a useful way to estimate parking area requirements in preliminary site planning.

The ratio, stated as being 2 to 1 or 3 to 1, for example, allows for a preliminary measurement of the site's parking capacity including allocations for the car stalls, the moving aisles, access drives, planting spaces, pedestrian walkways—the appurtenances of parking.

In estimating the site's parking capacity by the ratio method, it is best to allow 400 square feet of area per car. This allowance includes access drives, storage spaces, and incidental areas such as landscape plots and unusable corners.

(The recommended standard of 5.5 spaces per 1,000 sq. ft. of GLA is equivalent to a parking ratio of 2.2 sq. ft. of parking area for one sq. ft. of gross leasable area. In other words, a 2.2 to 1 ratio is more appropriate than a 3 to 1 ratio if the ratio formula is to be used in a zoning ordinance.)

SOURCE: By Permission From *"The Community Builders Handbook"* Prepared by the Executive Group of the Community Builders Council of Urban Land Institute, Edited by J. Ross McKeever, Copyright 1968, Urban Land Institute, 1200 18th Street, Wash. D. C. 20036 526 PP& 20.

(b) Parking Index

The relationship between the number of car parking spaces and the retail space furnishes the index for parking need.

The area in retail selling space varies according to the tenant type; the display of goods; the method of selling; the number, size, and variety of items, etc. For this reason, selling space as a unit against which to make comparisons is too variable for reliable computation. But the gross leasable area, i. e., the total gross floor area within buildings which is occupied exclusively by individual tenants and upon which the tenants pay rent, is measurable. Each tenant's gross leasable area is described in the lease document. Gross leasable area (abbreviated GLA) becomes, then, a known factor for measuring parking spaces in relationship to retail area for statistical analyses.

The type of tenancy has much to do with the number of parking spaces needed—for example a supermarket requires more spaces than does a furniture store. Ordinarily there is overlap and turnover of space from one tenant's use to another.

The parking index is the number of car parking spaces per 1,000 square feet of gross leasable area.

As a unit to indicate the number of parking spaces needed in relation to tenant occupancy, the parking index has the advantage of not requiring adjustments or explanations to show the assignments made for area per car, arrangement of the spaces, provision for car circulation, size and shape of the site, etc.

(c) Recommended Standard

The Community Builders Council in 1949[1] formulated the parking ratio as a basis for parking in relation to shopping center planning. Since then, the number of on-site parking spaces needed to accommodate retail customers and other users of a center's facilities has been a problem with several answers. Shopping center owners have often held one point of view, tenants another, and public officials have had local zoning ordinances incorporate requirements for off-street parking that have proved unrealistic or excessive in actual practice.

For a long time, shopping center owners, lenders, and tenants have been striving to arrive at scientifically determined guidelines that would establish valid yardsticks based on experience at shopping centers serving the public[2] Accordingly, Urban Land Institute conducted a survey of conditions existing in shopping centers. The summary of these findings[3] follows:

1. In operational practice and hence for development planning purposes, where there is virtually no walk-in trade nor public transit usage, the provision of 5.5 car parking spaces per thousand square feet of gross leasable area is adequate as a standard to meet the demand for parking space at shopping centers. This standard accommodates the need for parking spaces at shopping centers for all but the ten highest hours of demand during an entire year. These ten highest hours occur during the three peak days of the year. It is uneconomic to provide parking space for such limited peak demands.

1. *Shopping Centers, An Analysis.* Technical Bulletin 11 (out-of-print), Urban Land Institute.
2. One step toward this yardstick was the formulation of the parking index as the measurement for number of spaces created rather than an area as an evidence for adequacy.
3. See *Parking Requirements for Shopping Centers.* Technical Bulletin 53, Urban Land Institute.

2. Office space usage up to 20% of the gross leasable area can be added to the center's complex without a noticeable increase in the peak parking demand.

3. Where there is a significant volume of walk-in customers or arrivals by means of public transit, or where there are other mitigating circumstances such as a limited trading area of unusual arrays of tenant classifications that have unusually low parking requirements, then the parking space provision cited above can be reduced proportionately.

4. As found in zoning ordinances at present, most of the regulations for shopping center parking call for a substantially greater amount of parking spaces than are found to be necessary in actual practice.

The findings lead to the following general conclusions: off-street parking needs have been overestimated by shopping center developers, lenders, and tenants; similarly, off-street parking requirements being asked for are excessive in many zoning ordinances.

Accordingly, for shopping centers of all sizes it is recommended that a standard of 5.5 parking spaces per thousand square feet of gross leasable area be established generally.[1]

In determining area for parking purposes, 400 square feet should be allotted for each car. This figure includes space assignable to moving lanes, access drives, pedestrian walks, drive-up windows, and grocery loading areas, as well as landscaped areas to be incorporated in the site layout as a part of the circulation and parking for the center.

It is impractical to design the parking provision for the peak load—the Saturday before Christmas, for example. At other times the parking area will have a deserted look. Barren parking lots react on people unfavorably. In addition, an excessive parking space allocation cannot be justified by the economics involved. Variations in shopping hours, types of tenancy and rates of turnover help level peak parking demands.

Parking space demand at a shopping center is tempered by the fact that a shopper buys in several stores while parking his car only once—"one stop shopping," while at a single detached store the parking services only a single transaction. This shopping characteristic differentiates parking space requirements for shopping centers from parking provisions at free-standing, commercial enterprises—a difference not accounted for in most zoning ordinances which set parking for business on a single unit relationship. A large furniture store is an example of a tenant with low parking requirements; a supermarket generates the greatest need for parking space at any location.

Since the area required by a parking space varies with a parking lot's layout, the Community Builders Council uses the parking index, or number of car spaces provided per 1,000 square feet of gross leasable area, rather than the parking ratio which relates the area of the parking space to the building area.

[1] The basic study (*op. cit.*) shows that this standard would satisfy the parking requirements for all shopping periods during a year with the possible exception of ten peak hours or less than one-half of one percent of the total shopping hours during a year. The standard includes parking spaces for employees and incorporates a reserve allocation enabling free traffic movement within the parking area. The calculations assumed 400 square feet per parking space.

SOURCE: By Permission From "The Community Builders Handbook" Prepared by the Executive Group of the Community Builders Council of Urban Land Institute, Edited by J. Ross McKeever, Copyright 1968, Urban Land Institute, 1200 18th Street, Wash. D.C. 20036 526 PP & 20.

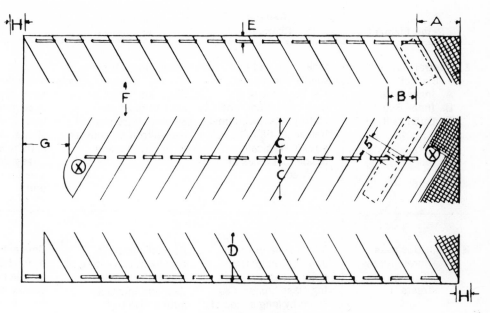

Dimension Table

Dimensions when parking at any of these angles

		45°	50°	55°	60°	90°
Offset	A	18′	15′8″	13′4″	11′	1′6″
Car Space	B	12′	11′4″	10′8″	10′	8′7″
Stall Depth	C	16′	16′8″	17′4″	18′	18′6″
Stall Depth	D	18′	18′4″	18′8″	19′	19′
Overhang	E	2′	2′1″	2′2″	2′3″	2′9″
Driveway	F	13′	14′6″	16′	17′6″	25′
Turnaround	G	17′	16′	15′	14′	14′
Extra	H	6′	5′	4′	3′	0

Parking Lot Layout (Diagram)

The schematic drawing above illustrates 60-degree diagonal parking within an area approximately 100′ × 150′. The table shows the dimensions for 45, 55, 60, and 90-degree parking which are the most used patterns.

To determine the number of cars that can be parked in each of the four banks:

1. Deduct the area lost in parking the first car. (Dimension "A" in the above sketch)
2. Then divide the car space, (dimension "B") into the total length of each bank of cars, plus the extra factor "H", if there is any extra space.

The shaded space may be used for planting. Dotted lines illustrate two large cars in parking position with alternate wheels against block—bumpers separated. Light standards are represented by "X".

Source: BUILDINGS, The Magazine of Building Management.

Retail Element	General Character	Source of Customers	Store Types	Parking	Traffic	Goods Sold
1. Central Business District A. Inner Core B. Inner Belt C. Outer belt	Inner core and belt solidly commercial. The business and recreational heart of metropolitan economy. Residents fill in back streets. Typically, residential areas are blighted.	Come from all parts of city and tributary area. Sites are most accessible to most consumers. Intra-city transportation converges in this element.	Largest in floor space and volume. Multi-story department store is symbolic. Home of leading specialty shops. Outer belt activity less intense. These stores do smaller volume per unit.	Totally inadquate in inner core and belt. Trend to provide public lots and commerical parking lots to supplement limited curb parking in inner belt and outer belt.	Extremely heavy, congested during peak periods.	Shopping and specialty goods emphasis. Area is center of apparel, home furnishings, other department store lines. Service and other commerical activities found in belts.
2. Main Business Thoroughfares ("String streets")	Mixed zone or retail and light industrial enterprises and working class homes. Featured by long series of miscellaneous stores.	Basically trade is transient, consisting of commuters, suburbanites, and inter-city automotive traffic. Some patronage also from neighorhood residents.	Concentration of larger food stores, automobile dealers, and supply houses, service and convenience goods stores.	Usually dependent on curb parking. Inadequate during most periods.	Streets are main traffic arteries. Usually heavy, but particularly so during commuting peaks.	Essentially business streets. Stores are widely spaced over length of artery.
3. Secondary Commercial Sub-districts (un-planned) A. Neighborhood B. Community or District S. Suburban or Outer	More residential than first two elements. Owner occupied residences increase with distance from general business districts. The sub-districts tend to appear, island-like, along string streets.	Come basically from A, B, or C trade areas. The districts developed as city grew at focal points of intra-city transportation. Dependent on traffic brought by public carriers.	Unplanned competition featuring convenience and shopping goods. "B" and "C" tend to be miniatures of central business districts.	Mostly curb, plus some off-street parking provided by individual merchants.	Since stores typically clustered at key intersections and transfer points of public carriers, this traffic is heavy.	Convenience goods featured in "A". Increasing shopping goods emphasis in "B" and "C".

Retail Element	General Character	Source of Customers	Store Types	Parking	Traffic	Goods Sold

3a. Controlled Secondary Sub Centers
  a. Neighborhood
  b. Community or District
  c. Suburban or Outer
	Waste area and marginal stores at a minimum. Found near more prosperous residential areas. Unified architecturally. Most built after World War II. New, fresh appearance compared to 3.	Greater dependence on automotive traffic. Parking provided so customers drawn from greater distances than in case of unplanned centers. generally found in suburban districts.	Balanced collection of supplementary stores possessing aesthetic appeal.
			Centers stress convenience and service, not price appeals.
				Provided on a cooperative basis within the center. Parking and other facilities related in size to surrounding trade area.	Parking for private automobiles key consideration. Even so, peak periods automotive traffic heavy.	Attempt made to present an integrated retail organism to customers coming from a, b, or c distances: a stresses convenience goods; b and c feature shopping and specialty merchandise.

4. Neighborhood Business Streets	Residential with commercial usage distinctly secondary.	Neighborhood is primary source. Most customers come from within walking or five minute driving distance.	Usually rows of convenience goods outlets found in center of neighborhood community.	Mostly curb. Due to convenience goods nature of most items sold, parking turnover is rapid.	Heavy during peak hours. Otherwise not a handicap to trade.	Emphasis on food and drugs. Grocery store-drug combination frequent. Service stores common.
5. Small Clusters and Scattered Individual Stores	More thinly populated residential areas. Neighborhoods served tend to be middle class.	Come from homes not within easy reach of larger elements in structure. Many walk to stores.	Smallest outlets in structure. Many are marginal. This classification dominated by food and general stores.	Curb and small lot parking usually adequate.	Usually not a problem. The lack of traffic congestion, plus the availability of parking, represents an appeal of this element to customers beyond their normal range.	Usually supplementary and not directly competitive.
6. Controlled Regional Shopping Centers	Overall unity obvious at a glance. Landscaped frequently. Off-street parking. Harmonious effect is objective. May be equipped to serve as area's civic and cultural center.	Draw from families within 30 minute driving range. Customers typically come from a number of suburban communities. Pull varies with effectiveness of central business district retailers and competing centers.	Attempt made to duplicate shopping facilities of central business district with minimum of overlapping. "One stop shopping in the suburbs."	Usually best facilities in metropolitan area. Adequate for all but occasional peak periods.	Problem usually under control as a result of co-ordinated planning.	One or two department store branches and satellite stores offer widest range of merchandise and services outside central business district.

SOURCE: Eugene J. Kelley, Shopping Centers, Tne ENO Foundation for Highway Traffic Control, Saugatuck, Conn.—1956

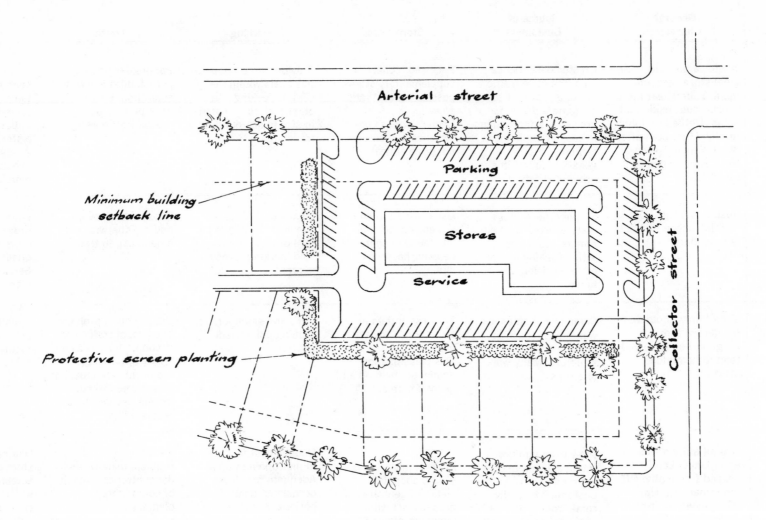

The location of the neighborhood shopping center is generally located on the arterial street at the intersection of a collector street. Adequate parking in relationship to number of stores must be provided. The houses adjacent to the shopping center must be properly protected with planting or fences.

SOURCE: Land Subdivision Regulations, Housing and Home Finance Agency, Washington, D. C.

INDUSTRIAL DEVELOPMENT AND ECONOMIC BASE

1. Basic Relationships:
    (a) Working Force as a percent of total population.   35–40%
    (b) Workers in industrial areas as percentage of total Working Force.   30–35%
    (c) Workers in Heavy Industry as percentage of workers in industrial areas.   60–70%
    (d) Workers in Light Industry as percentage of workers in industrial areas.   30–40%
    (e) Workers in basic industry (manufacture of goods for export from area) as percentage of theoretical community size.   10%

2. Worker-Area Ratios:

Average Number of Workers Per Gross Acre of Industrial Land

	Heavy Industry	Light Industry	Industrial Park
Present Ratios	8	28	18
Expected Future Ratios	6	22	16

3. Land Requirement of Industry:
    (a) Total Gross Land requirement for all Industry.   12 acres/1,000 popluation
    (b) Land requirements for Light Industry.   2 acres/1,000 population
    (c) Land requirements for Heavy Industry.   10 acres/1,000 population
    (d) Land requirements for pre-planned industrial complex (Industrial Park):*
         Minimum   320 acres
         Ideal   640 acres
    (e) Requirements for industrial land reserve:
         reserve land for minimum of 50 years future growth

4. General Requirements for Industrial Location:
    (a) Fast, easy and convenient access to good tratransportation facilities including rail, highway and air.
    (b) Reasonable location with respect to labor supply, raw materials source and markets.
    (c) An adequate amount of suitable land, free from foundation and drainage problems with a sufficient reserve for future growth.
    (d) An adequate and reliable supply of utilities: water, waste disposal, power and fuel.
    (e) Protection from encroachment of residential or other land uses.
    (f) Location so as to minimize obnoxious external effects on neighboring non-industrial land uses.

SOURCE: George Nez, Standards for New Urban Development—The Denver Background,
Reprinted by Permission of Urban Land, Vol 20, No 5 Urban Land Institute, 1200 18th Street, N. W., Wash., D. C.

PURPOSE OF THE CLASSIFICATION

The Standard Industrial Classification was developed for use in the classification of establishments by type of activity in which engaged; for purposes of facilitating the collection, tabulation, presentation, and analysis of data relating to establishments; and for promoting uniformity and comparability in the presentation of statistical data collected by various agencies of the United States Government, State agencies, trade associations, and private research organizations.

SCOPE OF THE CLASSIFICATION

The Classification is intended to cover the entire field of economic activities: agriculture, forestry, and fisheries; mining; construction; manufacturing; transportation, communication, electric, gas, and sanitary services; wholesale and retail trade; finance, insurance, and real estate; services; and government.

PRINCIPLES OF THE CLASSIFICATION

The Classification was prepared by the Technical Committee on Standard Industrial Classification.

In preparing the Classification, the Technical Committee was guided by the following general principles:

1. The Classification should conform to the existing structure of American industry.

2. The reporting units to be classified are establishments, rather than legal entities or companies.

3. Each establishment is to be classified according to its major activity.

4. To be recognized as an industry, each group of establishments must have significance from the standpoint of the number of persons employed, volume of business, and other important economic features, such as the number of establishments.

BASIS OF ESTABLISHMENT CLASSIFICATION-CODE ASSIGNMENT

Each establishment is assigned an industry code on the basis of its major activity, which is determined by the product or group of products produced or handled, or services rendered. Ideally, the principal product or service should be determined by reference to "value added." In practice, however, it is rarely possible to obtain this information for individual products or services, and it becomes necessary to adopt some other criteria which may be expected to give approximately the same results. It is recommended, therefore, that, as far as possible, the following characteristics be used for each of the major economic sections:

Economic Section	Characteristics
Agriculture, forestry, and fisheries (except agricultural services)	Value of production
Mining	Value of production
Construction	Value of work done
Manufacturing	Value of production
Wholesale and retail trade	Value of sales
Finance, insurance, and real estate	Value of receipts
Services (including agricultural services)	Value of receipts
Transportation, communication, electric, gas, and sanitary services	Value of receipts
Government	Function

Occasionally, in cases of mixed business, the above characteristics cannot be determined or estimated for each product or service, and less frequently a classification based upon the recommended characteristic will not represent adequately the process or activity of the establishment. In such cases, if employment information is available, the major activity should be determined by the activity in which the greatest number of employees worked.

SOURCE: The Standard Industrial Classification, Executive Office of the President, Bureau of the Budget

STRUCTURE OF CLASSIFICATION

The structure of the Classification makes it possible to classify establishments by industry on a two-digit, a three-digit, or a four-digit basis, according to the degree of detail in information which may be needed. It permits an agency to select the level of detail considered most appropriate for presentation of its data. Also, it permits an agency to use additional subdivisions in adopting this Classification for its own use, while still retaining comparability with the classifications used by other agencies. Furthermore, comparability with the Classification may be maintained on a two-digit basis by combining groups or industries within a Major Group; similarly, comparability may be maintained on a three-digit basis by combining industries within a three-digit group.

DEFINITION OF ESTABLISHMENT

The Standard Industrial Classification distinguishes two broad classes of establishments: (1) "operating establishments" or economic units which produce goods or services; and (2) central administrative office and auxiliary units which manage or provide services for other establishments of the same company.

Operating Establishments.—An "operating establishment" is an economic unit which produces goods or services—for example, a farm, a mine, a factory, a store. In most instances, the establishment is at a single physical location; and it is engaged in only one, or predominantly one, type of economic activity for which an industry code is applicable.

Where a single physical location encompasses two or more distinct and separate economic activities for which different industrial classification codes seem applicable, such activities should be treated as separate establishments and classified in separate industries, provided it is determined that: (1) such activities are not ordinarily associated with one another at common physical locations; (2) no one industry description in the Standard Industrial Classification includes such combined activities; (3) the employment in each such economic activity is significant; and (4) reports can be prepared on the number of employees, their wages and salaries, and other establishment type data. An establishment is not necessarily identical with the business concern or firm, which may consist of one or more establishments. Also, it is to be distinguished from organizational subunits, departments, or divisions within an establishment. Supplemental interpretations of the definition of an establishment are included in the industry descriptions of the Standard Industrial Classification.

Central Offices and Auxiliary Units.—A central administrative office is an establishment primarily engaged in management and general administrative functions performed centrally for other establishments of the same company.

An auxiliary unit is an establishment primarily engaged in performing supporting services for other establishments of the same company rather than for the general public or for other business firms.

Activities of the type performed at separate central administrative office and auxiliary establishments are, in fact, normally carried on as an integral part of individual operating establishments. Hence, this type of activity is only partially measured by the statistics on separately reported central administrative office and auxiliary establishments.

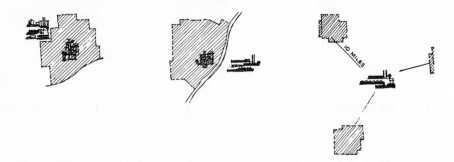

Three locations: peripheral, central and rural locations

A peripheral location outside city limits is characteristic, especially where transportation is paramount, but it must be within the urban distribution area. This means:

Containment within central express and pickup districts where rates are lowest. (In Chicago this zone extends 18 mi. beyond the city.) A powerful district may itself cause extension of low rates.

Containment within the local switching district of at least one railroad, and preferably in a terminal district so freight rates will not exceed adjoining metropolitan areas, especially in handling less-than-carload lots, which are highly important to small plants, and service may be better. In a big city where there is a terminal railroad its line may be preferable to a trunk line as a site because it will save some 24 hours on each interchange.

Situation on a good highway close enough to town so less-than-truckload quantities can be organized.

Lower land costs for today's one-story spread-out plants favor the peripheral location.

Labor must likewise be available, at distances that require no excessive travel time.

A central location may be preferable for the class of industry that may be called market- or contact-dominated. Example, a type of medium-sized plant whose salesmen have to keep running back and forth from the plant to clients' purchasing offices and would not easily be talked into moving to a suburban location.

Atop high land prices the city center usually offers difficulties of assembly short of condemnation under the federal redevelopment title; atop that, difficulties are increasingly imposed through requirements of off-street parking and loading.

Rural locations are still more exceptional. Plants that need to be close to raw materials, low-cost electric power or bodies of water may locate in rural areas.

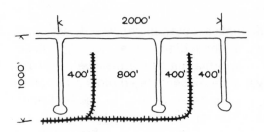

Interlaced, railway and auto transportation systems avoid crossings. Rail lead can be located off center to give any variation in depth of lots which may be desired by prospect.

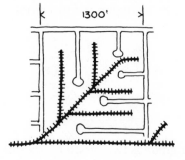

Diagonal rail lead interlaced with roads offers greater choice of lot shapes and sizes than in system illustrated (above). Diagonal system has further advantage of requiring less space for track to become parallel to buildings.

Minimum size for a profitable operation is not less than 80 acres; the maximum depends on the size of the individual plants, with 150 acres the preferred top limit where plants average 50,000 sq. ft., but more land where plants are bigger.

Size of lots depends on plant sizes, land coverage (anywhere from 30% to 60% as a maximum, the latter more typical) and distance from street to railroad siding (at least 200' and seldom over 500'). Lot sizes and shapes are more easily varied where railroads come in at the diagonal.

Expansion can be handled by requiring each tenant to rent a certain amount of expansion land (few tenants foresee their need) or options may be given, say for two years, on adjacent lots.

SOURCE: Reprinted from the Architectural Forum, April—1954. Copyright by Urban America, Inc.

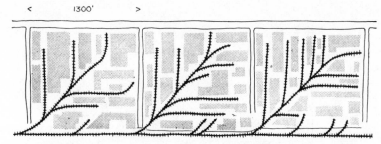

Rail-dominated district, such as early Clearing Industrial District (p. 114), has large plants, high densities, frequently uses more than one spur track per plant and makes relatively little provision for trucking as part of industrial process.

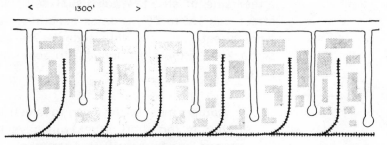

Balanced transportation is provided in practically all new districts. Plants in general cover less area and use both trucks and railway cars. Flow is not always from railway to truck but may be reversed or mixed.

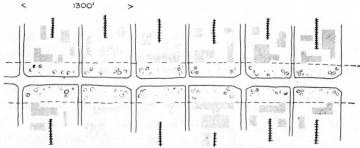

Auto-dominated district has some industries, such as research laboratories, which could very well get along without railroad. Employees' parking is the dominant factor, although trucks and railways are necessary for some of the industries in an ''Industrial Park.''

A basic problem of the district is to avoid rail and road interference. Ideally, the rail leads and the dead-end access streets come in from the main lines at opposite sides like interlacing fingers, avoiding crossings (middle sketch). In a diagonal scheme the rails lie in a tree pattern diagonal to the lot, and access streets are fed in from around the periphery, again interlacing without crossings.

The typical block may have rails coming in at a diagonal to the buildings (see uppermost of the three sketches). The ¼-mi. square block served by a diagonal railroad lead with branches is particularly suitable to districts where rail traffic is to be dominant. Within this ¼-mi. block it is possible to get an almost infinite variety of side-track layouts and shapes and sizes of lots.

An alternate is a series of blocks with railroad spurs coming in at right angles between the access roads, the way an alley runs up the middle of an ordinary city block (middle sketch).

This type of plan leads to an orderly looking community but it is neither so flexible nor so economic in its use of land in relation to the railraod as the diagonal type.

Water is no longer important except in unusual cases; truck transportation is universal, and virtually all districts also use rails. Opinions vary as to the relative advantage of having a district served by one railroad or two, since a single line may be expected to do more to promote the district but two lines may compete giving more attentive service.

SOURCE: Reprinted from the Architectural Forum, April—1954. Copyright by Urban America, Inc.

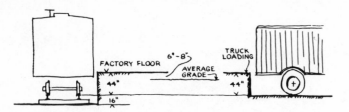

Depressed tracks and loading area bring floors of vehicles level with factory floor. It costs less usually to lay plant floor on grade and excavate tracks and trucks than to raise floor. In most districts railway leads and side tracks are depressed throughout entire district. In early districts only truck-loading areas were below grade. Some recent districts have entire street systems about 3' below grade.

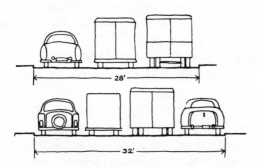

Paving width should be 28' or 32' wide. Paving 30' wide has been extensively used but is wider than needed for three vehicles, not wide enough for four. Major streets are now being laid out with 40' paving needed for four lanes if traffic is to be kept moving while cars are parking on one side of street.

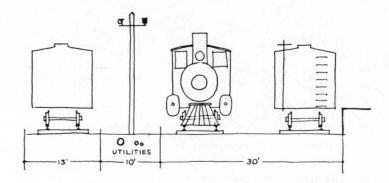

Utility strip alongside railway lead and side tracks is preferred to utilities in parking area on either side of street. When usual setback from street was 15' to 25', utilities generally came in from street side, but with today's 75' to 100' setbacks it is more economical to come in from rear.

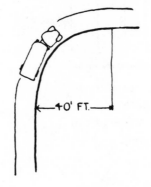

Corners must be designed to take trucks. If radius is too short, truck will have to use second lane to make turn. Throughout Southwest where combinations of tractor, semi-trailer and four-wheel trailer are used, it is desirable to use still longer radius.

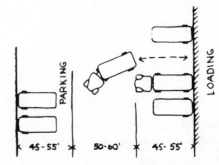

Plenty of truck space is needed for loading, parking and maneuvering. It is better to overdesign than skimp on space as time costs more than space. Warehousing is becoming increasingly important to industrial districts. Half the Clearing District's current construction is for warehouses. Photo shows truck terminals.

1. NOISE

A "decibel" is a unit of measurement of the intensity of sound (the sound pressure level).

A "sound level meter" is an instrument standardized by the American Standards Association, which is used for measurement of the intensity of sound and is calibrated in decibels.

An "octave band" is one of a series of eight bands which cover the normal range of frequencies included in sound measurements. Such octave bands serve to define the sound in term of its pitch components.

An "octave band analyzer" is an instrument used in conjunction with a sound level meter to measure sound in each of eight octave bands.

An "impact noise analyzer" is an instrument used in conjunction with the sound level meter to measure the peak intensities of short duration sounds

METHOD OF MEASUREMENT

For the purpose of measuring the intensity or frequency of sound, the sound level meter, the octave band analyzer, and the impact noise analyzer shall be employed.

The "C" network and the "slow" meter response of the sound level meter shall be used. Sounds of short duration, as from forge hammers, punch presses, and metal shears, which cannot be measured accurately with the sound level meter, shall be measured with the impact noise analyzer as manufactured by the General Radio Company, or its equivalent, in order to determine the peak value of the impact.

MAXIMUM PERMITTED DECIBEL LEVELS

The sound pressure level resulting from any activity, whether open or enclosed, shall not exceed, at any point on or beyond any lot line, the maximum permitted decibel levels for the octave band as set forth in the following table.

MAXIMUM PERMITTED SOUND PRESSURE LEVEL
(in decibels)

Octave band (cycles per second)	
20 to 75	79
75 to 150	74
150 to 300	66
300 to 600	59
600 to 1,200	53
1,200 to 2,400	47
2,400 to 4,800	41
Above 4,800	39

SOURCE: *Adapted from New York City Zoning Ordinance—1961*

2. VIBRATION

"Steady state vibrations" are earth-borne oscillations that are continuous. Discrete pulses that occur more frequently than 100 times per minute shall be considered to be steady state vibrations.

"Impact vibrations" are earth-borne oscillations occurring in discrete pulses at or less than 100 pulses per minute.

A "frequency" is the number of oscillations per second of a vibration.

A "three-component measuring system" is a device for recording the intensity of any vibration in three mutually perpendicular directions.

MAXIMUM PERMITTED STEADY STATE VIBRATION DISPLACEMENT

No activity shall cause or create a steady state vibration at any point on any lot line, with a displacement in excess of the permitted steady state vibration displacement for the frequencies as set forth in the following table.

MAXIMUM PERMITTED IMPACT VIBRATION DISPLACEMENT

No activity shall cause or create an impact vibration, at any point on any lot line, with a displacement in excess of the permitted impact vibration displacement for the frequencies as set forth in the following table.

MAXIMUM PERMITTED STEADY STATE VIBRATION DISPLACEMENT
(in inches)

Frequency (cycles per second)	
10 and below	.0008
10–20	.0005
20–30	.0003
30–40	.0002
40–50	.0001
50–60	.0001
60 and over	.0001

MAXIMUM PERMITTED IMPACT VIBRATION DISPLACEMENT
(in inches)

Frequency (cycles per second)	M1
10 and below	.0016
10–20	.0010
20–30	.0006
30–40	.0004
40–50	.0002
50–60	.0002
60 and over	.0002

3. SMOKE, DUST, AND OTHER PARTICULATE MATTER

"Particulate matter" is any finely divided liquid or solid matter capable of being air- or gas-borne.

"Dust" is solid particulate matter capable of being air- or gas-borne.

"Process weight" is the total weight of all materials used in any process which discharges dust into the atmosphere. Such materials shall include solid fuels, but not liquid or gaseous fuels or combustion air.

"Combustion for indirect heating" is the burning of fuel in equipment, such as steam boilers, water or air heaters, stills, or brew kettles, where there is no contact between the products of combustion and the materials being heated.

"Standard Smoke Chart numbers" are the numbers on the Standard Smoke Chart indicating graduations of light-obscuring capacity of smoke.

"Smoke" is any visible emission into the open air from any source, except emissions of an uncontaminated water vapor.

A "smoke unit" is a measure of the quantity of smoke being discharged and is the number obtained by multiplying the smoke density in a Standard Smoke Chart number by the time of emission in minutes. For example, the emission of Standard Smoke Chart number 1 for one minute equals one smoke unit.

MAXIMUM PERMITTED EMISSION OF SMOKE

The density of emission of smoke during normal operations shall not exceed Standard Smoke Chart number 2, and the quantity of smoke shall not exceed a maximum of 10 smoke units per hour per stack.

MAXIMUM PERMITTED EMISSION OF DUST

a. RELATED TO COMBUSTION FOR INDIRECT HEATING

The emission into the atmosphere of dust related to combustion for indirect heating from any source shall not exceed the maximum number of pounds of dust per million British thermal units heat input per hour as set forth herein:

The maximum permitted emission shall be 0.50 pounds per minimum-size plants producing a heat input of 10 million or less British thermal units per hour and 0.15 for maximum-size plants producing a heat input of 10,000 million or more British thermal units per hour. All intermediate values shall be determined from a straight line plotted on log graph paper.

b. RELATED TO PROCESSES

The emission into the atmosphere of process dust or other particulate matter which is unrelated to combustion for indirect heating or incineration shall not exceed 0.50 pounds per hour for 100 pounds of process weight or 50 pounds per hour for 100,000 pounds of process weight. All intermediate values shall be determined from a straight line plotted on log graph paper.

4. ODOROUS MATTER

The emission of odorous matter in such quantities as to be readily detectable at any point along lot lines or to produce a public nuisance or hazard beyond lot lines is prohibited.

5. TOXIC OR NOXIOUS MATTER

"Toxic or noxious matter" is any solid, liquid, or gaseous matter, including but not limited to gases, vapors, dusts, fumes, and mists, containing properties which by chemical means are:

a. Inherently harmful and likely to destroy life or impair health, or

b. Capable of causing injury to the well-being of persons or damage to property.

REGULATION OF TOXIC OR NOXIOUS MATTER

The emission of such matter shall be so controlled that no concentration at or beyond lot lines shall be detrimental to or endanger the public health, safety, comfort, and other aspects of the general welfare, or cause damage or injury to property.

6. RADIATION HAZARDS

"Fireproof containers" shall include steel or concrete containers and shall not include lead or other low-melting metals or alloys, unless the lead or low-melting metal or alloys are completely encased in steel.

MAXIMUM PERMITTED QUANTITIES OF UNSEALED RADIOACTIVE MATERIAL

Unsealed radioactive materials shall not be manufactured, utilized, or stored (unless such materials are stored in a fireproof container at or below ground level) in excess of one million times the quantities set forth in Column 1 of the table in Section 38-2 of the Industrial Code Rule No. 38, relating to Radiation Protection of the New York State Department of Labor.

SOURCE: ADAPTED FROM New York City Zoning Ordinance—1961

MAXIMUM PERMITTED QUANTITIES OF FISSIONABLE MATERIALS

No one of the following fissionable materials shall be assembled at any one point, place, or work area on a zoning lot in a quantity equal to or in excess of the amount set forth herein:

Material	Quantity
Uranium-233	200 grams
Plutonium-239	200 grams
Uranium-235	350 grams

7. FIRE AND EXPLOSIVE HAZARDS

"Slow burning" materials are materials which will not ignite or actively support combustion during an exposure for 5 minutes to a temperature of 1,200°F. and which, therefore, do not constitute an active fuel.

MODERATE BURNING

"Moderate burning" materials are materials which in themselves burn moderately and may contain small quantities of a higher grade of combustibility.

FREE BURNING

"Free burning" materials are materials constituting an active fuel.

INTENSE BURNING

"Intense burning" materials are materials which by virtue of low ignition temperature, high rate of burning, and large heat evolution burn with great intensity.

FLAMMABLE OR EXPLOSIVE

"Flammable or explosive" materials are materials which produce flammable or explosive vapors or gases under ordinary weather temperature including liquids with an open cup flash point of less than 100°F.

The "open cup flash point" is the temperature at which a liquid sample produces sufficient vapor to flash but not ignite when in contact with a flame in a Tagliabue open cup tester.

ORIGINAL SEALED CONTAINERS

"Original sealed containers" are containers with a capacity of not more than 55 gallons.

CLASSIFICATIONS

Materials are divided into four classifications or ratings based on the degree of fire and explosive hazard. The rating of liquids is established by specified open cup flash points.

a. Class I includes slow burning to moderate burning materials. This shall include all liquids with an open cup flash point of 182°F. or more.

b. Class II includes free burning to intense burning materials. This shall include all liquids with an open cup flash point between 100°F. and 182°F.

c. Class III includes materials which produce flammable or explosive vapors or gases under ordinary weather temperature. This shall include all liquids with an open cup flash point of less than 100°F.

d. Class IV includes materials which decompose by detonation, including but not limited to all primary explosives.

REGULATIONS APPLYING TO CLASS I MATERIALS OR PRODUCTS

Class I materials or products may be stored, manufactured, or utilized in manufacturing processes or other production.

REGULATIONS APPLYING TO CLASS II AND CLASS III MATERIALS OR PRODUCTS

Class II materials or products may be stored, manufactured, or utilized in manufacturing processes or other production only in accordance with the following provisions:

1. Such storage, manufacture or utilization shall be carried on only within buildings or other structures which are completely enclosed by incombustible exterior walls;

2. Such buildings or other structures shall either be set back at least 40 feet from any lot lines, or in lieu thereof, all such buildings shall be protected throughout by an automatic fire extinguishing system.

8. HUMIDITY, HEAT, OR GLARE

Any activity producing excessive humidity in the form of steam or moist air, or producing intense heat or glare, shall be carried out within an enclosure and in such a manner as not to be perceptible at or beyond any lot line.

SUBDIVISION

Size and location requirements of individual industries vary widely. The areas of the Park, should be subdivided into parcels averaging ten acres each. This size parcel permits initial construction of 200-foot by 200-foot buildings, covering about ten percent of the area (40,000 square feet) with allowance for ultimate expansion of two to three times the initial construction. Depending on the specific needs of industries desiring to locate here, the parcels may be further subdivided or combined. Such modifications, if executed with care, will not adversely affect the overall master plan. A minimum parcel size of not less than two acres should be established.

The following site standards have been established and must be adhered to by all industries locating in the Industrial Park.

- Minimum land-to-building ratio of 4:1.
- Minimum building setback of 50 feet from main roads. Such setback areas must be appropriately landscaped.
- Minimum side lot setback of 50 feet. Such side lot areas may be devoted to paved parking.
- A 200-foot buffer strip is required by zoning regulations and must be maintained. It serves to protect the character of the park.
- All parking must be to the rear or side of buildings.
- All parking lots must be paved.
- No truck loading docks or doors are permitted on the front of buildings. Such docks or doors shall be located at sides or rears of buildings. This requirement also applies to rail siding facilities.

The following provisions relative to types of industry and architecture must be met.

- Plans of all proposed buildings must be submitted for approval prior to the start of construction.
- Building exteriors on all four sides shall be constructed of materials considered first class exterior finishes. In the case of expansion walls only, concrete blocks will be allowed as the finish of the exterior wall. Stucco is not considered a first class finish.
- All buildings must have a sprinkler system for fire protection.
- Outside storage must be appropriately screened on all sides.

CRITERIA FOR SIDETRACK SERVICE

The standards presented below relative to track layout, clearances, grade crossings and grade crossing protection, are based on requirements of the New Haven Railroad and the standards for highway grade crossings are based on the Commonwealth of Massachusetts requirements. These standards are as follows:

- No. 10 connections off the main track.
- No. 8 connections off switching tracks.
- Minimum track centers—13 feet.
- Maximum curvature—19 degrees (i.e. minimum radius—300 feet).
- Maximum grade—1.5 percent.

The railroad has in certain instances relaxed its requirements for curvature and grade. This should be discussed in detail prior to entering into any agreements.

INTERIOR ROADS

To insure smooth flow of traffic and easy access to individual plants by truck and trailers, minimum interior roads should have 100-foot right-of-way and 40-foot pavements. Any turn-arounds should have a minimum 60-foot radius.

COMMERCIAL SERVICES

Dependent upon size of the park, commercial facilities may be provided to serve the employees and visitors. Such facilities may include a branch bank, restaurant, stores of various types, small office building, and a motel.

UTILITIES

Adequate provisions for present and future requirements of water supply, sanitary sewers, storm sewers, electric and gas lines must be provided.

SOURCE: ARA Casebook No. 12, Area Redevelopment Agency, U. S. Dept of Commerce—1965

Local expenditures in the fiscal year ending June 30, 1965 amounted to $55.9 billion and accounted for 27% of the expenditure of all governments in the United States.

Elementary and high school education—the most important local governmental function—accounted for 41% of total local expenditure. The remainder was parceled out among more than 25 functions and subfunctions (according to the classification of the U. S. Bureau of the Census), none of which accounted for more than 8% of total expenditures. These functions constitute the diverse services provided by municipalities, townships, counties, and special districts; they include such basic services as, for example, police and fire protection, welfare, sanitation, highways, and recreation.

1. MAJOR LOCAL FUNCTIONS

a. SCHOOLS

Elementary and high school expenditures are the single most important item in local budgets—particularly in the suburbs, where the school population is on the average 10% to 20% higher than in central cities.

b. MUNICIPAL FUNCTIONS

Municipal functions consist of such services as garbage removal, traffic control, fire protection, and others directly concerned with the conditions of health and safety maintained by a community for its residents, workers, and businessmen. They are the responsibility of local units of governments, mainly of cities and towns.

c. AREA FUNCTIONS

Area functions represent those activities of local governments which, in addition to their value to the community, have widespread effects on the surrounding communities. Transportation is the prime example. The highways and rapid transit facilities developed by an area will affect the growth pattern of the entire surroundings; airports and water terminals may be of importance to centers of population several thousand miles away. Other area functions range from welfare and hospitals to higher education and libraries.

d. "Overhead" expenditures such as administration, interest, and employee-retirement expenses, a heterogeneous group of expenditures that are part of the general "cost of doing business" for nearly all governments.

PER CAPITA LOCAL DIRECT EXPENDITURES, BY FUNCTION, FISCAL 1965

	Fiscal 1965		Fiscal 1970	
	$ Per Capita	Per Cent of Total	Per Cent of Total	Real Growth Rate 1965–70
Local schools	114.46	41.7	39.6	1.8
Municipal functions	48.89	17.8	17.7	2.2
Sanitation	12.17	4.4	4.9	3.4
Water supply (utility)	12.92	4.7	4.2	1.9
Police	11.36	4.1	4.1	1.1
Fire	6.74	2.5	2.2	1.1
Local parks	5.70	2.1	2.3	3.2
Area functions	85.68	31.2	33.3	3.5
Transportation	29.83	10.9	9.4	0.0
Highways	20.67	7.5	6.1	−0.7
Transit (utility)	5.81	2.1	2.1	2.7
Other transportation	3.35	1.2	1.1	0.3
Public welfare	17.10	6.2	6.5	3.8
Cash	9.75	3.6	2.7	0.0
Other than cash	7.35	2.7	3.8	9.4
Hospitals and health	13.73	5.0	4.7	1.6
Hospitals	11.39	4.1	4.0	1.9
Health	2.33	0.8	0.7	−0.5
Urban renewal	6.30	2.3	3.0	6.8
Other and unallocable	18.72	6.8	9.6	7.7
Higher education	3.12	1.1	1.8	8.8
Other and unallocable	15.60	5.7	7.8	7.5
"Overhead"	25.53	9.3	9.3	2.7
Administration	9.42	3.4	3.0	0.2
Interest	8.61	3.1	3.8	5.0
Insurance trust	4.02	1.5	1.7	4.2
Public buildings	3.48	1.3	0.9	0.2
Total direct expenditures	274.56	100.0	100.0	2.5

Sources: U. S. Bureau of the Census, Governmental Finances in 1964–65, U. S. Government Printing Office, Washington, D. C., 1966; The Conference Board.

SOURCE: Juan De Torres, Financing Local Government, Studies in Business Economics, No. 96, The National Industrial Conference Board, New York—1967

COMPOSITION OF LOCAL GOVERNMENT REVENUES AND EXPENDITURES
1902 1965

Growth of Local Government Expenditures and Revenues, Fiscal 1902–1965

	Fiscal 1902 ($ Billions)	Fiscal 1927 ($ Billions)	Fiscal 1948 ($ Billions)	Fiscal 1965 ($ Billions)	Average Annual Growth Rate 1902–27 (Per cent)	Average Annual Growth Rate 1948–65 (Per cent)
Total Expenditures	$ 1.0	$ 6.3	$ 12.9	$ 53.6	7.8%	8.8%
Total Revenues	0.9	6.2	12.6	51.7	8.0	8.6
State and Federal Aid	0.1	0.6	3.5	15.2	10.0	9.0
Revenue from Own Sources	0.9	5.6	9.1	36.4	7.8	8.5
Service Charges	0.1	1.1	2.3	10.0	8.3	9.0
Tax Revenue	0.7	4.5	6.6	25.5	7.7	8.3
Property	0.6	4.4	5.9	22.2	8.1	8.1
Sales	—	*	0.4	2.1	—	10.1
Income	—	—	*	0.4	—	14.4
Other	0.1	0.1	0.3	0.8	0.6	5.9
Addendum:						
Gross National Product	21.6	96.3	244.4	653.9	6.2	6.0
Personal Disposable Income	15.0[a]	72.6[a]	178.8	450.5	6.3[a]	5.5

* Less than $0.05 billion.
[a] Personal consumption expenditure (PDI not available for year prior to 1929).
Note: All data exclude gas and electric utilities. Components may not add up to totals or subtotals because of rounding.
Sources: U.S. Bureau of the Census, Governmental Finances in 1964–1965; U.S. Bureau of the Census, Census of Governments: 1962, Vol. VI, No. 4, Historical Statistics on Governmental Finances and Employment; U.S. Department of Commerce, Survey of Current Business, August, 1965 and July, 1966; John W. Kendrick, Productivity Trends in the United States.

During the postwar period, total revenues of local governments grew nearly as rapidly as total expenditures; local revenues (excluding gas and electric utilities) rose at an average annual rate of 8.6% during fiscal 1948-1965, from $12.6 billion to $51.7 billion. (During fiscal 1902-1927, they had risen at an average annual rate of 8.0%—slightly faster than local expenditures—from $0.9 billion to $6.2 billion.) While revenues remained below expenditures during every fiscal year since 1948, the over-all "revenue gap" widened only moderately despite the very rapid postwar increase in local spending. This gap rose from about $0.3 billion in fiscal 1948 to $1.9 billion in fiscal 1965, necessitating continuous, but manageable annual increases in local borrowing. Thus, at first glance, the financial problems of the local governments do not appear to have been too serious.

Yet the comparison of total local revenues and expenditures does not properly reveal the true dimensions of the financial difficulties of many local communities for two reasons: (1) Total local revenues include a sizable

and rapidly growing amount of state and Federal aid, a component that is almost completely outside the control of the local government units, and (2) any "global" comparison masks the diversity of local experiences. Among these, there are at least two special problem areas that deserve separate consideration: (a) "unbalanced" communities and (b) large metropolitan cities (see Section C below).

a. GRANTS-IN-AID

Combined state and Federal aid to local governments has risen much faster than either local taxes or other local revenues. During fiscal 1948-1965, total grants-in-aid increased at an average annual rate of 9.0% (from $3.5 billion to $15.2 billion), whereas local revenues from own sources rose at an average annual rate of only 8.5% (from $9.1 billion to $36.4 billion).

SOURCE: Juan De Torres, Financing Local Government, Studies in Business Economics, No. 96, The Conference Board, New York—1967

Table III-2: Real Estate Assessement Ratios in Ten Largest States, Fiscal
1961[a]
(Per Cent of Market Value)

	Nonfarm Residential			Commercial and Industrial	Acreage and Farm	Vacant Lots
	Statewide Average	High[1]	Low[1]			
California	19.7	24.7	11.8	16.5	11.0	14.0
New York	42.8	65.4	14.0	55.1	31.0	28.0
Pennsylvania	33.8	59.4	17.1	34.7	18.2	20.4
Illinois	43.1	55.1	35.5	55.1	35.7	32.1
Ohio	37.8	45.7	29.8	23.5	23.6	22.8
Texas	19.4	29.7	8.8	17.2	8.6	12.4
Michigan	33.4	47.2	17.2	28.8	27.3	30.6
New Jersey	27.7	44.6	17.0	37.1	13.5	18.8
Florida	48.4	79.4	29.5	38.2	30.6	23.6
Massachusetts	38.3	81.2	24.4	36.7	28.9	25.1

[a] Ranked according to projected population as of July 1, 1965.

[1] For the local areas sampled in each state: California, 33; New York, 30; Pennsylvania, 31; Illinois, 20; Ohio, 30; Texas, 31; Michigan, 16; New Jersey, 16; Florida, 17; Massachusetts, 18.

Source: U. S. Bureau of the Census, Census of Governments: 1962, vol. II, Taxable Property Values, U. S. Government Printing Office, Washington, D. C., 1963.

SOURCE: *Juan De Torres, Financing Local Government, Studies in Business Economics, No. 96, The National Industrial Conference Board, New York—1967*

3. TYPES OF PROPERTY

The general scheme according to which property is usually classified for tax purposes divides it into personal and real property. Real property consists of land, its improvements, and the buildings thereon; all other property is considered personal property regardless of whether it is owned by an individual or a corporation.

a. PERSONAL PROPERTY

There are three types of personal property. Each presents its own peculiarities with respect to the assessment and recording of property. First, there are "intangibles," which consist of demand deposits, bonds, mortgages, and similar financial claims. These usually have an easily ascertained market value, but the owner can keep them with as much ease and security in other states as in his own community. Therefore, placing intangibles on the property tax roll is a task that is beyond the capabilities of local assessors, and even of the states.

Second, there are the "tangibles" of private persons such as jewelry, cars, and appliances. Many of these are also difficult to place on the property roll, because to do so would require governmental inquiry into the private lives of individuals, and this is barred by the traditional objections to government intrusions into private affairs.

Third, there are business tangibles consisting of machinery, inventories, and fixtures. Business tangibles are frequently traded. Therefore, they can be assessed with relative ease at full market value. They can be recorded with little intrusion into private affairs. But, in practice, it has been found that taxing business tangibles at full market value leads to heavy taxes on businesses that require large inventories. Thus, in most states, to avoid discriminating against these businesses, either business tangibles are left off the property roll or legal provision is made for their assessment at relatively low percentages of full market value.

b. REAL PROPERTY

Real property is recorded with relative ease, but it nearly always presents assessment problems to local assessors, for it is less standardized, is traded less frequently, and is sold in larger units than most personal property.

Housing, farmland, certain types of standardized space for commerce and manufacturing, and vacant lots furnish the local assessor with a fairly continuous record of sales, which can serve him as a reasonable guide for assessments. Yet, the value of such a record can often be vitiated by wide fluctuations in price from year to year. For example, prices of vacant lots, in particular, fluctuate very widely, so that a record of previous sales is often not a good guide to present values.

However, a large proportion of commercial and industrial property is either so specialized in its uses or so large, and is traded so seldom, that a current market value or "replacement" value has to be imputed to it.

NEIGHBORHOOD UNIT AND NEW TOWN CONCEPTS

Three different descriptions of land use patterns have been devised to describe resulting spatial organization of urban areas. Eech theory sets forth certain general tendencies of arrangement which allegedly will prevail unless modified by topographical or other disturbing influences. These descriptions indicate that urban land uses are distributed within concentric zones, sectors, or multiple nuclei. A condensed description of each theory follows. 6

Concentric zone. The most influential advocate of the concentric zone theory was Ernest W. Burgess, whose theory was cited by Fisher and Fisher and others writing in the area of community organization. Burgess assumed that the modern American city would take the form of five concentric urban zones. In outline, the zones are:

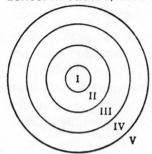

Concentric Zone Description
(Supposedly applicable to all cities.)
Zones
I. The Central Business District.

II. Zone in Transition.

III. Zone of Independent Workingmen's Homes.

IV. Zone of Better Residences.

V. The Commuters' Zone.

a Adapted from E. W. Burgess, "Urban Areas," Chicago: An Experiment in Social Science Research, ed. by T. V. Smith and L. D. White (Chicago: University of Chicago Press, 1929), p. 115.

Sector: This theory holds that residential land uses tend to be arranged in sectors or wedges radiating from the center of a city. While each community has a different pattern, rent areas tend to conform to a pattern of sectors rather than to concentric circles.

Sector Description
(Arrangement of sectors differs from city to city.)
Theoretical Pattern of Monthly Rent Distribution

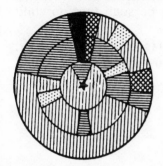

less than $10

$10-$19.99

$20-$29.99

$30-$49.99

$50 and over

b Theoretical pattern of rent distribution in Indianapolis. From The Structure and Growth of Residential Neighborhoods in American Cities (Washington, D. C.: Federal Housing Adm), p. 77.

SOURCE: Eugene J. Kelley Shopping Centers, The ENO Foundation for Highway Traffic Control, Saugatuck, Conn.—1956

Multiple Nuclei. Harris and Ullman combine the concentric zone and sector theories to explain the arrangement of land uses.

In many cities the land use pattern is built not around a single center but around several discrete nuclei. In some cities these nuclei have existed from the very origins of the city; in others they have developed as the growth of the city stimulated migration and specialization. . . . The initial nucleus of the city stimulated may be the retail district in a central place city, the port or rail facilities in a breakoff city, or the factory, mine, or beach in a specialized function city.

The rise of separate nuclei and differentiated districts reflects a combination of the following four factors:

1. Certain activities require specialized facilities.

2. Certain like activities group together because they profit from cohesion.

3. Certain unlike activities are detrimental to each other.

4. Certain activities are unable to afford the rents of the most desirable sites.

The number of nuclei which result from historical development and the operation of localization forces vary greatly from city to city. The larger the city, the more numerous and specialized are the nuclei.

Multiple-Nuclei Description
(Arrangement of nuclei differs from city to city.)
District

1. Central Business District.

2. Wholesale Light Manufacturing.

3. Low-Class Residential.

4. Medium-Class Residential.

5. High-Class Residential.

6. Heavy Manufacturing.

7. Outlying Business District.

8. Residential Suburb.

9. Industrial Suburb.

c From C. D. Harris and E. L. Ullman, "The Nature of Cities," The Annals of the American Academy of Political and Social Science, Vol. 242 (November 1945), p. 13.

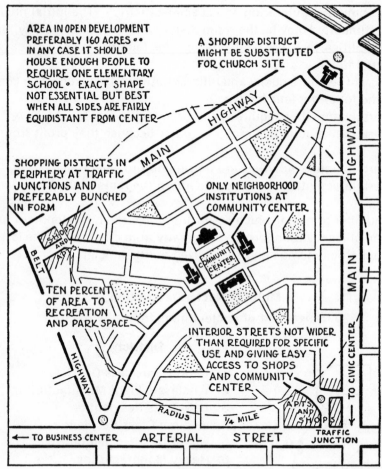

AREA IN OPEN DEVELOPMENT PREFERABLY 160 ACRES •• IN ANY CASE IT SHOULD HOUSE ENOUGH PEOPLE TO REQUIRE ONE ELEMENTARY SCHOOL ∘ EXACT SHAPE NOT ESSENTIAL BUT BEST WHEN ALL SIDES ARE FAIRLY EQUIDISTANT FROM CENTER

A SHOPPING DISTRICT MIGHT BE SUBSTITUTED FOR CHURCH SITE

SHOPPING DISTRICTS IN PERIPHERY AT TRAFFIC JUNCTIONS AND PREFERABLY BUNCHED IN FORM

ONLY NEIGHBORHOOD INSTITUTIONS AT COMMUNITY CENTER

TEN PERCENT OF AREA TO RECREATION AND PARK SPACE

INTERIOR STREETS NOT WIDER THAN REQUIRED FOR SPECIFIC USE AND GIVING EASY ACCESS TO SHOPS AND COMMUNITY CENTER

COMMUNITY CENTER

SHOPS AND APTS

HIGHWAY / MAIN / BELT / HIGHWAY / MAIN / TO CIVIC CENTER

RADIUS ¼ MILE

APTS AND SHOPS

← TO BUSINESS CENTER   ARTERIAL   STREET   TRAFFIC JUNCTION

Reproduced from New York Regional Survey

In a preliminary study in 1926 and in a report published by the Committee on the Regional Plan of New York and Its Environs in 1929, Perry enunciated his Neighborhood Theory. Its six basic principles were:

1. Major arterials and through traffic routes should not pass through residential neighborhoods. Instead, these streets should provide the boundaries of the neighborhood.

2. Interior street patterns should be designed and constructed through use of cul-de-sacs, curved layout and light duty surfacing so as to encourage a quiet, safe, low volume traffic movement and preservation of the residential atmosphere.

3. The population of the neighborhood should be that which is necessary to support its elementary school. (When Perry formulated his theory, this population was estimated at about 5,000 persons; current elementary school size standards probably would lower the figure to 3,000-4,000 persons.)

4. The neighborhood focal point should be the elementary school centrally located on a common or green, along with other institutions that have service areas coincident with the neighborhood boundaries.

5. The neighborhood would occupy an approximately 160 acres with a density of 10 families per acre. The shape would be such that no child would walk more than one-half mile to school.

6. The unit would be served by shopping facilities, churches, a library, and a community center located near the elementary school.

SOURCE: New York Regional Survey of New York and its Environs—1929

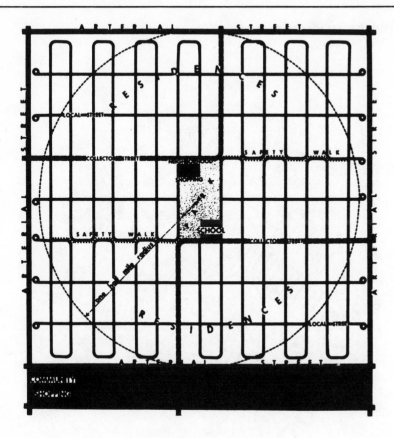

A sound area for living with:

1. Adequate school and parks within a half mile walk

2. Major streets around rather than through the neighborhood

3. Separate residential and non-residential districts

4. Population large enough to support an elementary school, usually 5,000 to 10,000 people

5. Some neighborhood stores and services

SOURCE: Reproduced from Comprehensive Planning for The Whittier Neighborhood, courtesy of Minneapolis City Planning Commission

THE NEIGHBORHOOD UNIT—CLARENCE STEIN

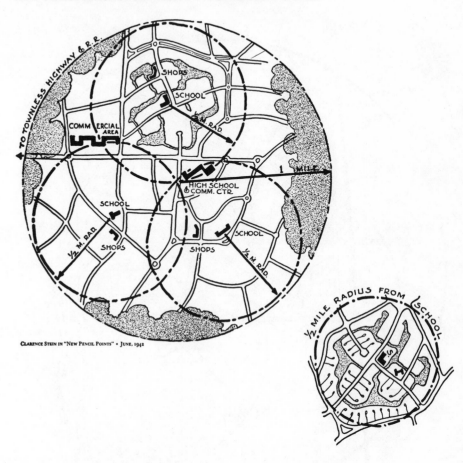

Clarence Stein in "New Pencil Points" • June, 1942

The elementary school is the center of the unit and within a one-half mile radius of all residents in the neighborhood. A small shopping center for daily needs is located near the school. Most residential streets are suggested as cul-de-sac or "dead-end" roads to eliminate through traffic, and park space flows through the neighborhood in a manner reminiscent of the Radburn plan.

The grouping of three neighborhood units served by a high school and one or two major commercial centers, the radius for walking distance to these facilities being one mile.

GENERAL PLAN SHOWING NEIGHBORHOODS

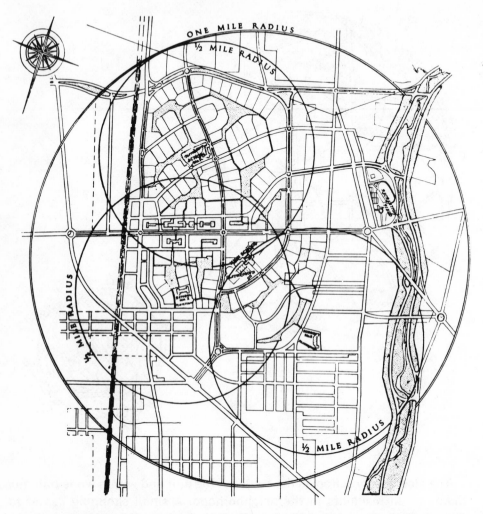

NORTHWEST NEIGHBORHOOD

In their design of the suburb of Radburn in New Jersey, C. S. Stein and Henry Wright introduced a new approach to residential planning. They originated the superblock idea, the main feature of which, is the separation of pedestrian and automobile traffic. At Radburn, houses are grouped around a series of culs-de-sac which are linked by walkways with the park, the school, and the shops, all of which are located in the interior of the superblock. The superblock is considered an ideal solution to the circulation problem since it provides a means of locating the houses off the main road.

SOURCE: Clarence Stein, Toward New Towns for America, Reinhold Publishing Corp., New York—1957

The illustration shows a typical cul-de-sac street employed at Radburn. Its characteristics may be summarized as follows: The short cul-de-sac acts as a service lane only; it provides vehicular access to houses and garages, permitting delivery and other services, and it also serves for most of the parking; footways located on the perimeter of each cul-de-sac house group serve as sidewalks. As opposed to established planning practices, houses have been "turned around," the living rooms, porches, and as many bedrooms as possible facing the gardens at rear of dwellings, and kitchens and cellar storage, the service lane.

The dwellings are loosely disposed around the dead-end streets and, as a group, they show little of formal architectural discipline. The landscaping, judiciously planned, undoubtedly is the most important uniting element in the composition. Other uniting elements are the consistency in the use of building materials and the continuity in roof lines. Also, by joining houses by means of coupling their garages, the usual disorderly appearance of the free standing houses in relation to each other has been eliminated and sufficient space left on either side of the buildings. The architectural informality of the Radburn cul-de-sac distinguishes it from the British dead-end street in which a formal correlation of the houses predominates.

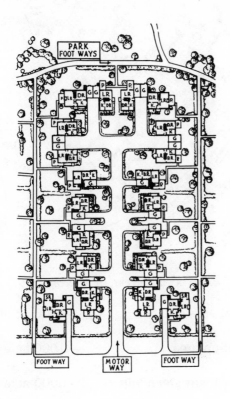

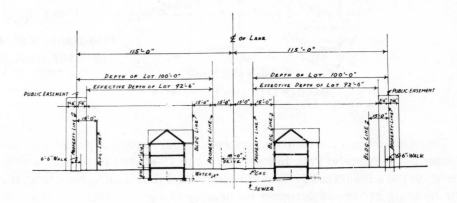

Plan of a typical "lane" at Radburn. The park in the center of the superblock is shown at the top; the motor ways to the houses are at right angles to the park.

Typical transverse section of a "lane" in the first unit of Radburn.

SOURCE: Clarence Stein, Toward New Towns for America, Reinhold Publishing Corp., New York—1957

GARDEN CITIES OF TOMORROW

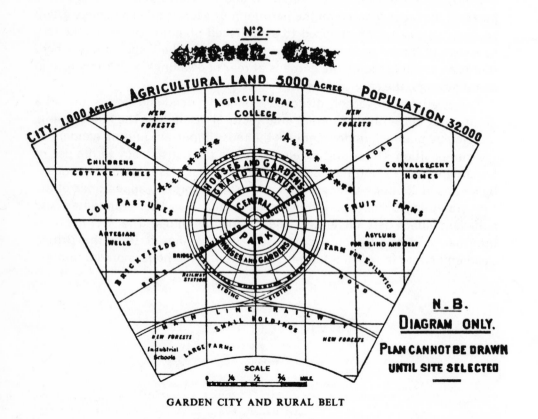

GARDEN CITY AND RURAL BELT

WARD AND CENTRE OF GARDEN CITY

N.B. A DIAGRAM ONLY. PLAN MUST DEPEND UPON SITE SELECTED.

Total area of city	—6000 acres
Built-up area	—1000 acres
Permanent green belt	—5000 acres
Total population	—32,000 people

City organization—

Center—	civic buildings
1st Ring—	central park
2nd Ring—	housing of various types bisected by Grand Avenue
3rd Ring—	crystal palace or covered promenades
4th Ring—	factories and warehouses
Green belt—	permanent open space

Ebenezer Howard put forth his concept of a garden city in a book entitled **Tomorrow: A Peaceful Path to Real Reform** in 1898. The basic goal was to combine the advantages of town life with that of the country. He advocated the building of "towns designed for healthy living and industry; of a size that makes possible a full measure of social life, but not larger; surrounded by a rural belt; the whole of the land being in public ownership, or held in trust for the community."

SOURCE: Ebenezer Howard, Garden Cities of Tomorrow—1946, Faber & Faber—London

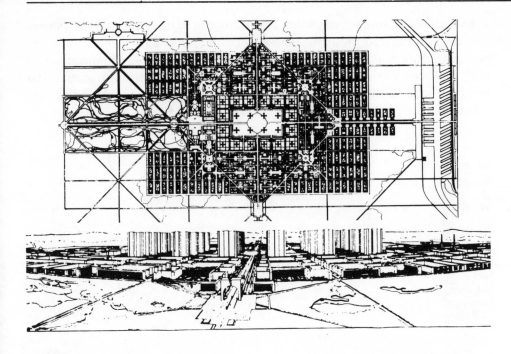

"LA VILLE CONTEMPORAINE" BY LE CORBUSIER

The City of Tomorrow for 3,000,000 people was proposed by Le Corbusier in 1922. Sixty-story office buildings with a density of 1,200 persons per acre and covering only 5 per cent of the ground area are set within landscaped open space. Eight-story apartment buildings with a density of 120 persons per acre surround the office skyscrapers and the cite jardins of single houses occupy the outskirts of the city. The hub of the plan is the transportation center for motor and rail lines, the roof of which is the airfield. Main highways are elevated.

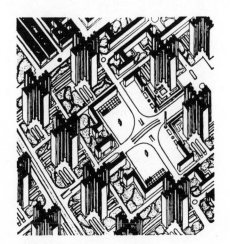

After the introduction of "La Ville Contemporaine," Le Corbusier applied the same theories to a section of Paris. In this "Voisin Plan," the 60-story skyscraper office buildings are set in vast open space, main traffic highways are defined with complete separation of traffic, and parking space for vehicles is provided. The plan is a rectangular arrangement of streets, but local and through traffic are distinctly separated, and the large open spaces are treated with informal pedestrian circulation and landscaped. The difference in scale of open space and building coverage is indicated in the plan sketch.

"PLAN VOISIN" by Le Corbusier, Paris, 1925

CONTRAST Between Old and New in "Plan Voisin"

SOURCE: From Gallion and Eisner The Urban Pattern, Copyright 1963 D. Van Nostrand Co., Inc., Princeton, N.J.

Essentially a "linear" city form, Frank Lloyd Wright's proposal distributes industry, commerce, housing, social facilities, and agriculture along the railroad artery and his access to highways. The unit which dominates this plan is the minimum of one acre of land for each family rather than the neighborhood unit, although the various neighborhood facilities are provided.

Area of Plan is
Two Square Miles

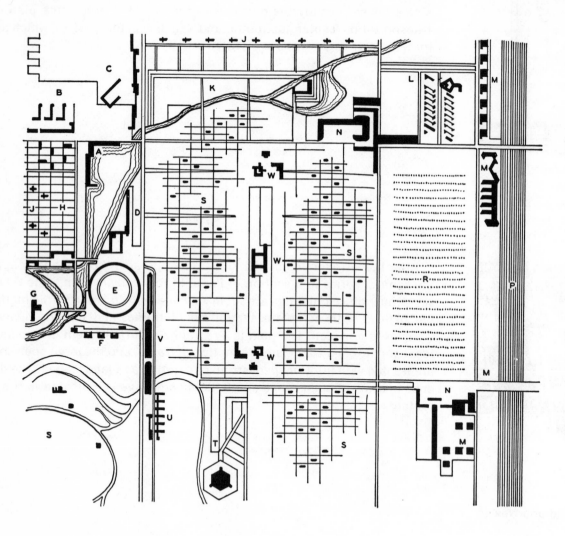

A	County Seat Administration	**M**	Industry
B	Airport	**N**	Merchandising
C	Sports	**P**	Railroad
D	Professional Offices	**R**	Orchards
E	Stadium	**S**	Homes and Apartments
F	Hotel	**T**	Temple and Cemetery
G	Sanitarium	**U**	Research
H	Small Industry	**V**	Zoo
J	Small Farms	**W**	Schools
K	Park		
L	Motor Inn		

SOURCE: From Gallion and Eisner The Urban Pattern, Copyright 1963 D. Van Nostrand Co., Inc., Princeton, N.J.

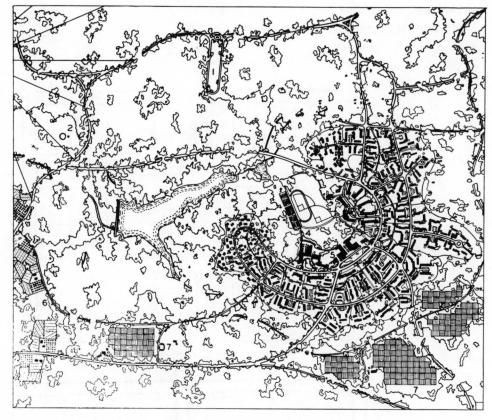

GREENBELT, Maryland

1 Water Tower

2 Disposal Plant and Incinerator

3 Picnic Center and Lake

4 Community Center

5 Store Group

6 Rural Homesteads

7 Allotment Gardens

SOURCE: From Gallion and Eisner The Urban Pattern, Copyright 1963 D. Van Nostrand Co., Inc., Princeton, N.J.

This development is on a 2,100-acre site about 25 minutes' drive by automobile from Washington, D.C., and includes 712 dwellings in group houses and 288 in apartments, a total of 1,000 units occupying an area of 250 acres. There are 500 garages. The sixteen-room elementary school is jointly used as a community center, and the shopping center includes space for a post office, food stores, a drug store, a dentist's and a doctor's offices, a 600-seat theater, and such service shops as shoe repair, laundry, tailor, barber, and beauty shops. There are a bus terminal, a garage and repair shop, a fire station, and a gas station. The recreation facilities include an athletic field, picnic grounds, and an artificial lake. The superblock is used, each block containing about 120 dwellings with interior play areas. Underpasses provide continuous pedestrian circulation without crossing main roads. The commercial and community center, in the approximate center of the plan, reduces to a minimum the walking distance from all dwellings.

As a component part of the Federal government's search for ways and means to cope with the modern city and its living environment, the Resettlement Administration planned four "greenbelt towns" beginning in 1935. They were satellite communities near large cities. The designs were inspired by Howard's Garden City idea, but they were not planned as self-contained towns; they were more like dormitory villages, the sources of employment for the residents being in the near-by cities. Each was surrounded by a belt of permanent open space, part of which could be farmed or gardened. A full complement of community facilities was included in each town— shopping, schools, and recreation space.

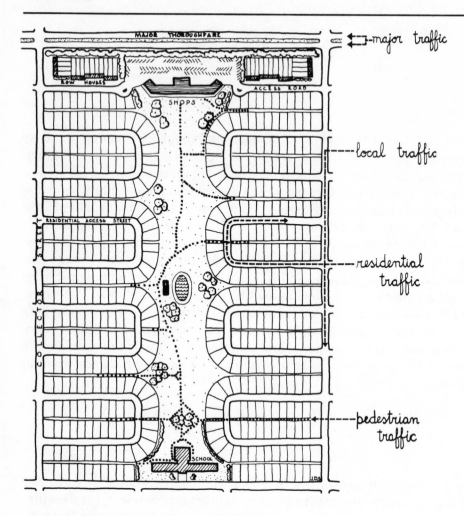

— major traffic

— local traffic

— residential traffic

— pedestrian traffic

STANDARD GRID SYSTEM
—No separation of pedestrian and vehicular traffic
—All roads used for all traffic purposes
—All lot sizes standard

OPEN PLAN
—Pedestrians and vehicles separated
—Roads planned for specific uses

STREET TYPES
    Major thoroughfares
    Collector Streets
    Access roads
    Minor residential roads

MODIFIED GRID PATTERN
—Some separation of pedestrians and vehicles by provision of foot paths
—Channelling of traffic—less road

SOURCE: Principles of Small House Grouping, Central Mortgage and Housing Corp., Ottawa, Canada

Year	Proposed By	Area Involved	Proposal	Density Per Gross Acre	Optimum Population
1898	E. Howard	City	Book—Garden Cities	8–12 Dwelling Units	32,000 persons
1924	Le Corbusier	City	La Ville Contemporaine	1,200 persons	3,000,000 persons
1929	Clarence Perry	Neighborhood Unit	Neighborhood Unit Concept	5 dwelling units	5–9,000 persons
1932	Frank Lloyd Wright	City	Broadacre City	1 dwelling unit	no limit
1944	Jose L. Sert	Residential Unit	Book—Human Scale in City Planning	3–5 dwelling units	5–10,000 persons
1945	Walter Gropius & M. Wagner	Residential Unit	Book—A Program for City Reconstruction	4–10 dwelling units	5000 persons
1946	L. Justement	City	Book—New Cities for Old	10–35 dwelling units	1,000,000 persons
1947	P. Goodman P. Goodman	City	Book—Communitas	100 dwelling units	6–8 million persons

ELEMENTS OF CITYSCAPE

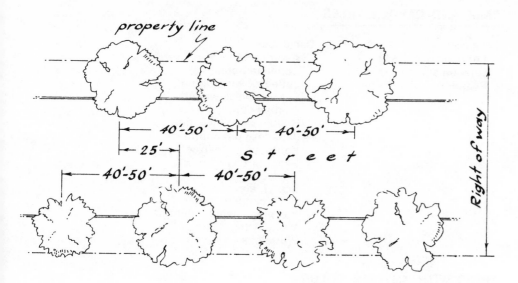

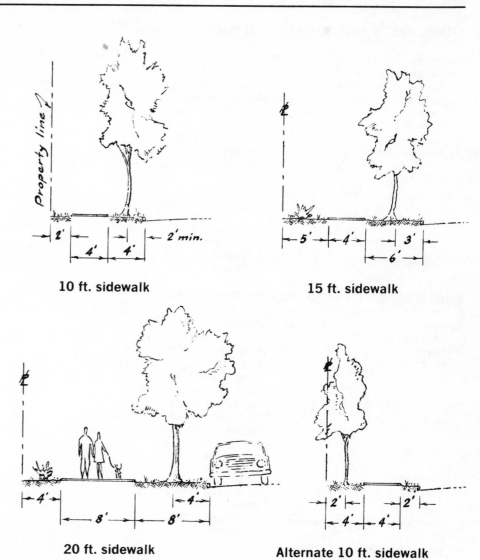

10 ft. sidewalk

15 ft. sidewalk

20 ft. sidewalk

Alternate 10 ft. sidewalk

GENERAL CRITERIA

- Trees should be spaced alternately on each side.
- Trees should be spaced at regular intervals without regard to property lines. This will give the street a well-balanced appearance.
- Trees for an entire block should be planted at the same time.
- Some typical spacing of trees:

Elms, White Oaks	50 ft.
Planet Tree, Soft Maples	45 ft.
Ginkgo, Red Maples	40 ft.

- All trees should be the same kind on a street except to achieve special effects.

There are several advantages of placing trees between sidewalk and property line, which are:

1. House has better screening from street.
2. There is less interference with overhead wires.
3. Tree roots are less likely to be cut with street repairs.
4. Trees usually have better soil.

SHADE TREES FOR SUBURBAN HOMES

Evergreen:
- Canada hemlock
- Colorado blue spruce
- Eastern white pine
- Nikko fir
- White fir

In northern part only
- Balsam fir
- white spruce

Deciduous:
- Ame. hornbeam
- Amer. mountain-ash
- Amer. yellowwood
- European beech
- Eur. linden
- Littleleaf linden
- Norway maple
- Panicled goldenrain-tree
- Pin oak
- Scarlet oak
- Schwedler maple
- Silver linden
- Sugar maple
- Sweetgum
- Tuliptree
- Whiteoak

ROADSIDE, BOULEVARD AND AVENUE TREES

Evergreen:
- Canada hemlock
- Eastern white pine
- red pine

Decidious:
- Amer. linden
- Ame. yellowwood
- Black tupelo
- Common hackberry
- Ginkgo (staminate form)
- London planetree
- Northern red oak
- Norway maple
- pin oak
- red maple
- scarlet oak
- silver linden
- Schwedler maple
- sugar maple
- sweetgum
- Tuliptree

STREET TREES

Evergreen:
- None

Deciduous:
- Ailanthus (pistallate form)
- Amur corktree
- Ginkgo (staminate form)
- London planetree
- Norway maple
- Pin oak
- Thornless common honeylocust
- Tuliptree

PARK AND GARDEN TREES

Evergreen:
- Common Douglas-fir
- Oriental spruce
- Red pine

Deciduous:
- Amur corktree
- Bolleana poplar
- cutleaf weeping birch
- Eastern black walnut
- English elm
- Golden weeping willow
- Japanese pagodatree
- Kentucky coffeetree
- Paper birch
- Rock elm
- Scotch elm
- Silverpendent linden
- Weeping silverpendent linden
- White Ash
- White oak

TREES WITH AUTUMN COLOR

- American hornbeam (orange, scarlet)
- American yellowwood (yellow)
- Black tupelo (scarlet)
- Ginkgo (yellow)
- Northern red oak (red)
- Norway maple (yellow)
- Pin oak (scarlet, dark red)
- Red maple (orange, red, scarlet)
- scarlet oak (scarlet, dark red)
- sugar maple (yellow, orange, scarlet)
- Sweetgum (red, scarlet)
- tuliptree (yellow)

TREES WITH CONSPICUOUS COLOR

- American mountain-ash (white)
- American yellowwood (white)
- Common horsechestnut (pinkish white)
- Japanese pagodatree (yellowish white)
- Panicled goldenrain-tree (yellow)
- Red maple (red)
- Sugar maple (yellowish green)
- Tulliptree (greenish yellow)

SOURCE: Trees—Yearbook of Agriculture—1949, U. S. Dept. of Agriculture

■ SOUTHEASTERN REGION

SHADE AND ROADSIDE TREES

Deciduous:
American beech
American elm
American sycamore
Laurel oak
Pecan
Sugarberry
Sweetgum
Water oak
Weeping willow
White oak
Willow oak
Winged elm
Yellow popular

Evergreen:
Live oak
Southern magnolia

STREET TREES

Deciduous:
American elm
American sycamore
Cabbage palmetto
Common crapemyrtle
Laurel oak
Sugar berry
Sweetgum
Water oak
White oak
Willow oak
Winged elm

Evergreen:
Camphor-tree
Live oak
Southern magnolia

PARK AND LAWN TREES

Deciduous:
American beech
American elm
American sycamore
Common crapemyrtel
Eastern redbud
Flowering dogwood
Mimosa
Panicled goldenrain-tree
red maple

Evergreen:
American holly
Southern magnolia

TREES WITH AUTUMN COLOR

Deciduous:
Flowering dogwood
Pin oak
Red maple
Scarlet oak
Sweetgum
Yellow-popular

■ SOUTHERN ROCKY MOUNTAIN REGION

STREET TREES

Deciduous:
Green ash
Lanceleaf poplar
Linden
London Planetree
Narrowleaf poplar
Northern catalpa
Norway maple
Siberian elm
Velvet ash
White Ash

SHADE TREES

Deciduous:
Amer. elm
Boxelder
Plains poplar
red mulberry
white mulberry

TREES WITH CONSPICUOUS FLOWERS

Deciduous:
Black locust
Northern Catalpa

TREES FOR DIFFICULT SITES

Deciduous:
Black locust
Boxelder
Common hackberry
Russian-olive
Siberian elm
Tamarisk
Thornless honeylocust
Tree-of Heaven ailanthus
Velvet ash

TREES WITH AUTUMN COLOR

Deciduous:
Lanceleaf poplar
Lombardy poplar
Narrowleaf poplar
Norway maple
Plains poplar

ROADSIDE TREES

Deciduous:
Black locust
Lombardy poplar

Evergreen:
Arizona cypress
Eucalyptus
Ponderosa Pine

PARK AND GARDEN TREES

Deciduous:
Common hackberry
Russian olive
Tamarisk
Thornless honeylocust
tree of heaven ailanthus

Evergreen:
Aleppo pine
Austrian pine
Colorado pinyon pine
Colorado spruce
Englemann spruce
Rocky mountain juniper
Scotch pine

Evergreen:
Eucalyptus

SOURCE: Trees: Yearbook of Agriculture—1949, U. S. Dept. of Agriculture

SHADE AND PARK TREES

Deciduous:
American Elm
Bur oak
Cottonwood
Green ash
Hackberry
Honeylocust
Russian-olive

Evergreens:
Austrian pine
Eastern redcedar
Ponderosa pine
Rocky mountain cedar

NEBRASKA NORTHWARD:

Deciduous:
Boxelder
Hawthorn
Maples
Willows

Evergreens:
Douglas fir
Scotch pine
Spruce
White fir

NEBRASKA SOUTHWARD:

Deciduous:
Ailanthus
American sycamore
Black locust
Black walnut
Catalpa
Russian mulberry

OKLAHOMA AND TEXAS:

Deciduous:
Chinese elm
Desertwillow
Kentucky coffeetree
soapberry

Evergreen:
Arizona cypress (texas)
Loblolly pine
Shortleaf pine

TREES WITH SNOWY FLOWERS

Black locust
Catalpa
Desertwillow
Hawthorn
Honeylocust

SOURCE: Trees: Yearbook of Agriculture—1949, U. S. Dept. of Agriculture

STREET TREES

Deciduous:
American elm
American sycamore
Boxelder
Bur oak
Green ash
Hackberry
Maples
Russian mulberry
Siberian elm

Evergreens:
Austrian pine
Ponderosa pine

TREES WITH SHOWY FOLIAGE IN AUTUMN

Cottonwood (yellow)
Green ash (golden yellow)
Maple (gold and red)
Oak (yellow to red)
Sycamore (clear yellow)

Trees suitable for use on phymatotrichum root rot infected soil:

Deciduous:
Ailanthus
Desertwillow
Hackberry
Mulberry
Soapberry

Evergreens:
Eastern redcedar
Rocky Mountain cedar

■ NORTH PACIFIC COAST AREA

SHADE TREES

American yellowwood

Common hackberry
European linden
pin oak

LAWN TREES

Amer. yellowwood
Atlas-cedar (conifer)
Common hackberry
Eur. Linden
Himalayan pine (conifer)
Oregon white oak
Pacific madrone
Pin oak
Sweet gum, Tuliptree

TREES WITH SHOWY FALL FOLIAGE

Amer. yellowwood
Pin oak
Sweetgum

TREES WITH SHOWY OR FRAGRANT FLOWERS

American yellowwood
Eur. linden
Pacific madrone

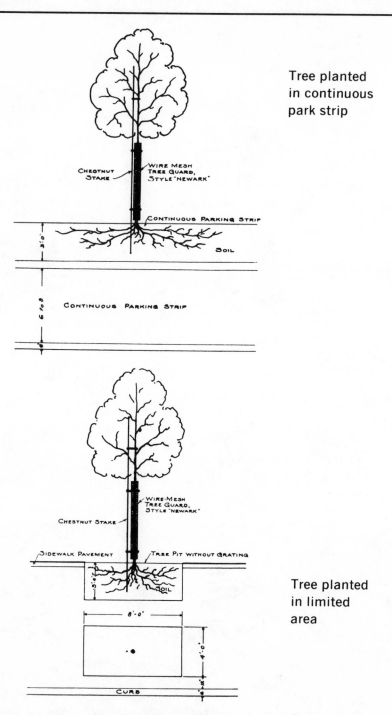

Tree planted
in continuous
park strip

Tree planted
with brick
surface over
tree pit

Tree planted
in limited
area

Tree planted
with grating
over tree pit

SOURCE: A Street Tree System for New York City, Bulletin of NYS College of Forestry at Syracuse University

a. Acer platanoides — Norway Maple. A wide round-headed, densely foliaged tree. Leaves are five-lobed, quite large, and deep green, turning a golden yellow in the fall. A fine tree for a symmetrical, impenetrable look. Height 40 feet, spread 35 feet.

b. Aesculus hippocastanum — Horse Chestnut. The famous tree which grows on the Champs Elysees. The flowers bloom like white candles in May, coming out with the lovers. A wonderful tree with a handsome, five-fingered leaf, it grows up to 50 feet high with a 30-foot spread.

c. Ailanthus altissima — Chinese Tree of Heaven. The tree that grows in Brooklyn will grow anywhere. It has a fine tropical quality and handsome fruits which hang in clusters. Thin, very often multistemmed, finely divided leaves. Height 40 feet, spread 35 feet.

d. Carpinus betulus—European Hornbeam. A fine tree for shearing and pleaching. This was the tree used mostly in Versailles for the high hedges pleached down the allees. A small, elegant leaf and a clean, upright, black-barked trunk. Height 35 feet, spread 25 feet.

e. Fraxinus pennsylvanica lanceolata — Green Ash. A good, all-around, tough, vigorous tree. The bark is most interesting: marked diagonally, and quite black in color. Height 35 feet, spread 30 feet.

f. Ginkgo biloba — Maidenhair Tree. A living fossil which owes its life to the fact that it has been planted for centuries in the temple gardens of China. The females of this species produce evil-smelling fruits, so use only the male. Height 60 feet, spread 35 feet.

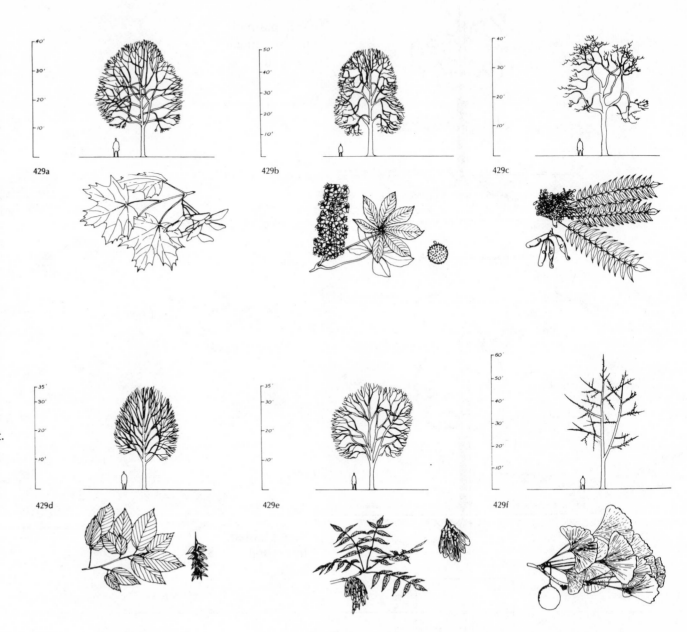

429a

429b

429c

429d

429e

429f

SOURCE: Lawrence Halpirin, Cities, Reinhold Publishing Corp, NY 1963

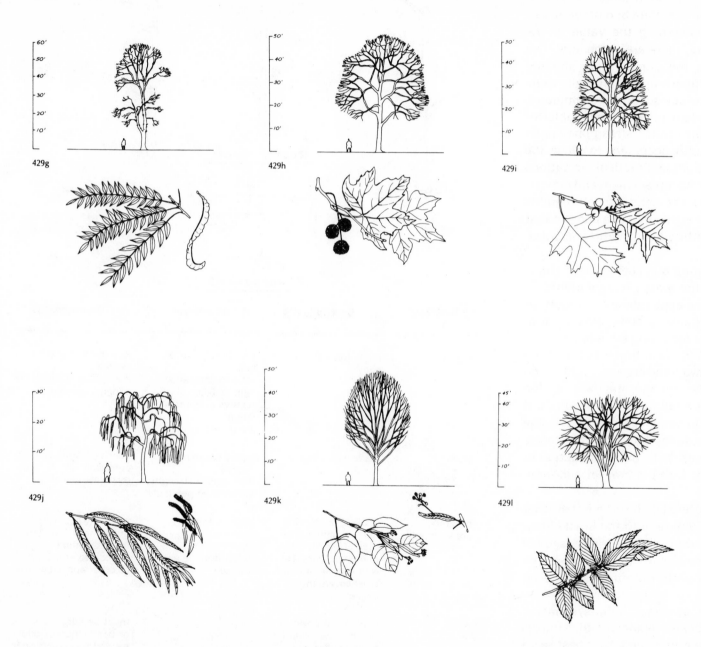

429g

429h

429i

429j

429k

429l

g. Gleditsia triacanthos—Honey Locust. Very high-headed, spreading, umbrella-shaped tree with a beautiful silhouette, deep black bark, and fine textured leaves. Tough and handsome. Height 50 feet, spread 40 feet.

h. Platanus acerifolia — London Plane Tree, Sycamore. The most planted street tree in North America. It can be sheared, pleached, or pollarded with excellent effects, withstands winds and soot admirably. Other excellent sycamores. Platanus orientalis—the Oriental Plane Tree, Platanus racemosa—the California Plane Tree. Height 50 feet, spread 40 feet.

i. Quercus borealis — Red Oak. The best of the Oaks for city conditions, clean, handsome, upright, and all-American. A deeply serrated leaf which turns a brilliant red in the fall. Height 50 feet, spread 40 feet.

j. Salix babylonica — Weeping Willow. Actually a native of China, this willow is not good for a street tree but is wonderful for small parks, playgrounds, backyard gardens. Its long, yellow, whiplike twigs have a fine color when the leaves have fallen. Height 30 feet, spread 30 feet.

k. Tilia cordata — Linden Basswood. The famous "Unter den Linden" tree, an extremely popular street tree in Europe. A beautiful round shape, handsome heart-shaped leaves, and delightful small flowers. The American species, Tilia american (called basswood), makes some of the tastiest honey in the world. Height 50 feet, spread 30 feet.

l. Zelkova serrata — Japanese Zelkova. Very much like the American elm in its shape and leaf, though smaller, and can be used in its place since it is not susceptible to the Dutch elm disease. Height 45 feet, spread 50 feet.

A street lighting pole is the assembly of a shaft and bracket or equipment used for supporting a street lighting luminaire and other appurtenances. Because of the divided opinion concerning the value of the psychological effect of white-way street lighting, there are, in general, two types of street light poles available for use: the upright pole and the pendant pole. The upright pole acts as a strut supporting and luminaire while the pendant pole has single or double brackets which support the luminaire. Various types and heights of upright and pendant poles are available for most any condition. However, the trend is towards taller, streamlined units with supporting brackets of the type and length necessary to place the luminaires over the area of the roadway to be lighted. Practical limitations of present-day mechanical equipment used in lamp replacement and maintenance work has for the present, standardized the pendant pole heights generally within the range of 25 to 35 ft. Such heights must be coordinated with the proper lamp type, pole spacing, mounting height ratio and transverse location.

While the primary function of the street lighting brackets or mast arm is to position the luminaire where it will render the most effective nighttime service, adequate strength and pleasing daytime appearance are important factors. The brackets and mast arms are available in steel, aluminum or concrete. Both single and twin-unit brackets for mounting the luminaire are available for the requirements of the installation. Twin brackets are sometimes used on the center esplanades for parkway and freeway lighting on wide divided streets, while single brackets remain the standard for the majority of the installations. Common bracket sizes vary from 4 ft to 16 ft in nominal length and are of horizontal or upsweep design to suit the individual luminaire requirements. On some upsweep brackets, it is necessary to use one and sometimes two sway braces. With the introduction of fluorescent street lighting there are indications that the bracket and luminaire are becoming an integral unit.

With the varying amounts of upsweep encountered in the different bracket styles, no set rules for the attachment of the luminaire to the bracket can be established. However, a cardinal point to be considered during assembly is to have the axis of the luminaire perpendicular to the surface to be lighted except where the type of illumination pattern desired is achieved through varying the axis angle.

The engineer will find that the planning of street light systems is enhanced by the wide selection of poles and brackets available which makes it relatively easy to design an installation of functional beauty to best serve the needs of the community.

SOURCE: American Standard Practice for Roadway Lighting, American Standards Association, New York, New York, 1963.

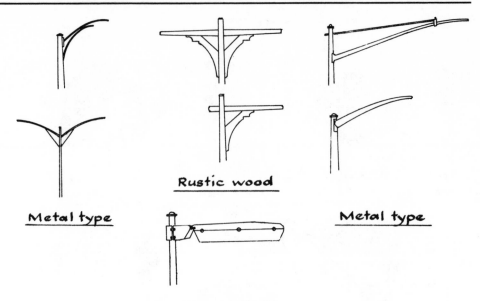

Rustic wood

Metal type

Fluorescent

Metal type

Type Pole	Description	Advantages	Disadvantages
Aluminum	made from aluminum alloy	resistant to corrosion little maintenance light weight relative easy installation lower cost	less durable and rugged low tensile strength for hanging pendants
steel	made with alloy steels	highly durable and rugged high tensile strength for hanging pendants	needs painting against corrosion relatively heavy
concrete, pre-stressed	made by a centrifugal machine process of pre-stressed, reinforced concrete with marble or crushed granite aggregate	little or no maintenance no corrosion highly durable and rugged	relatively heavy, requires heavy equipment for installation difficult to attach signs or other appurtenances
wood	made from hewn western red cedar, turned cedar, or pine	rustic character little or no initial maintenance	must be fully creosoted or pentachloro-phenol treated for proper wear solid post does not permit interior wiring or other equipment

LIGHTING POLE SPACING

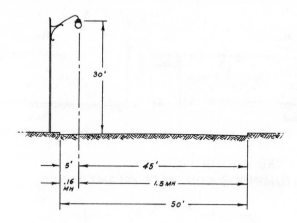

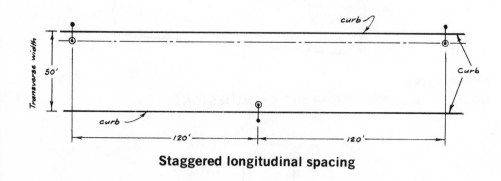

Staggered longitudinal spacing

Typical layout of luminaires

SOURCE: *American Standard Practice for Roadway Lighting, American Standards Association, New York, New York, 1963.*

HYDRANT SPACING

The choice of hydrants for public service is based on the same considerations as the choice of hydrants for private fire service. One point in which private and public practice may differ is that public hydrants are generally equipped with a gate valve between the hydrant and the main so as to make repairs to the hydrant possible without shutting down the street main.

In general, hydrants should be placed with consideration to their possible use. Hose lines more than 400 or 500 ft long result in delay and undue pressure losses in hose lines. Therefore, hydrants should be distributed not more than 300 or 400 ft from the buildings to be protected. Where it is the fire department practice to use hose lines direct from hydrants, to prevent undue friction losses, lines must be kept shorter than in the case of lines from pumpers, and hydrants must be spaced about 100 ft closer together.

A rough rule to follow is to place one hydrant near each street intersection and to set intermediate hydrants where the distance between intersections exceeds 350 to 400 ft.

CEMENT CONCRETE CURBS

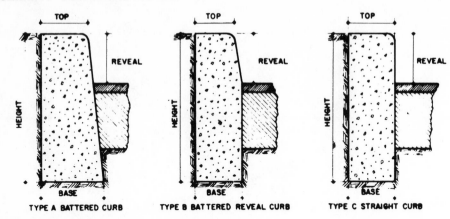

TYPE A BATTERED CURB

TYPE B BATTERED REVEAL CURB

TYPE C STRAIGHT CURB

CEMENT CONCRETE VALLEY GUTTER

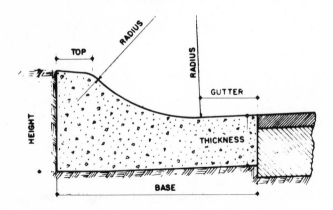

CEMENT CONCRETE ROLLED CURB AND GUTTER

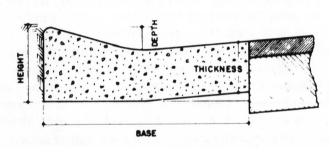

CEMENT CONCRETE CURBS AND GUTTERS

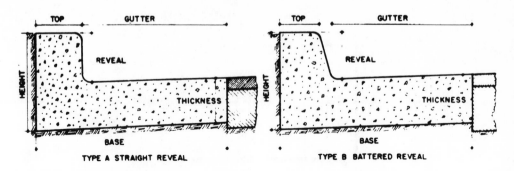

TYPE A STRAIGHT REVEAL

TYPE B BATTERED REVEAL

BITUMINOUS CURB AND GUTTER
COLD LAID BITUMINOUS CONCRETE (PLANT MIXED)

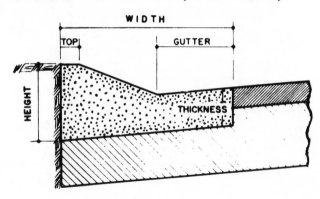

STONE CURB
GRANITE, MEDINA SANDSTONE OR BLUESTONE

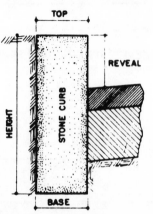

SOURCE: Federal Housing Administration, Data Sheets, 100, 200, 250, 300, 500, 600

TREE LOCATION

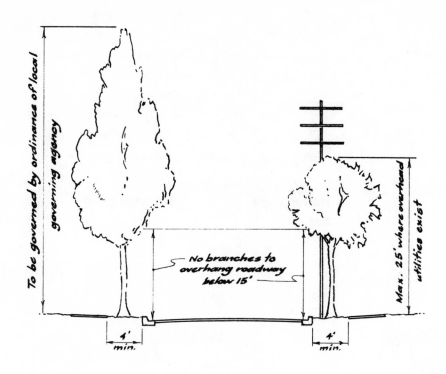

Spacing of trees to depend upon specie and growth characteristics, with min. of 25' apart. All trees within right of way to be planted by permit from governing agency.

STREET NAME SIGN LOCATION

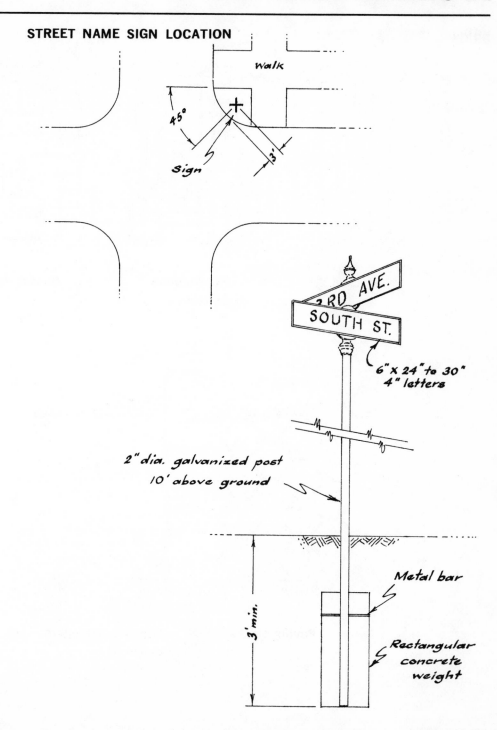

BRICK

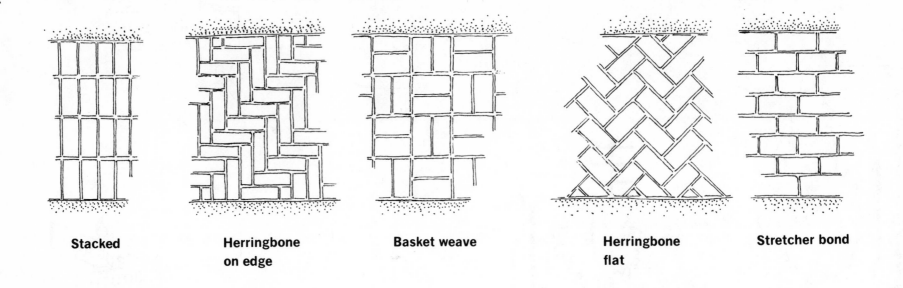

Stacked

Herringbone
on edge

Basket weave

Herringbone
flat

Stretcher bond

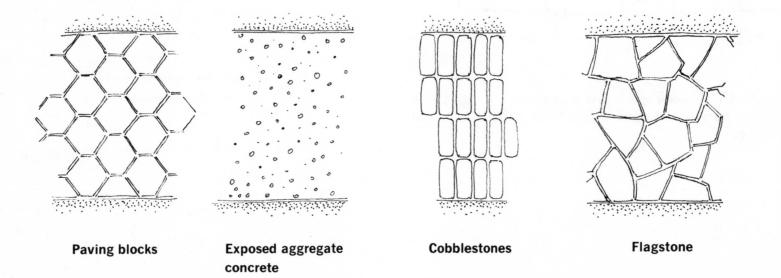

Paving blocks

Exposed aggregate
concrete

Cobblestones

Flagstone

Wood pole lines

Steel tower lines

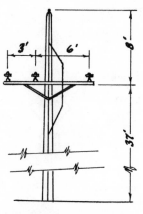

Average span 300'

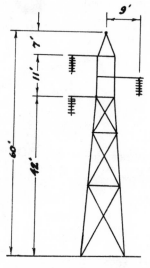

Average span 700'

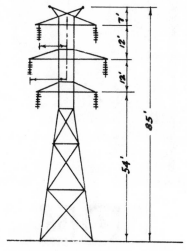

Average span 800'

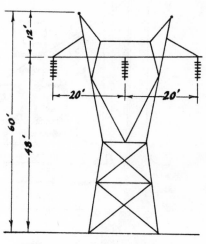

Average span 1000'

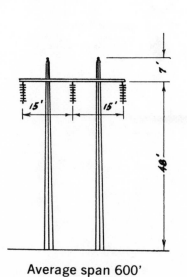

Average span 600'

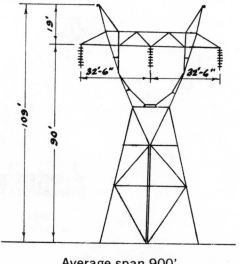

Average span 900'

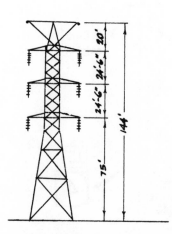

Average span 850'

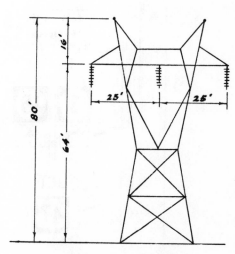

Average span 1000'

Typical route markings at intersections (for one direction of travel only)

Height and lateral location of signs—typical installations.

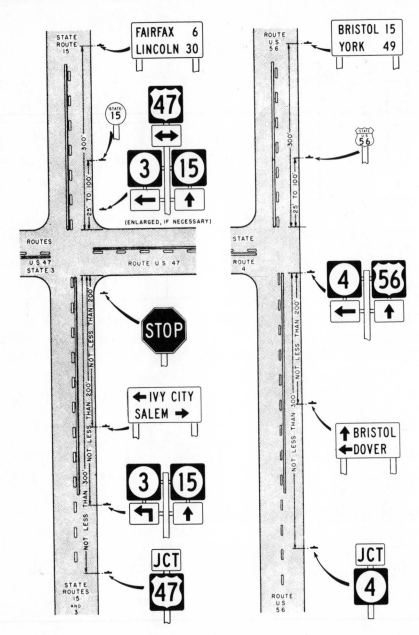

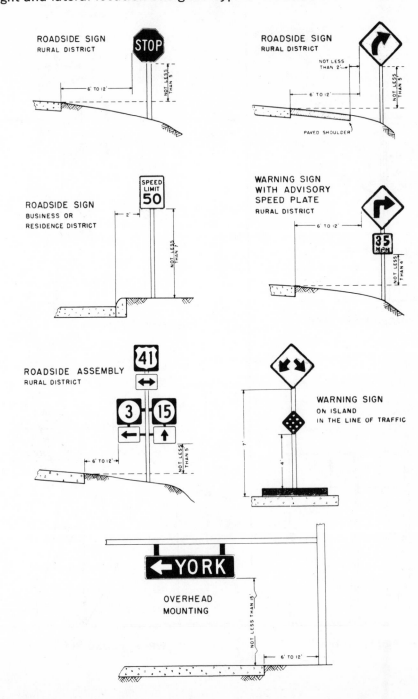

SOURCE: Manual on Uniform Traffic Control Devices, U. S. Dept. of Commerce, Wash., D. C.—1961

PUBLIC AND PRIVATE UTILITIES

PUBLIC WATER SUPPLY

(a) Quantity: Sufficient quantity for projected growth plus reserve for dry periods.

(b) Quality: Meets United States Public Health standards.

(c) Treatment Facilities: Adequate capacity to meet demands of maximum day plus fire flow.
Provision for stage expansion.
Adequate to insure degree of treatment needed.

(d) Distribution System: Proper design to insure complete coverage of logical service area, and to assure delivery of required flow.
Storage facilities where needed.
Maintenance of minimum pressure of 40 psi everywhere in system.

SEWAGE DISPOSAL

(a) Collection System: Proper design of interceptors, laterals, and trunks to insure complete coverage of logical service area.
Maintenance of minimum gradient in lines.
Provision for sewage life stations where required.

(b) Sewage Treatment System: Complete treatment required, preferably through consolidated area-wide system.
Location away from residential or commercial districts.
Plant layout and total space adapted for expansion.

STORM DRAINAGE

(a) Reasonable basis for assumed quantity of runoff from design storm (generally 5 year storm).

(b) Adequate provision for handling storm waters originating in upper basin as well as lower basin.

(c) Preserve natural drainage courses where possible with adequate channel rights of way (generally flood plain of 25 year storm).

(d) Prohibit storm drainage into active irrigation ditches.

(e) Provision of storm sewers where necessary with sizes capable of serving logical service area (drainage basin).

ELECTRICITY, GAS, AND TELEPHONE SERVICE

(a) Insure adequacy of coverage and capacity.

(b) Encourage underground installation wherever possible.

SOURCE: *George Nez, Standards for New Urban Development—The Denver Background,*
Reprinted by Permission of Urban Land, Vol 20, No 5 Urban Land Institute, 1200 18th Street, N. W., Wash. D. C.

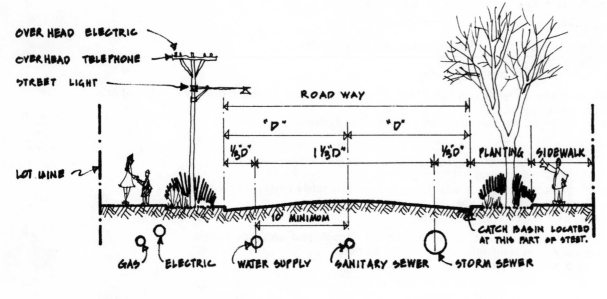

The street cross section is ideal and actual conditions can have all or some of the elements indicated.

STREET CROSS SECTION   no scale

DEFINITIONS OF UTILITY LOCATION

SANITARY SEWER

Generally located on center line of road. The line is a clay tile pipe. If it was located in the planting strip the roots of the trees might cause breaks in the pipes. This center line location also locates the pipe equidistant from building lines on both sides of the street.

STORM SEWER

Generally located the distance from curb line to center line of street. It is always located on the opposite side of the street from the water line.

WATER SUPPLY

May be located under sidewalk, in planting strip, or under street. Minimum design requirements will locate it at least 10 feet from nearest sewer or gas main and above highest sewer or gas main.

GAS

Generally located under sidewalk or in planting strip.

ELECTRICITY AND TELEPHONE

Best located in underground conduit. Sometimes located in overhead lines over planting strips. This causes interference with trees, danger of falling wires, and unsightly appearance.

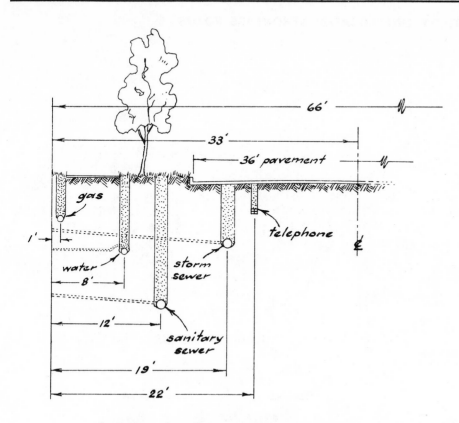

Location of underground utilities in soils of uncertain characteristics

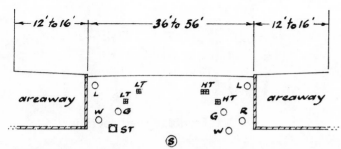

(a) Most common arrangement no original plan

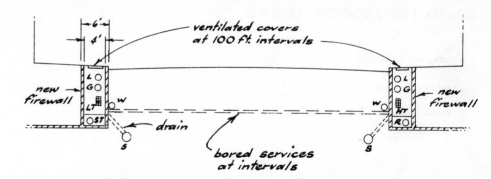

(b) Desirable plan when part of areaways can be recovered

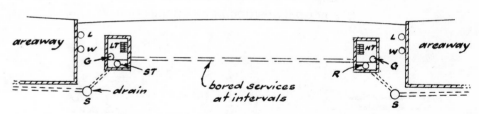

(c) Pipe tunnels where areaways cannot be used

Fig. a, b, and c, typical sections, central business section of Cincinnati, Ohio

Legend

L—Lighting circuit	LT—Telephone, telegraph fire alarm
W—Water	HT—Electric light and power
G—Gas	R—Refrigeration
ST—Steam	S—Sewer

SOURCE: *Committee of the City Planning Division on Location of Underground Utilities, American Society of Civil Engineers—1937*

UTILITY LINE LOCATIONS-GENERAL

① Carry utility around corner

② Stay on same side of street

③ Return utility to normal side of street at intersection

Utility line

Example of a utility relocation
to a normal position at an intersection

UTILITY LINE LOCATIONS-FRONTAGE ROADS

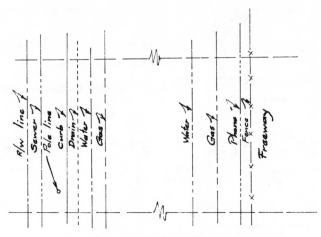

Frontage road plan

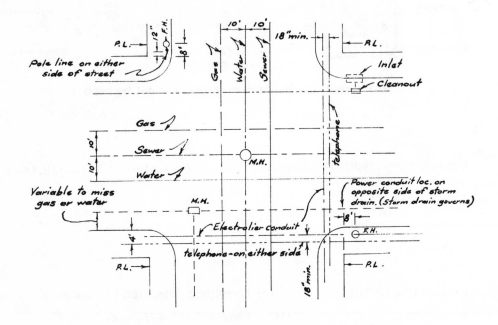

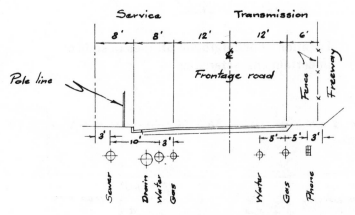

Frontage road section

SOURCE: Street and Urban Road Maintenance, Street Maintenance Committee, American Public Works Association, Public Administration Service, Chicago, Ill.

Combined

Separate

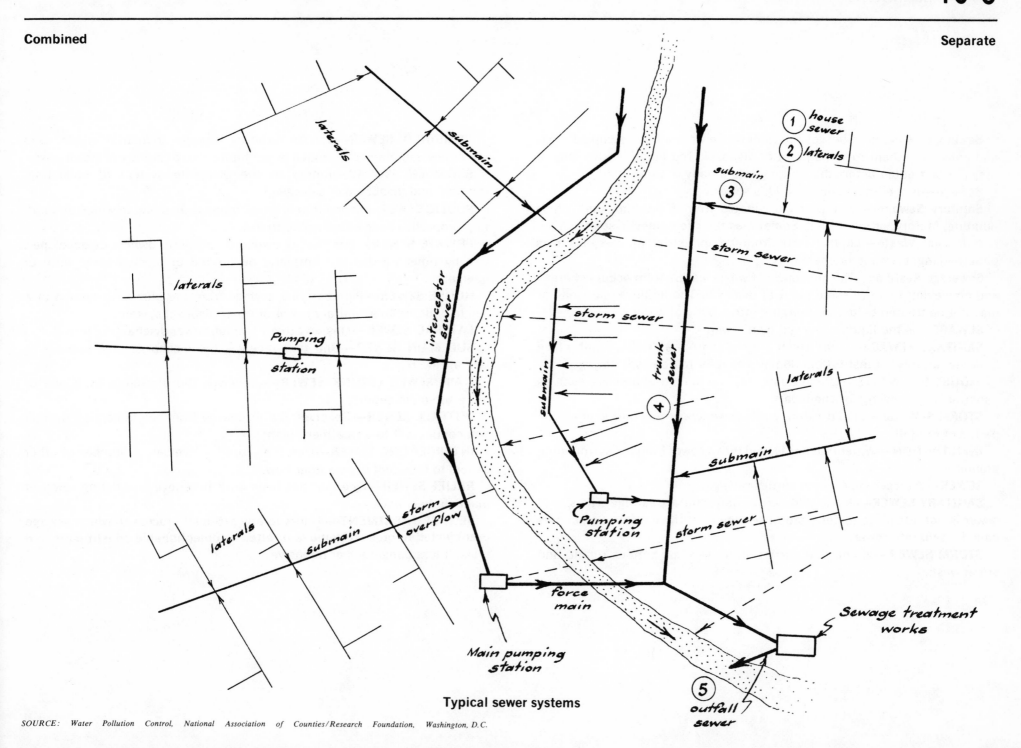

Typical sewer systems

SOURCE: *Water Pollution Control, National Association of Counties/Research Foundation, Washington, D.C.*

Sewerage System:—The collection of waste waters from occupied areas and conveying them to some point of disposal. The liquid wastes may or may not be treated before discharging into a body of water.

Sewage—is the liquid conveyed by a sewer.

Sanitary Sewage—That which originates from a dwelling unit, office building, factory, or institution. Sometimes refer to domestic sewage.

Industrial Waste—Liquid waste from an industrial process, such as papermaking, brewing, or chemicals.

Sewerage System:—The collection of waste waters from occupied areas and conveying them to some point of disposal. The liquid wastes may or may not be treated before discharging into a body of water.

SEWAGE—is the liquid conveyed by a sewer.

SANITARY SEWAGE—That which originates from a dwelling unit, office building, factory, or institution. Sometimes refer to domestic sewage.

INDUSTRIAL WASTE—Liquid waste from an industrial process, such as papermaking, brewing, or chemicals.

STORM SEWAGE—Liquid entering into sewers resulting during or after a period of rainfall.

INFILTRATION—Water that has leaked into a sewer from the surrounding ground.

SEWER—A closed pipe which carries sewage.

SANITARY SEWER—is one that carries only sanitary sewage. The size of sewer is not adequate to carry storm sewage or surface water. Sometimes called a separate sewer.

STORM SEWER—is one that carries storm sewage, surface runoff, and street wash.

COMBINED SEWER—carries sanitary sewage industrial waste, and storm sewage. Diameter is much larger than either a sanitary or storm sewer.

SEWERAGE WORKS—Refers to the complete system of collecting, treating, and disposing of sewage.

PUBLIC SEWER—is one that is municipally-owned and in which all abutting properties have equal rights to use.

PRIVATE SEWER—one that is owned by property owners or developer. Use by other parties will normally be limited or involve some form of payment.

HOUSE SEWER—Pipe carrying sewage from the plumbing system of a single building to a sanitary sewer or other disposal system.

LATERAL SEWER—Has no other common sewer discharging into it.

SUB MAIN SEWER—One that receives the discharge of a number of lateral sewers.

MAIN SEWER (TRUNK SEWER)—Receives the discharge from one or more sub-main sewers.

OUTFALL SEWER—Receives the discharge from the collecting system and conducts it to a treatment plant.

INTERCEPTING SEWER—One that cuts transversely a number of other sewers to intercept dry-weather flow.

RELIEF SEWER—One that has been built to relieve an existing sewer of inadequate capacity.

SEWAGE TREATMENT—Refers to any artificial process to which sewage is subjected in order to remove or alter its objectionable constituents and make it less dangerous or offensive.

AREAS SERVED

To make the following evaluations the sewerage service map is compared with (1) the present population density map, to determine current service needs and (2) the future population density map, to determine these areas which the future will find most in need of sewerage service. In this connection, there is considerable evidence that, within limits, the construction of new sewer systems to serve anticipated growth areas is often "self-insuring"; that is, the presence of adequate public sewerage facilities attracts home builders and home owners alike to the areas so served and in this way stimulates population growth in these areas. By computing the area provided with sewerage service as a percentage of the total area in each density grouping, the percentage of homes served for each of the population groupings may be determined.

Example:
49.6 sq. mi.—total in study area
7.9 sq. mi.—total area in "over 5,000 persons per sq. mi." density group
6.8 sq. mi.—of this 7.9 sq. mi. served by public sewerage service

Therefore: $100 \times \dfrac{6.8}{7.9} = 86$ per cent of this density group is served

Example:

The following chart relates the economic justification of public sewerage service with various population densities. The chart does not necessarily reflect the justification of public sewerage service from a health standpoint, since this cannot be determined except as a judgment factor.

With this limitation, the chart should serve as a "rule-of-thumb" guide for planning purposes. Local characteristics such as topography and subsoil conditions may alter the criteria, which are based on research results for average soil and topographic conditions.

Population Density	Equivalent Lot Size	Service Economic Justification
Over 5,000 persons/sq. mi.	Less than ½ acre	Public sewerage is justified
2,500–5,000 persons/sq. mi.	½ to 1 acre	Public sewerage is normally justified
1,000–2,500 persons/sq. mi.	1 to 2 acres	Public sewerage is not normally justified
Less than 1,000 persons/sq. mi.	Over 2 acres	Public sewerage is rarely justified

SOURCE: *Environmental Health Planning Guide, Public Health Service, U. S. Dept. of Health, Education, and Welfare—1962*

SERVICE AREA

Service areas should be based on population density and topography. A multiplicity of small sewage treatment plants indicates a lack of coordinated area planning. The practice of constructing many small plants, each designed to serve only its immediate area, is less desirable and often more expensive than a few large plants designed to serve entire drainage areas. A comparison of the service area map with the map previously prepared for drainage and soil conditions will be helpful in determining (a) most logical locations of treatment facilities and service areas, and (b) areas where public sewerage is most needed due to soil conditions which preclude the proper operations of private septic tank systems.

JURISDICTIONAL AREA

Jurisdictional areas should be related to drainage areas and should reflect anticipated growth patterns.

SEWERAGE MASTER PLAN

A sewerage master plan showing future needs and facilities is necessary in attacking the problem of urban growth. In areas currently without serious problems, such a plan will assist greatly in preventing future problems. Along with the master plan, a capital budget (long-range financial plan) is needed, in which expenditures are allocated for periods of several years. Both the master plan and the capital budget should be related to other community needs.

EXPANSION NEEDS

A sewerage system which allows flexibility to meet changing conditions is desirable. This can be accomplished by designing sewer sizes to handle both present and future needs, and by a treatment plant which will allow expansion at minimum expense. Where economics do not justify large sewer main construction in all areas, temporary pumping stations have been used until population densities warrant permanent trunk line installations.

SEWER CONNECTION REQUIREMENTS

When public facilities are available, connection to such a system should be required, since this allows better system planning. A determination is needed for availability, and a definite distance should be set. Some areas also use a time factor, allowing one to two years before connection is required. Still another system is that of requiring payment of a front foot benefit charge where a line is available regardless of whether connection is made.

SEWER LINE EXTENSIONS

The community should have a definite policy for determining the method by which service extensions are made. Whatever method is used, it should allow extensions to be made where economic and health factors make this desirable.

The policy should include provision for extension of lines across vacant lots. This requires a decision as to the method of payment or cost sharing. For over-sized lines designed to serve a large drainage area, a common method is for the government agency to pay the difference in cost between a sewer sized only for the immediate development area and the larger size which will be needed ultimately for the total drainage area.

ADEQUACY OF TREATMENT

The community should provide treatment for all sewage. In urban areas, the discharge of untreated sewage into the environment constitutes a definite health hazard. If such conditions exist, or if the present facilities do not provide treatment of all sewage, steps should be taken toward corrective measures for the community.

RATE STRUCTURE

A determination of total sewerage service costs is useful to compare local system costs with each other and with costs in adjacent areas. Average monthly residential sewerage cost is a convenient basis for this comparison. In some communities sewerage costs are paid from a general fund supported by ad valorem taxes and in this case, an estimate of average monthly residential cost should be made.

In other areas sewerage costs are based on water usage. If this is the case, a standard water consumption figure must be assumed and used throughout the study area for comparison purposes. One thousand cubic feet per residence per month (about 75 gallons per person per day) is suggested for this purpose.

SOURCE: Environmental Health Planning Guide, Public Health Service, U. S. Dept. of Health, Education, and Welfare—1962

1. Cheaper
2. Larger pipes
3. Difficulty of treatment

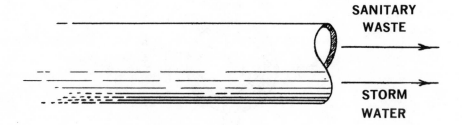

Combined—Storm water and sanitary waste are carried in the same line

1. Better in areas of large rainfall
2. Small pipes
3. Easier to maintain
4. Treatment plant smaller

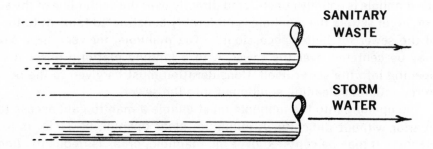

Separate—Two separate lines are used for storm water drainage and sanitary waste disposal

SOURCE: Ernest W. Steel, Water Supply and Sewerage, 3rd Edition, McGraw Hill Book Co., Inc.

Combined vs. Separate Sewers. Present-day construction of sewers is largely confined to the separate system except in those cities where combined systems were constructed many years ago. In newly developing urban areas the first need is for collection of sanitary sewage, and, since the sanitary sewers are relatively small and inexpensive, they can usually be constructed without long delay. For years the storm water will be cared for by the street gutters and the natural watercourses. As the city grows, however, underground conveyance of storm-water runoff may be needed, and a storm sewer system will be built. Many of the cities having combined systems were highly developed before the establishment of water-carried sewerage and already had storm sewer systems. It is interesting to note that a century ago in some cities the discharge of household wastes into the sewers was actually forbidden, but later the storm sewers received all liquid wastes and became combined sewers. Further extensions of such systems were then specially designed as combined sewers, often with provision for separating the dry-weather flow, which is largely sanitary sewage, from the large wet-weather flow.

Separate sewers are favored under the following conditions: where there is an immediate necessity for collection of sanitary sewage but not for the larger conduits required for the storm flow; where conditions are favorable for carrying storm sewage long distances over the ground surface; where disposal of the combined flow would necessitate pumping but where the separated storm flow need not be pumped; where mixture of storm and sanitary sewage would necessitate treatment of both while separation will allow disposal of storm flow without treatment; where an existing system of storm or combined sewers is inadequate in capacity and can be used for sanitary sewage alone, supplemented by another system for the storm waters.

Combined sewers are favored under the following conditions: where both types of sewage must be carried underground and it is necessary to keep the cost as low as possible; where the combined flow can be disposed of near by without objectionable conditions; where the storm flow, because of organic matter in street wash, is itself objectionable and requires treatment; where, as in crowded city streets, it is inadvisable to have more than one sewer.

It should also be pointed out that a system of sanitary sewers needs careful supervision to prevent unauthorized connection of roof gutters and other drains which will overload the sewers with rainwater during storms. Such supervision and danger are not a factor with combined sewers.

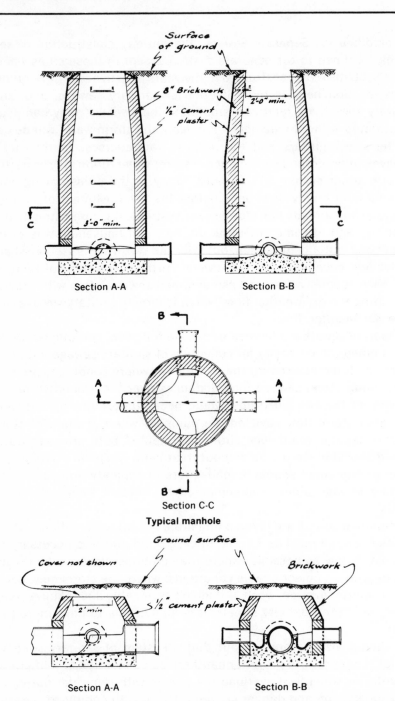

Section A-A   Section B-B

Section C-C

Typical manhole

Section A-A   Section B-B

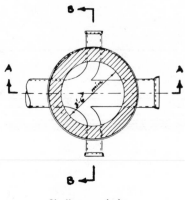

Shallow manhole

Manholes are among the most common appurtenances found in sewerage systems. Their principal purpose is to permit the inspection and cleaning of the sewers and the removal of obstructions.

Most manholes are circular in shape, with the inside dimension sufficient to perform inspecting and cleaning operations without difficulty. A minimum inside diameter of 4 ft for circular manholes has been widely adopted. However, 3 ft 6 in. is used in some localities, and where used solely for access into large sewers a diameter of 3 ft has been successful.

When the width of the sewer does not exceed the width of the manhole, the manhole is usually constructed directly over the center line of the sewer. For larger sewers the manhole is preferably constructed tangent to the side of the sewer for better accessibility. The manhole, for very large sewers, may be centered over the sewer, with a landing platform offset from an opening into the sewer itself. Consideration must be given to the need for introduction of cleaning equipment into the sewer.

The opening into the manhole must enable a man to gain access to the interior without difficulty. A minimum clear opening of 21 in. is recommended; it may be centered over the manhole, or, as is frequently done, it may be constructed off center in such a way as to provide a vertical side for the entire depth.

Typical manholes of the types used by many engineers and municipalities are shown.

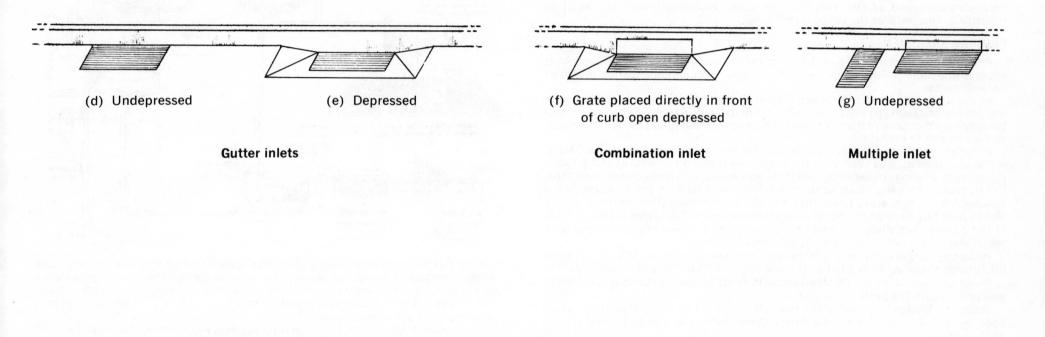

(d) Undepressed   (e) Depressed   (f) Grate placed directly in front   (g) Undepressed
                                                                              of curb open depressed

Gutter inlets   **Combination inlet**   **Multiple inlet**

(a) Undepressed   (b) Depressed   (c) Deflector inlet

Curb inlets

SOURCE: *Design and Construction of Sanitary and Storm Sewers, Joint Committee of American Society of Civil Engineers and the Water Pollution Control Federation—1960*

A wastewater treatment plant speeds up natural processes of stabilization. A reduction of the pollutants in water which might take weeks or days in the receiving water is accomplished in hours in a treatment plant.

Wastewater treatment is of two general types, primary and secondary. In primary treatment solids are allowed to settle out. This reduces pollution by about 25-40%. Secondary treatment, a further step in purifying, uses biological processes in addition to settling. This reduces the pollution 85-95%.

PRIMARY TREATMENT

Primary treatment may be suitable when the receiving waters are large and swift enough to handle pollutants by natural processes without endangering health or causing odors.

As the wastewater enters the plant, it flows through a bar screen to remove large pieces of material which might clog or damage machinery. A comminutor or barminutor may take the place of the bar screen. These units shred or cut the solid material and it remains in the liquid.

In the grit chamber, sand, grit, cinders, and stones are allowed to settle out. Next, a coarse screen may be used to protect equipment and processes. At this point, a pumping station may be necessary to lift the wastewater into the sedimentation tank. In this tank, remaining solids settle to the bottom or float on top as scum. These solids, called sludge, are removed from the tank by skimming the scum from the top and by pumping the sludge from the bottom of the tank to the sludge digestion tank. In the digester, the sludge is reduced in volume and stabilized by bacterial action which results in material that can be disposed of safely.

While the sludge is digesting, a large volume of gas is produced. This gas contains 60-70% methane and has a net heat value of 540-675 B.T.U.'s per cubic foot.

Sludge gas produced by digestion is used in many treatment plants as a source of energy for operating parts of the plant.

Stabilized sludge is periodically drawn off and dried by being spread on drying beds, by centrifuging or by vacuum filters. Dried sludge can then be burned or used as land-fill.

However, there are some problems in disposal and use of dried sludge. The demand for it as fertilizer is limited. When used by homeowners, sludge should be sterilized to protect the public health.

As a final step in primary treatment, the settled wastewater may be passed through a chlorine contact tank where chlorine is added for disinfection. The effluent is then discharged to receiving waters through an outfall sewer.

SECONDARY TREATMENT

In secondary treatment, certain units are added to the primary treatment plant to treat the settled wastewater from primary sedimentation. These additional units are needed when the receiving waters are small or slow-flowing or wastes come from a large population. Secondary treatment involves biological processes which oxidize dissolved and finely suspended materials. The basic methods of providing this biological treatment are:

Trickling filers. Settled wastewater from the sedimentation tank is distributed over beds of gravel or crushed stone, usually by a rotary distributor. As the wastewater trickles through the stones, it contacts the biological slime which grows on the stones. The organisms in the slime oxidize most of the remaining impurities in the liquid, reducing the pollutional load.

Activated sludge or aeration. Settled wastewater from the sedimentation tanks is mixed with compressed air and biologically active sludges. This method also oxidizes the organic materials and reduces impurities.

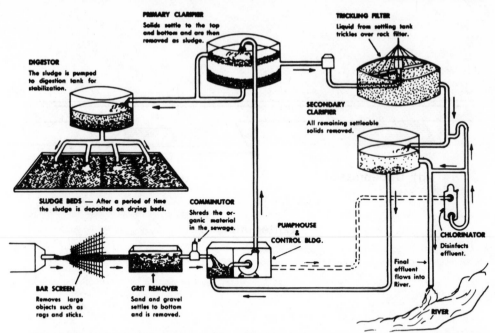

After this biological treatment, secondary sedimentation removes the remaining solids. A portion of the settled solids is returned to the aeration tank to provide the necessary biologically active material. The remainder is pumped to the digestor with the sludge from the primary sedimentation tank for treatment. The final effluent may be chlorinated before discharge.

Since the activated sludge process is more complex, it is more difficult to operate than a trickling filter. The trickling filter, however, is less efficient and requires a larger land area. There are many modifications of these basic processes available for use with particular types of wastes.

OTHER METHODS OF TREATMENT

There are several other processes in addition to these basic methods of treatment.

The Imhoff tank combines sedimentation and sludge digestion in a two-story tank. This is a common method of primary treatment in small communities because it is cheaper and requires less skilled operation than a standard primary treatment plant with separate digestion tanks. However, it is low in efficiency and provides less reliable sludge digestion, particularly in northern latitudes.

The Zimmerman Process is a patented method of treating sludge under high pressure and high temperature in a small area. If there is high sludge concentration the process is self-supporting in heat and power. For this method to be practical, an equivalent population of 30,000 is necessary.

Another patented method of sludge digestion involves the centrifuging of raw sludge followed by incineration under low pressure and high temperature. There are still other patented processes. Their applicability in a given situation must be evaluated by competent sanitary engineers.

Automation is an important new factor in wastewater treatment plant operation. Much progress has been made in the automation of recording and control equipment.

SOURCE: Water Pollution Control, National Association of Counties/Research Foundation, Washington, D. C.

SERVICE AREAS

A small number of community water utilities is preferable to a multiplicity of uncoordinated systems. Where practical, interconnection between distribution lines is recommended. A large number of relatively small water companies or municipal departments is often the result of a lack of a coordinated policy for community water resources. Widely different rate systems, insufficient capacity in some areas, and deficient fire protection service can often be traced to these conditions and illustrate the need for an area-wide coordinated plan for water service.

WATER MASTER PLAN

A master plan which shows future needs and facilities in relation to the area's growth and water resources is necessary for effective planning. Such a plan should be developed in connection with a sewerage master plan, and should encompass the long-range watershed needs, storage facilities, and, if appropriate, flood-control plans. Pipe networks, pumping facilities, treated water storage needs, and fire protection demands should also be considered.

Still another factor needed for a good community water program is a long-range financial plan. Both the master plan and capital budget should be related to other community needs.

CONNECTION REQUIREMENTS

Regulations calling for mandatory connection to public water supplies, where public water service is, or could be made available, are recommended for allowing better system planning and financing.

EXTENSION OF SERVICES

The community should have a definite policy for determining the method by which service extensions are made. Where water is provided by a private utility firm, extensions are largely dictated by economic factors. Where the system is publicly operated, there should be clear-cut processes by which service can be extended without undue "red tape."

Population Density	Equivalent Lot Size	Service Economic Justification
Over 2,500 persons/sq. mi.	Less than 1 acre	Public water supply is justified
1,000 2,500 persons/sq. mi.	1 to 2 acres	Public water supply is normally justified.
500 1,000 persons/sq. mi.	2 to 4 acres	Public water supply is not normally justified.
Less than 500 persons/sq. mi	Over 4 acres	Public water supply is rarely justified.

SOURCE: Environmental Health Planning Guide, Public Health Service, U. S. Dept. of Health, Education, and Welfare—1962

Where vacant areas must be crossed, or where the pipe network calls for oversized lines, a policy should be firmly established describing any special financial arrangements for such cases.

WATER QUALITY

The treated water should meet State and Public Health Service quality standards. A recommended minimum standard suitable for States and local areas is given in Public Health Service Drinking Water Standards.

WATER QUANTITY

Capacity and storage should be such as to provide quantities adequate for maximum day demands, without significant loss of pressure. The system should also be capable of meeting fire flow demands. In most cities under 200,000 population, the water required for fire fighting purposes, plus the maximum day consumption, is the governing factor in design. Requirements for fire fighting needs are usually based on standards set by the National Board of Fire Underwriters.

RATE STRUCTURE

Although no emperical figure can be provided as a "reasonable" water rate, the cost of water should be fairly consistent throughout the study area and should be reasonable enough to encourage connection to the public supply. In some communities, water revenues are too low to allow sound fiscal planning for depreciation or anticipated expansion needs. In other areas, water rates are set high enough to give a surplus sometimes used for other purposes. A thorough study of the rate structure is desirable to avoid both of the above practices and to provide fiscally sound service rates.

AREAS SERVED

Public water supply service should be provided to those areas where service can be justified from health and economic standpoints. In making the following evaluation, the water service map should be compared with present and also future population density maps. The percentage of homes served in each population density group can then be determined.

This chart is based on average cost of public vs. private water supplies as compiled from various journals and reports. The policies of State public utility commissions regarding capital investment-financial return were also taken into account.

Local characteristics may indicate an adjustment to these criteria is needed in some cases, but they are suitable for average conditions as a "rule-of-thumb" guide in determining economic justification of public water service.

Quantities of Water

Population Density[1]	Avg. Daily (gpcd)	Water Use Acre-Ft.[2] per 1000 Pop.	Max. Daily Water Use[3] (gpcd)	Acre-Ft. per 1000 Pop.	Total Daily Water Requirements Per 100 Acres of Residential Development				Total Yearly Requirements Per 100 Acres of Residential Development		Total Yearly Requirements Per 100 Pop. Acre Feet
					Avg. Day 1000 Gal.	Ac. Ft.	Max. Day[3] 1000 Gal.	Ac. Ft.	1,000,000 Gal.	Acre Feet	
1. Less than 1 d.u./acre	300	0.92	900	2.76	57	0.18	171	.54	21	64	335
2. 1–2.9 d.u./acre	225	0.69	675	2.07	171	0.53	513	1.59	62	190	252
3. 3–4.9 d.u./acre	190	0.58	570	1.74	253	0.78	759	2.34	92	282	212
4. 5–15 d.u./acre	150	0.46	450	1.38	455	1.40	1365	4.20	166	512	168
5. Over 15 d.u./acre	125	0.38	375	1.14	950	2.92	2850	8.76	346	1065	139

[1] Assumes 3.8 persons per dwelling unit.
[2] One acre-foot equals 325,830 gallons.
[3] Maximum daily consumption equals 3 times average daily consumption.

SOURCE: George Nez, Standards for New Urban Development—The Denver Background,
Reprinted by Permission of Urban Land, Vol 20, No 5 Urban Land Institute, 1200 18th Street N. W., Wash. D. C.

—PLANNING GUIDE FOR WATER USE

Types of establishments	Gallons per day
Airports (per passenger)	3–5
Apartments, multiple family (per resident)	60
Bathhouses (per bather)	10
Camps:	
Construction, semipermanent (per worker)	50
Day with no meals served (per camper)	15
Luxury (per camper)	100–150
Resorts, day and night, with limited plumbing (per camper)	50
Tourist with central bath and toilet facilities (per person)	35
Cottages with seasonal occupancy (per resident)	50
Courts, tourist with individual bath units (per person)	50
Clubs:	
Country (per resident member)	100
Country (per nonresident member present)	25
Dwellings:	
Boardinghouses (per boarder)	50
Additional kitchen requirements for nonresident boarders	10
Luxury (per person)	100–150
Multiple family apartments (per resident)	40
Rooming houses (per resident)	60
Single family (per resident)	50–75
Estates (per resident)	100–150
Hotels with private baths (2 persons per room)	60
Hotels without private baths (per person)	50
Institutions other than hospitals (per person)	75–125
Hospitals (per bed)	250–400
Laundries, self-serviced (gallons per washing; i.e., per customer)	50
Livestock (per animal):	
Cattle (drinking)	12
Dairy (drinking and servicing)	35
Goat (drinking)	2
Hog (drinking)	4
Horse (drinking)	12
Mule (drinking)	12
Sheep (drinking)	2
Steer (drinking)	12

Types of establishments	Gallons per day
Motels with bath, toilet, and kitchen facilities (per bed space)	50
With bed and toilet (per bed space)	40
Parks:	
Overnight with flush toilets (per camper)	25
Trailers with individual bath units (per camper)	50
Picnic:	
With bath houses, showers, and flush toilets (per picnicker)	20
With toilet facilities only (gallons per picnicker)	10
Poultry:	
Chickens (per 100)	5–10
Turkeys (per 100)	10–18
Restaurants with toilet facilities (per patron)	7–10
Without toilet facilities (per patron)	2½–3
With bars and cocktail lounge (additional quantity per patron)	2
Schools:	
Boarding (per pupil)	75–100
Day with cafeteria, gymnasiums, and showers (per pupil)	25
Day with cafeteria but no gymnasiums or showers (per pupil)	20
Day without cafeteria, gymnasiums, or showers (per pupil)	15
Service stations (per vehicle)	10
Stores (per toilet room)	400
Swimming pools (per swimmer)	10
Theaters:	
Drive-in (per car space)	5
Movie (per auditorium seat)	5
Workers:	
Construction (per person per shift)	50
Day (school or offices per person per shift)	15

SOURCE: *Environmental Health Practice in Recreational Areas, Public Health Service, U. S. Dept. of Health, Education, & Welfare*

TYPES OF WELLS

Wells may be classified with respect to construction methods as dug, bored, driven, drilled, and jetted.

Drilled wells may be drilled by either the rotary or percussion method.

Each type of well has distinguishing physical characteristics and is best adapted to meet particular water-development requirements.

The following factors should be considered when choosing the type of well to be constructed in a given situation.

1. Characteristics of the subsurface strata to be penetrated and their influence upon the method of construction.

2. Hydrology of the specific situation and hydraulic properties of the aquifer; seasonal fluctuations of water levels.

3. Degree of sanitary protection desired, particularly as this is affected by well depth.

4. Cost of construction work and materials.

Characteristics of various types of wells[1]

Characteristics	Dug	Bored	Driven	Drilled		Jetted
				Percussion	Rotary	
Range of practical depths (general order of magnitude)	0–50 feet	0–100 feet	0–50 feet	0–1000 feet	0–1000 feet	0–100 feet
Diameter	3–20 feet	2–30 inches	1¼–2 inches	4–18 inches	4–24 inches	4–12 inches
Type of geologic formation:						
Clay	Yes	Yes	Yes	Yes	Yes	Yes
Silt	Yes	Yes	Yes	Yes	Yes	Yes
Sand	Yes	Yes	Yes	Yes	Yes	¼" pea gravel
Gravel	Yes	Yes	Fine	Yes	Yes	No
Cemented gravel	Yes	No	No	Yes	Yes	No
Boulders	Yes	Less than well diameter.	No	(In firm bedding)	(Difficult)	No
Sandstone	Soft	Soft	Thin layers	Yes	Yes	No
Limestone	Soft, fractured	Soft, fractured	No	Yes	Yes	No
Dense igneous rock	No	No	No	Yes	Yes	No

[1] The ranges of values in this table are based upon general conditions which may be exceeded for specific areas or conditions.

SOURCE: *Individual Water Supply Systems, Public Health Service, U. S. Dept. of Health, Education & Welfare*

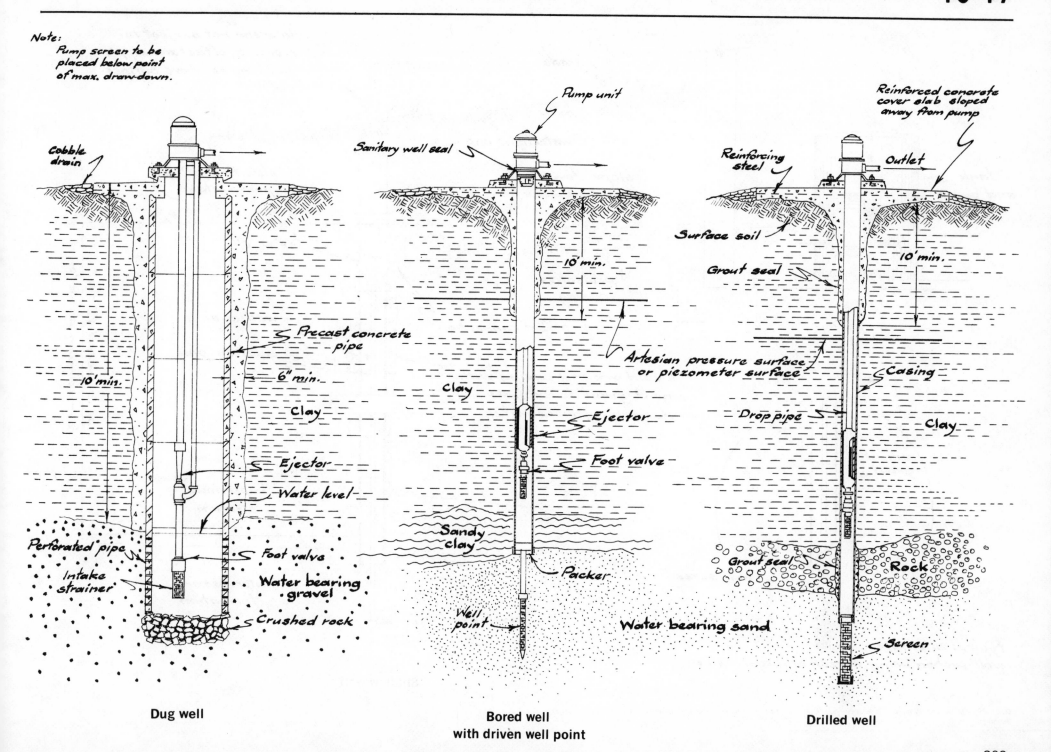

Note:
Pump screen to be placed below point of max. draw-down.

Cobble drain

Precast concrete pipe

10' min.

6" min.

Clay

Ejector

Water level

Perforated pipe

Intake strainer

Foot valve

Water bearing gravel

Crushed rock

Dug well

Pump unit

Sanitary well seal

10' min.

Clay

Ejector

Foot valve

Sandy clay

Packer

Well point

Bored well with driven well point

Reinforced concrete cover slab sloped away from pump

Reinforcing steel

Outlet

Surface soil

Grout seal

10' min.

Artesian pressure surface or piezometer surface

Casing

Drop pipe

Clay

Grout seal

Rock

Water bearing sand

Screen

Drilled well

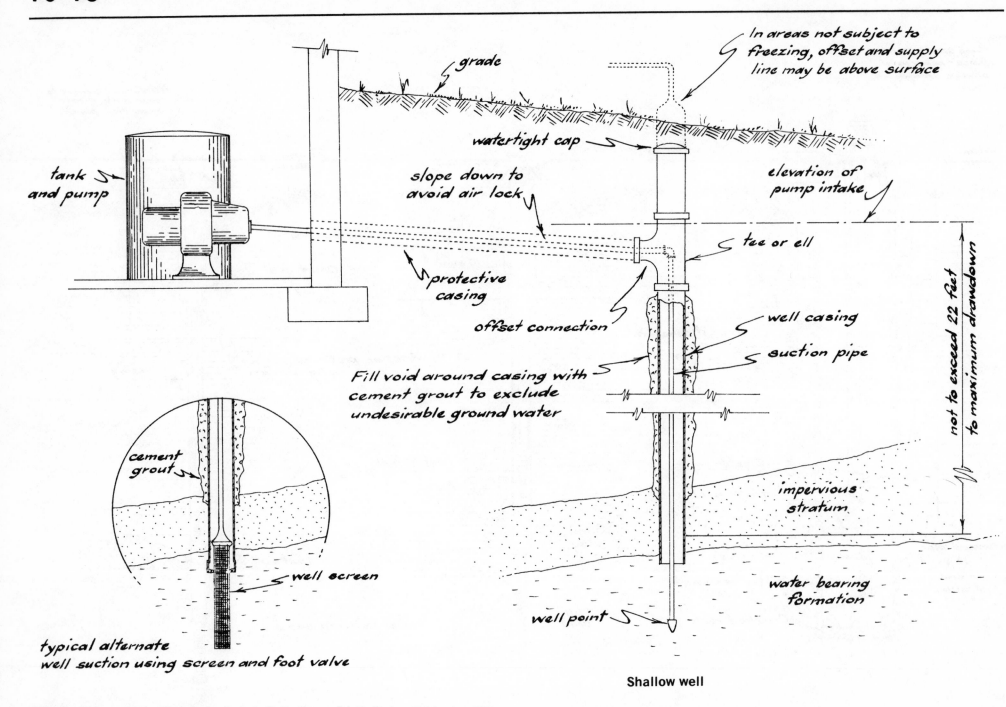

In areas not subject to freezing, offset and supply line may be above surface

grade

watertight cap

slope down to avoid air lock

elevation of pump intake

tank and pump

tee or ell

protective casing

well casing

suction pipe

offset connection

not to exceed 22 feet to maximum drawdown

Fill void around casing with cement grout to exclude undesirable ground water

impervious stratum

cement grout

water bearing formation

well screen

well point

typical alternate well suction using screen and foot valve

Shallow well

SOURCE: *Minimum Property Standards for 1 & 2 Family Houses, Federal Housing Administration, HUD, Washington, D. C.*

Deep well

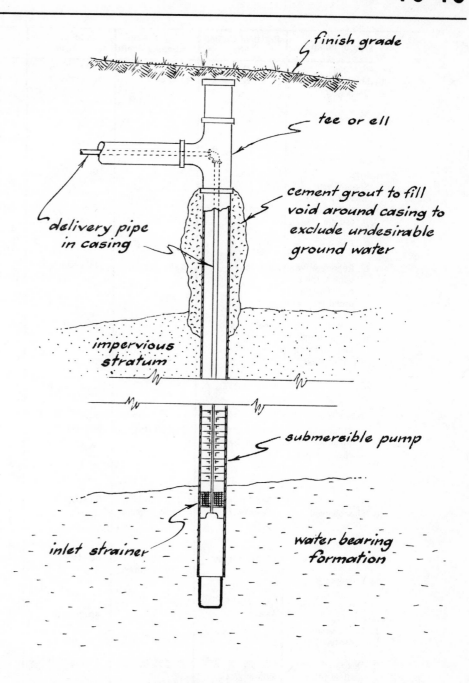

pressure pipe

suction pipe

grade

cement grout

casing

well casing must penetrate impervious layer

ejector pump

gravel pack and strainer (when required)

water bearing formation

bail plug

rock or other impervious formation

Note: Formations not subject to crumbling may not require the use of a casing

Alternate ejector type pump

finish grade

tee or ell

cement grout to fill void around casing to exclude undesirable ground water

delivery pipe in casing

impervious stratum

submersible pump

inlet strainer

water bearing formation

Submersible type

SOURCE: *Minimum Property Standards for 1 & 2 Family Houses, Federal Housing Administration, HUD, Washington, D. C.*

Type of pump	Practical suction lift[1]	Usual well-pumping depth	Usual pressure heads	Advantages	Disadvantages	Remarks
Reciprocating: 1. Shallow well 2. Deep well	22–25 ft. 22–25 ft.	22–25 ft. Up to 600 ft.	100–200 ft. Up to 600 ft. above cylinder.	1. Positive action. 2. Discharge against variable heads. 3. Pumps water containing sand and silt. 4. Especially adapted to low capacity and high lifts.	1. Pulsating discharge. 2. Subject to vibration and noise. 3. Maintenance cost may be high. 4. May cause destructive pressure if operated against closed valve.	1. Best suited for capacities of 5–25 gpm against moderate to high heads. 2. Adaptable to hand operation. 3. Can be installed in very small diameter wells (2" casing). 4. Pump must be set directly over well (deep well only).
Centrifugal: 1. Shallow well a. straight centrifugal (single stage)	20 ft. max.	10–20 ft.	100–150 ft.	1. Smooth, even flow. 2. Pumps water containing sand and silt. 3. Pressure on system is even and free from shock. 4. Low-starting torque. 5. Usually reliable and good service life.	1. Loses prime easily. 2. Efficiency depends on operating under design heads and speed.	1. Very efficient pump for capacities above 50 gpm and heads up to about 150 ft.
b. Regenerative vane turbine type (single impeller)	28 ft. max.	28 ft.	100–200 ft.	1. Same as straight centrifugal except not suitable for pumping water containing sand or silt. 2. They are self-priming.	1. Same as straight centrifugal except maintains priming easily.	1. Reduction in pressure with increased capacity not as severe as straight centrifugal.
2. Deep well a. Vertical line shaft turbine (multistage)	Impellers submerged.	50–300 ft.	100–800 ft.	1. Same as shallow well turbine.	1. Efficiency depends on operating under design head and speed. 2. Requires straight well large enough for turbine bowls and housing. 3. Lubrication and alignment of shaft critical. 4. Abrasion from sand.	
b. Submersible turbine (multistage)	Pump and motor submerged.	50–400 ft.	50–400 ft.	1. Same as shallow well turbine. 2. Easy to frost-proof installation. 3. Short pump shaft to motor.	1. Repair to motor or pump requires pulling from well. 2. Sealing of electrical equipment from water vapor critical. 3. Abrasion from sand.	1. Difficulty with sealing has caused uncertainty as to service life to date.
Jet: 1. Shallow well	15–20 ft. below ejector.	Up to 15–20 ft. below ejector.	80–150 ft.	1. High capacity at low heads. 2. Simple in operation. 3. Does not have to be installed over the well. 4. No moving parts in the well.	1. Capacity reduces as lift increases. 2. Air in suction or return line will stop pumping.	
2. Deep well	15–20 ft. below ejector.	25–120 ft. 200 ft. max.	80–150 ft.	1. Same as shallow well jet.	1. Same as shallow well jet.	1. The amount of water returned to ejector increases with increased lift—50% of total water pumped at 50 ft. lift and 75% at 100 ft. lift.
Rotary: 1. Shallow well (gear type)	22 ft.	22 ft.	50–250 ft.	1. Positive action. 2. Discharge constant under varible heads. 3. Efficient operation.	1. Subject to rapid wear if water contains sand or silt. 2. Wear of gears reduces efficiency.	
2. Deep well (helical rotary type).	Usually submerged.	50–500 ft.	100–500 ft.	1. Same as shallow well rotary. 2. Only one moving pump device in well.	1. Same as shallow well rotary except no gear wear.	1. A cutless rubber stator increases life of pump. Flexible drive coupling has been weak point in pump. Best adapted for low capacity and high heads.

[1] Practical suction lift at sea level. Reduce lift 1 foot for each 1,000 ft. above sea level.

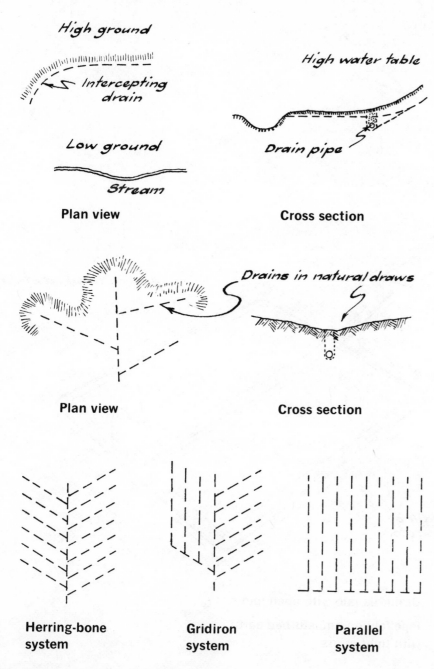

Plan view   **Cross section**

Plan view   **Cross section**

Herring-bone system   **Gridiron system**   **Parallel system**

LOCATING THE SYSTEM; SPACING, DEPTH, SLOPE

The main should, so far as possible, follow the line of natural drainage. Drains should be in straight lines, or in long easy curves.

Submains should also follow the line of natural drainage. Laterals should be laid in the line of greatest slope. Intercepting drains are an exception, generally being placed across the slope.

DESIGN OF LATERAL SYSTEM

Three principal types of lateral subdrainage systems are in common use, the herring-bone, gridiron and parallel systems. The parallel system is the most economical type because it involves the least duplication of drainage by laterals and mains. The preferable arrangement is short mains and long laterals rather than the reverse.

The spacing of laterals depends on the physical composition and texture of the soils.

A minimum slope of 0.1 percent (1 ft in 100 ft) is recommended. Steeper slopes are better.

SOURCE: Handbook of Drainage and Construction Products, ARMCO Drainage and Metal Products, Inc., Middletown, Ohio

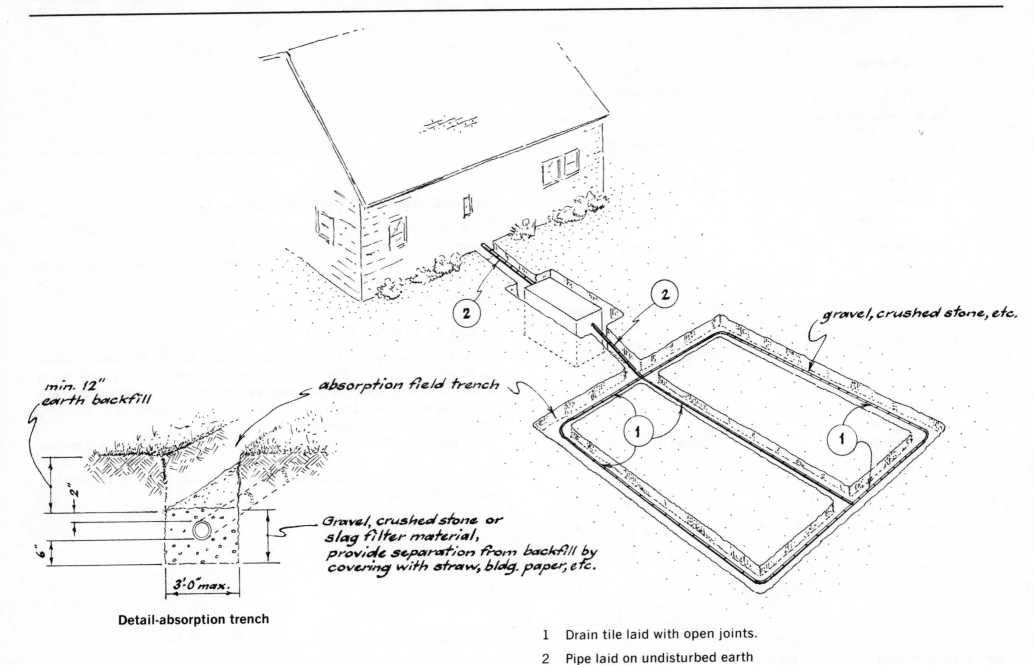

min. 12" earth backfill

absorption field trench

gravel, crushed stone, etc.

2"

6"

3'-0" max.

Gravel, crushed stone or slag filter material, provide separation from backfill by covering with straw, bldg. paper, etc.

Detail-absorption trench

1   Drain tile laid with open joints.

2   Pipe laid on undisturbed earth with tight joints.

SOURCE: *Minimum Property Standards for 1 & 2 Living Units, FHA No. 300, Washington, D. C.*

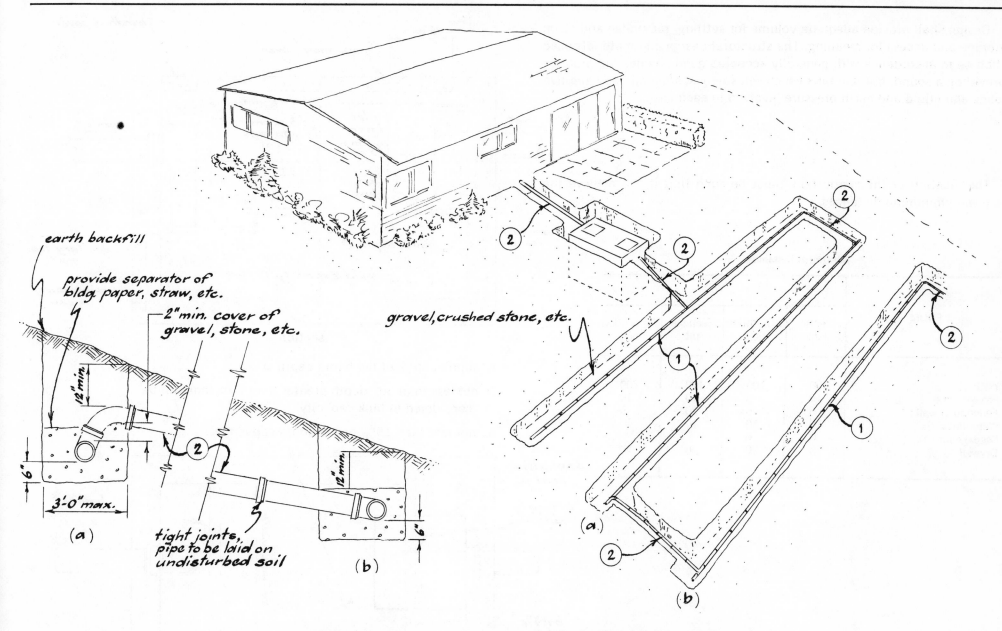

earth backfill

provide separator of
bldg. paper, straw, etc.

2" min. cover of
gravel, stone, etc.

12" min.

6"

3'-0" max.

(a)

tight joints,
pipe to be laid on
undisturbed soil

12" min.

6"

(b)

gravel, crushed stone, etc.

(a)

(b)

1   Drain tile laid with open joints

2   Pipe laid with tight joints

SOURCE: Minimum Property Standards for 1 & 2 Living Units, FHA No. 300, Federal Housing Administration

Design shall provide adequate volume for settling, for sludge and scum storage and access for cleaning. The structural design and materials used shall be in accordance with generally accepted good engineering practice providing a sound, durable tank which will safely sustain all dead and live loads and liquid and earth pressure involved in each case.

The location of the septic tank must be such that it will achieve the following minimum distances.

Minimum Distances

FROM	To			
	Septic tank	Absorption field	Seepage pit	Absorption bed
Well	50	100	100	100
Property line	10	5	10	10
Foundation wall	5	5	20	5
Water lines	10	10	10	10
Seepage pit	6	6		
Drywell	6	20	20	20

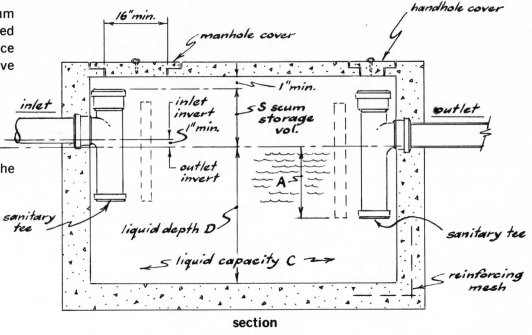

section

A approx. 40% of the liquid depth D

D not less than 30" depth greater than 6 ft. shall not be considered in tank capacity.

S not less than 15% of the liquid capacity C.

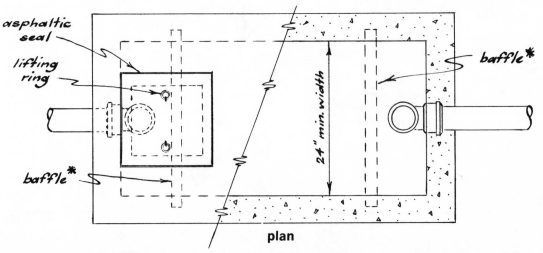

plan

*baffles optional to submerged inlet and outlet sanitary tee

SOURCE: Minimum Property Standards for 1 & 2 Living Units. FHA No. 300, Federal Housing Administration

Liquid capacity shall be based on the number of bedrooms proposed, or that can be reasonably anticipated in the dwelling and shall be at least as follows:

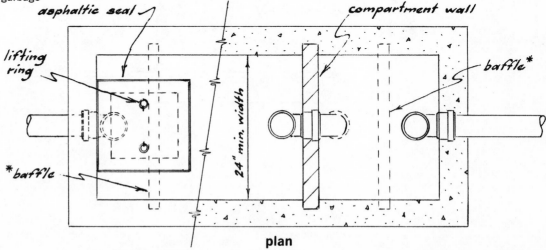

Minimum Capacities for Septic Tanks

Number of bedrooms	Minimum liquid capacity below outlet invert (gallons)
2 or less	750
3	900
4	1,000
Each additional bedroom, add	250

Note: These capacities provide for the plumbing fixtures and appliances commonly used in a single family residence (automatic sequence washer, mechanical garbage grinder and dishwasher included).

section

A approx. 40% of the liquid depth D

D not less than 30'' depth greater than 6 ft. shall not be considered in tank capacity.

S not less than 15% of the liquid capacity C.

plan

*baffles optional to submerged inlet and outlet sanitary tee

SOURCE: Minimum Property Standards for 1 & 2 Living Units, FHA No. 300, Federal Housing Administration

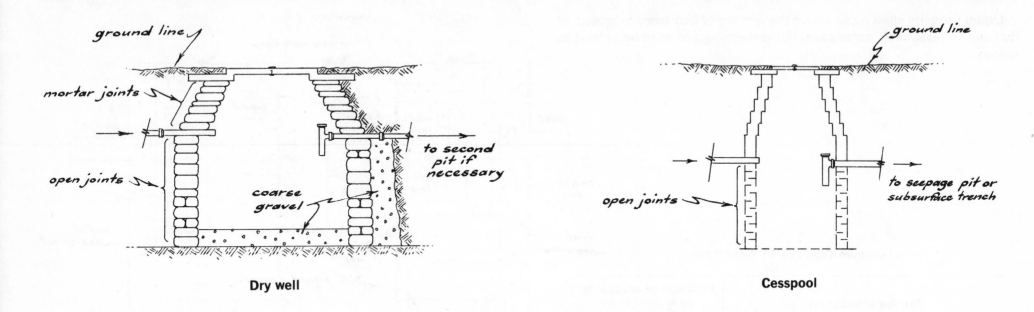

Dry well

Cesspool

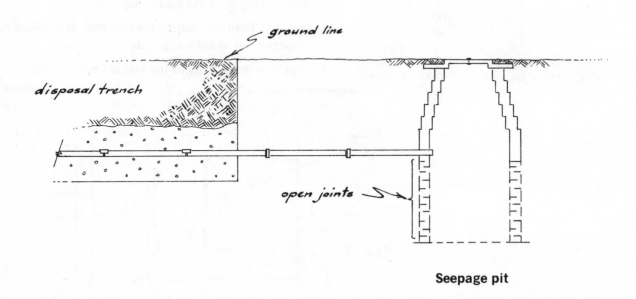

Seepage pit

SOURCE: Home Builders Manual for Land Development, National Association of Home Builders—1958

COLLECTION AGENCY

A governmentally regulated system of refuse collection is preferable to the practice of having individual competitive haulers deal directly with the homeowner. This regulation can be achieved by a governmentally operated system, by having private companies contract with the local government, or by having private companies franchised by the local government.

REFUSE MASTER PLAN

A master plan based on a thorough engineering analysis for the collection and disposal of refuse is vital in rapidly growing communities. The alternative is almost insurmountable future problems. Even the best planned refuse collection and disposal system will be one of the costliest services provided by a municipality. A poorly planned system is certain to place a continuous, undue burden on financial resources and create ill-will in the community.

Of prime economic importance is the proper location of disposal facilities in relation to future population concentrations. Sites for these facilities must be designated and acquired either through zoning, leasing, purchase, or condemnation to avoid future hostile public reaction as well as to avoid expensive future acquisition costs.

There must be close coordination of the refuse collection and disposal services (including any necessary transfer stations) and the community transportation plans to develop the most economic hauling system. Coordination with future recreational area plans may be mutually beneficial through improvement of low land by filling with refuse or incinerator residue.

EXTENSION OF SERVICE

A definite policy should be established for extending service areas. In contrast to water and sewerage services which require considerable long-range planning of physical needs, refuse collection lends itself to somewhat more flexible program planning.

Population Density	Equivalent Lot Size	Service Economic Justification
Over 2,500 persons/sq. mi.	Less than 1 acre	Service is justified
1,000 2,500 persons/sq. mi.	1 to 1 acres	Service is normally justified
500 1,000 persons/sq. mi.	2 to 4 acres	Service is not normally justified
Less than 500 persons/sq. mi	Over 4 acres	Service is rarely justified

SOURCE: *Environmental Health Planning Guide, Public Health Service, U. S. Dept. of Health, Education, and Welfare—1962*

COLLECTION

Collection should include both rubbish and garbage. Where only one type of refuse is collected routinely, experience has shown that the other type is often neglected. Closed body trucks are desirable for preventing material from scattering. Compaction trucks are advantageous under some circumstances because of larger capacity per unit volume. If garbage is collected, it should be done at least twice weekly during the warmer summer months. Weekly collection may suffice during winter months in many parts of the country.

Wrapping of garbage has been found to be an effective means of fly control during summer periods. A number of communities now require the installation of garbage grinders in newly constructed residences, and where sewage disposal facilities are capable of treating this load this practice is often desirable. Household incineration of combustible refuse should be carefully regulated to prevent insanitary conditions resulting from the possible introduction of non-combustible material, and to control air pollution. In those densely populated urban areas having adequate refuse collection, individual burning of refuse often creates serious air pollution problems and under these conditions communities may wish to restrict or prohibit this method of disposal.

DISPOSAL FACILITIES

Because of nuisance conditions and health hazards, open dumps are not acceptable. Other disposal methods such as the sanitary landfill or incinerator are satisfactory when properly operated. The disposal site should be as near as possible to the area it serves, preferably not more than 10 miles away.

AREAS SERVED

The refuse service area map should be compared with the population density maps to determine coverage in the various density groupings. The chart assumes average topography and reasonable length of haul, and is based on cost research using various numbers of collection stops per mile. As a "rule-of-thumb" guide, they can be used for determining the economic justifications of service under average conditions.

	ADVANTAGES	DISADVANTAGES	CENTRAL LOCATION	AREA REQ.
DUMP Refuse is simply dumped in a designated area. Garbage & rubbish may or may not be separated. Refuse is periodically burned, separated and plowed under. Generally utilized by small communities with ample open land.	Provides fill for marginal areas. Inexpensive Simple operation and supervision.	Propogation of insects. Propogation of rodent population. Offensive odors produced.	Distance from residential areas. Located so winds blow odors away from developed areas. Industrial areas.	Approximately 2 acres per 10,000 population served
SANITARY FILL Process is similar to dumping, except that refuse is covered over with earth. Dump areas are well organized and specified. Garbage decomposes and fill. Generally utilized by medium or high-density urban areas.	Relatively inexpensive. Simple operation. Provides fill for marginal areas.	Requires constant supervision. May develop insects and rodents if poorly operated.	Marginal areas requiring fill.	Approximately 4 acres per 10,000 population served.
INCINERATOR Destruction by fire of all refuse in a furnace. The refuse is delivered to the incinerator plant and burned. There are different types of incinerators and each must be carefully engineered. Usually restricted to large, high density urban areas.	No insects. No rodents. Clean operation. Used in combination with sanitary fill. Process can be used to make steam.	Relatively expensive in initial cost and operation. Building adds to air pollution. Complicated operation.	In most industrial areas regardless of wind directions.	10-20 acres.

ZONING, CODES, AND REGULATORY CONTROLS

FARM DISTRICTS

May be of the exclusive type or the cumulative type. Agriculture is the primary use. Other uses are secondary and accessory. Also permitted can be certain public and semi-public uses. Cumulative-type farm zoning districts can often serve as transition zones from agriculture to residential uses, including subdivisions. The transition may be facilitated by lowering lot size requirements. Usual minimum tract requirements for farm districts range from 10 to 80 acres.

FORESTRY DISTRICTS

Generally located in the Northwestern U. S. Developed from large acreage which is marginal for farming but valuable for forestry. Zoning is of the exclusive type. Such zones add to the recreational attraction of the area.

RECREATIONAL DISTRICTS

Primary use is for variety of recreational activities. This type of district can be used to protect and preserve mountainous, riverbank, lakeshore, or other areas that have natural or potential recreational features. Permitted uses can be agriculture, forestry, institutional uses, and limited commercial recreational uses.

FLOOD PLAIN DISTRICTS

Flood Plain Districts generally encompass all areas adjacent to rivers, streams, drainage channels, and ponds that are in danger of flooding. They can also include beds of water courses and of those portions of the adjoining flood plain that are required to carry and discharge the flood flow. Permitted uses usually include farming, forestry, and recreational activities.

WATERSHED DISTRICTS

Watershed districts reserve mountainous and hilly land for water production, forestry, wildlife, and recreation. Their purpose is to protect water sources and to avoid loss from improper use of land that has high water tables and is subject to periodic flooding. Forestry, agriculture, and grazing are deemed desirable principal uses. The types of recreation that need large acreages are suitable secondary uses.

OPEN-SPACE DISTRICTS

Open-space districts are used to reserve rural areas on the urban fringe for future generations, to provide permanent open space. Usually crop and tree farming may be allowed along with grazing and recreational activities.

LANDMARKS OR PRESERVATION DISTRICTS

Such districts are used to protect buildings and places that are of historical or cultural importance. Such districts help to safeguard our heritage and serve cultural educational, and recreational ends. The regulations pertain to buildings and structures of some significant architectural period. The concern is with exterior features only, mainly design, arrangement, texture, materials, and color. No changes can be made without approval from a review board.

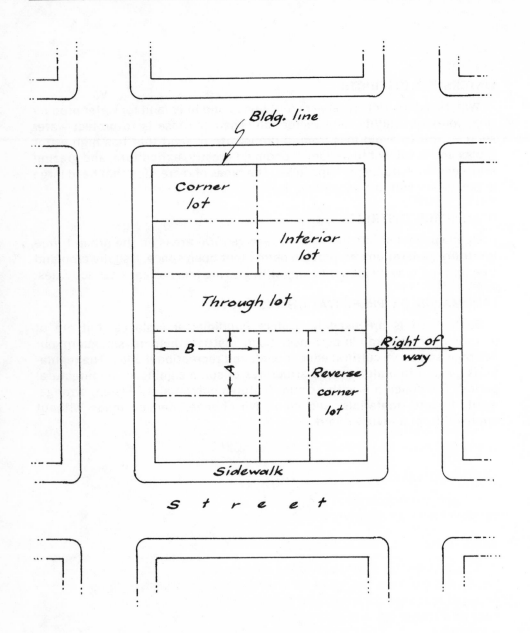

A—Width of lot

B—Length of lot

ZONING LOT

A "zoning lot" is either:

a. A lot of record existing on the effective date of the zoning ordinance or any applicable subsequent amendment thereto, or

b. A tract of land, either unsubdivided or consisting of two or more contiguous lots of record, located within a single block in single ownership.

LOT, INTERIOR

An "interior lot" is any zoning lot neither a corner lot nor a through lot.

LOT, CORNER

A "corner lot" is either a zoning lot bounded entirely by streets, or a zoning lot which adjoins the point of intersection of two or more streets and in which the interior angle formed by the extensions of the street lines in the directions which they take at their intersections with lot lines other than street lines, forms an angle of approximately 135 degrees or less.

LOT, THROUGH

A "through lot" is any zoning lot, not a corner lot, which adjoins two street lines opposite to each other and parallel or within 45 degrees of being parallel to each other. Any portion of a through lot which is not or could not be bounded by two such opposite street lines and two straight lines intersecting such street lines shall be subject to the regulations for an interior lot.

REVERSE CORNER LOT

A "reverse corner lot" is a corner lot which reverses the depth from the normal pattern of interior lots on a street. The front of the lot also changes from one street to the other.

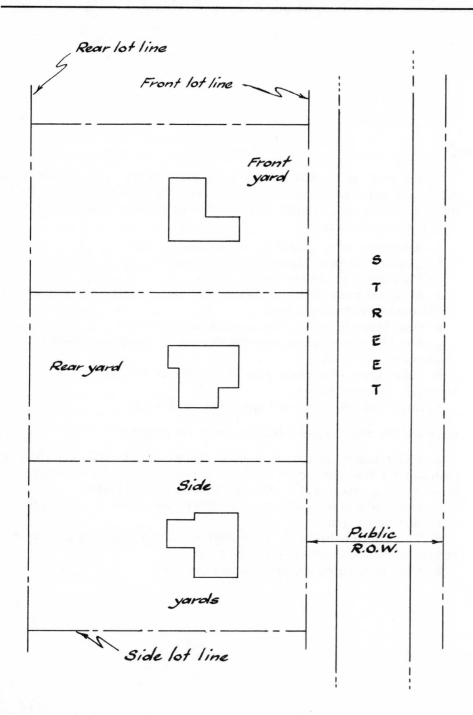

DEFINITIONS

YARD

A "yard" is that portion of a zoning lot extending open and unobstructed from the lowest level to the sky along the entire length of a lot line, and from the lot line for a depth or width set forth in the applicable district regulations.

YARD, FRONT

A "front yard" is a yard extending along the full length of a front lot line. In the case of a corner lot, any yard extending along the full length of a street line shall be considered a front yard.

YARD LINE, FRONT

A "front yard line" is a line drawn parallel to a front lot line at a distance therefrom equal to the depth of a required front yard.

YARD, REAR

A "rear yard" is a yard extending for the full length of a rear lot line.

YARD LINE, REAR

A "rear yard line" is a line drawn parallel to a rear lot line at a distance therefrom equal to the depth of a required rear yard.

YARD EQUIVALENT, REAR

A "rear yard equivalent" is an open area which may be required on a through lot as an alternative to a required rear yard.

YARD, SIDE

A "side yard" is a yard extending along a side lot line from the required front yard (or from the front lot line, if no front yard is required) to the required rear yard (or to the rear lot line, if no rear yard is required). In the case of a corner lot, any yard which is not a front yard shall be considered a side yard.

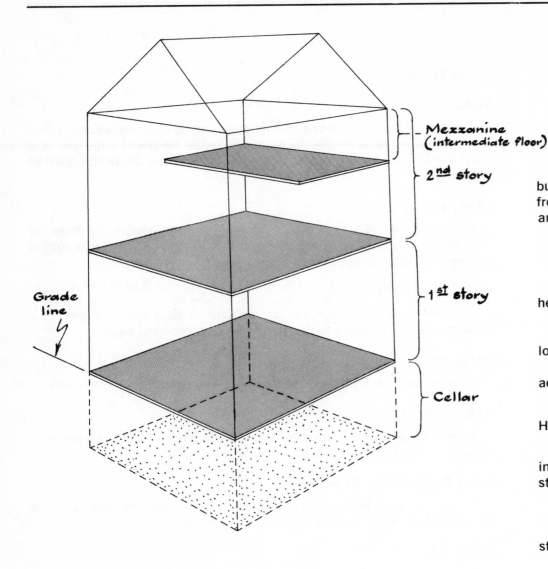

Mezzanine (intermediate floor)

2nd story

1st story

Grade line

Cellar

Floor area included

Floor area excluded

"Floor area" is the sum of the gross areas of the several floors of a building or buildings, measured from the exterior faces of exterior walls or from the center lines of walls separating two buildings. In particular, floor area generally includes:

    a. **Basement** space, except as specifically excluded
    b. Elevator shafts or stairwells at each floor
    c. Floor space in penthouses
    d. Attic space (whether or not a floor has been laid) providing structural headroom of eight feet or more
    e. Floor space in interior balconies or mezzanines
    g. Any other floor space used for dwelling purposes, no matter where located within a building
    h. Floor space in accessory buildings, except for floor space used for accessory off-street parking
    k. Any other floor space not specifically excluded.

However, the floor area of a building shall not include:

    a. **Cellar** space, except that cellar space used for retailing shall be included for the purpose of calculating requirements for accessory off-street parking spaces and accessory off-street loading berths
    b. Elevator or stair bulkheads, accessory water tanks, or cooling towers
    c. Uncovered steps
    d. Attic space (whether or not a floor actually has been laid) providing structural headroom of less than eight feet
    h. Floor space used for mechanical equipment

Floor area ratio is the total floor area on a zoning lot, divided by the lot area of that zoning lot.

$$FAR = \frac{\text{total floor area}}{\text{total lot area}}$$

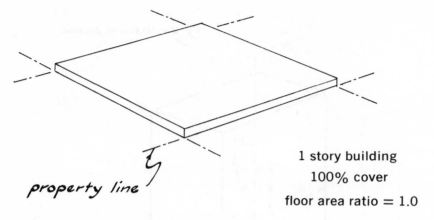

property line

1 story building
100% cover
floor area ratio = 1.0

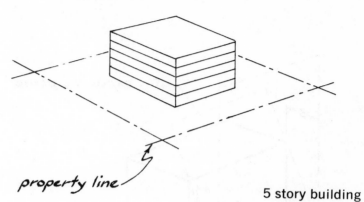

property line

5 story building
20% cover
floor area ratio = 1.0

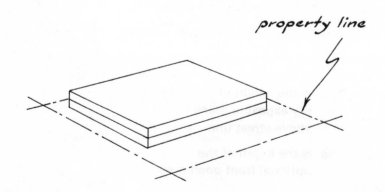

property line

2 story building
50% cover
floor area ratio = 1.0

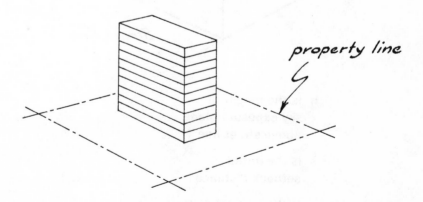

property line

10 story building
10% cover
floor area ratio = 1.0

A "Sky Exposure Plane" is an imaginary inclined plane beginning above the street line at a set height and rising over a zoning lot at a ratio of vertical distance to horizontal distance.

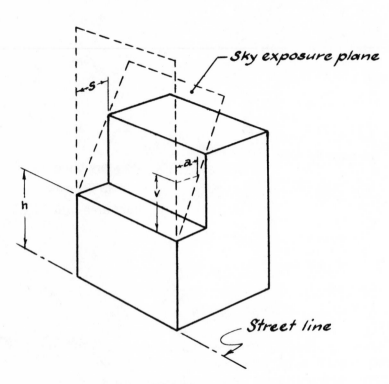

h is the height of
sky exposure plane
above **street line**

s is the **initial
setback distance**

v is the vertical distance

a is the horizontal distance

ILLUSTRATION OF SKY EXPOSURE PLANE

$$\text{Sky Exposure Plane} = \frac{\text{Vertical Distance}}{\text{Horizontal Distance}}$$

SOURCE: New York City Zoning Resolution—1961

h is the height of
sky exposure plane
above **street line**

s is the depth of the
optional front open area

v is the vertical distance

a is the horizontal distance

ILLUSTRATION OF ALTERNATE SKY EXPOSURE PLANE

On narrow streets, the slope will be less than on wide streets.
The height (h) should relate to the general scale of the neighboring structures.

BUILDING HEIGHT

H = Height of building

End view   **Gable roof**   Side view

End view   **Hip roof**   Side view

End view   **Gambrel roof**   Side view

Deck line

End view   **Mansard roof**   Side view

Building Height: Is the vertical distance measured from the established grade to the highest point of the roof surface for flat roofs; to the deck line of mansard roofs; and to the average height between eaves and ridge for gable, hip, and gambrel roofs.

BASEMENT, CELLAR

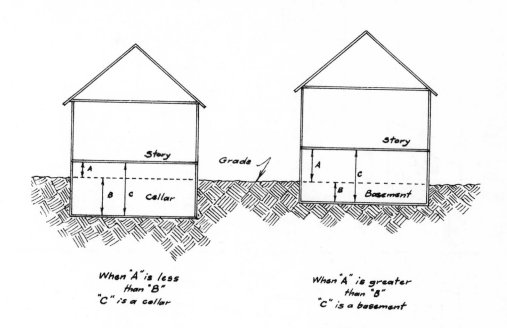

When "A" is less than "B" "C" is a cellar

When "A" is greater than "B" "C" is a basement

STORY

A "story" is that part of a building between the surface of a floor (whether or not counted for purposes of computing floor area ratio) and the ceiling immediately above. However, a cellar is not a story.

BASEMENT

A "basement" is a story (or portion of a story) partly below curb level, with at least one-half of its height (measured from floor to ceiling) above curb level. On through lots the curb level nearest to a story (or portion of a story) shall be used to determine whether such story (or portion of a story) is a basement.

CELLAR

A "cellar" is a space wholly or partly below curb level, with more than one-half its height (measured from floor to ceiling) below curb level. On through lots the curb level nearest to such space shall be used to determine whether such space is a cellar.

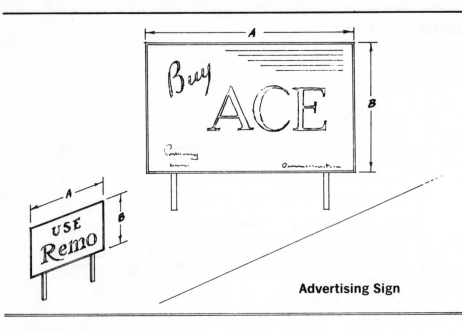

Advertising Sign

Business Sign

SIGN

A "sign" is any writing (including letter, word, or numeral); pictorial representation (including illustration or decoration); emblem (including device, symbol, or trademark); flag (including banner or pennant); or any other figure of similar character, which:

a. Is a structure or any part thereof, or is attached to, painted on, or in any other manner represented on a building or other structure, and

b. Is used to announce, direct attention to, or advertise, and

c. Is visible from outside a building. A sign shall include writing, representation, or other figure of similar character within a building only when illuminated and located in a window.

SIGN, ADVERTISING

An "advertising sign" is a sign which directs attention to a business, profession, commodity, service, or entertainment conducted, sold, or offered elsewhere than upon the same zoning lot.

SIGN, BUSINESS

A "business sign" is an accessory sign which directs attention to a profession, business, commodity, service, or entertainment conducted, sold, or offered upon the same zoning lot.

SIGN, FLASHING

A "flashing sign" is any illuminated sign, whether stationary, revolving, or rotating, which exhibits changing light or color effects, provided that revolving or rotating signs which exhibit no changing light or color effects other than those produced by revolution or rotation, shall be deemed flashing signs only if they exhibit sudden or marked changes in such light or color effects

SIGN, ILLUMINATED

An "illuminated sign" is a sign designed to give forth any artificial light or reflect such light from an artificial source.

SIGN, SURFACE AREA OF

Area of face of sign (A x B)

SIGN WITH INDIRECT ILLUMINATION

A "sign with indirect illumination" is any illuminated non-flashing sign whose illumination is derived entirely from an external artificial source and is so arranged that no direct rays of light are projected from such artificial source into residences or streets.

DENSITY (Families Per Acre)	GROSS AREA Per Family (Acre assumed to be 40,000 SF)	NO. OF PERSONS Per acre (4 Persons Per Family)	SUGGESTED Housing Type	DENSITY (Families Per Acre)	GROSS AREA Per Family (Acre Assumed to be 40,000)	NO. OF PERSONS Per Acre (4 Persons Per Family)	SUGGESTED Housing Type
1	40,000 SF	4	1 Family, Detached	50	800 SF	200	Low-Rise Multi-Family Apts. (6 Stories Max.)
2	20,000 SF	8	,, ,,	60	660 SF	240	,,
3	14,000 SF	12	,, ,,	70	580 SF	280	,,
4	10,000 SF	16	,, ,,	80	500 SF	320	,,
5	8,000 SF	20	,, ,,				
6	6,600 SF	24	,, ,,				
7	5,800 SF	28	,, ,,	100	400 SF	400	Medium-Rise Multi-Family Apartments (6-20 Stories)
8	5,000 SF	32	,, ,,				
10	4,000 SF	40	1 Family, Attchd. 2 Family, Detchd.	120	330 SF	480	,,
				140	280 SF	560	,,
12	3,300 SF	48	,, ,,	160	250 SF	640	,,
16	2,500 SF	64	,, ,,	180	220 SF	720	High-Rise Multi-Family Apts. (Over 20 Stories)
20	2,000 SF	80	Row Houses Or Garden Apts.				
				200	200 SF	800	,,
25	1,600 SF	100	,, ,,	300	150 SF	1200	,,
30	1,330 SF	120	,, ,,	400	100 SF	1600	,,
40	1,000 SF	160	,, ,,				

The height of building is limited by means of the Angle of Light Obstruction, so that adequate open air and light may reach the streets and rear yards. Each district is allotted a certain ALO. This is measured from the center line of the street and from the rear lot line. It is similar to many present regulations of height and setbacks, though expressed in angles instead of vertical and horizontal distances. However, to give more freedom of design and allow for more efficient building shapes, without sacrificing light and air, the ALO may be "averaged"; so that some sections of a building may rise above the allotted angle line, provided that an equally large or larger section drops below it. To avoid overlong stretches of high wall, this averaging is limited to a frontage length of not more than 1½ times the width of the street in residential districts and twice the width of the street in all other districts. To avoid too much height in any section on the street front, a minimum angle is set for calculating the low building sections, and buildings in residential districts may only exceed their allotted average angle for half the street frontage of the lot. And the overall bulk is still controlled by the Floor Area Ratio.

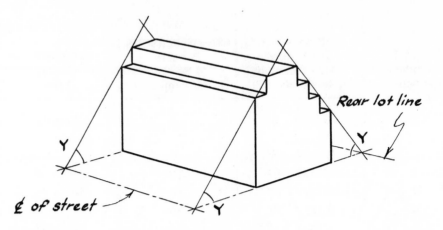

The Angle of Light Obstruction Y may be kept constant along the whole street frontage,

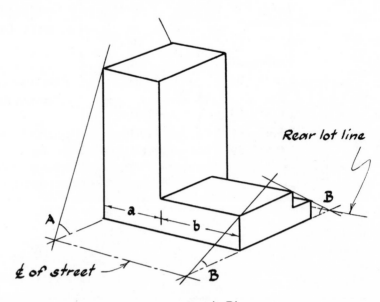

or averaged by the formula $Y = \dfrac{Aa + Bb}{a + b}$

SOURCE: *Rezoning New York City Edited and Designed by Baker-Funaro New York Chapter, American Institute of Architects*

All windows which are needed to satisfy the ventilation requirements of the Building Code and the Multiple Dwelling Law will have to give upon a certain minimum of open space known as the Area for Light Access. This can be easily and quickly measured with a graphic device marked off in a series of wedge-shaped sections.

The required ALA may be within the lot upon which the building is placed, or on the street, or on the required open yard of an adjoining lot.

The Area for Light Access is measured by a series of wedges marked out within the segments of a circle.

For residential buildings
the wedges are within the band between 40 and 60 ft. from the window.
Eight wedges (six of them contiguous) must be unobstructed.

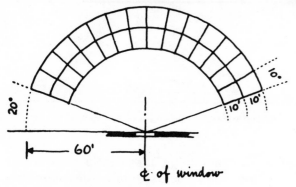

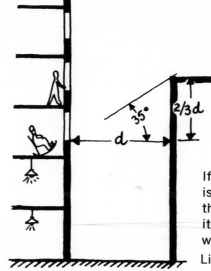

If an obstruction in front of the window is not higher (from the sill line) than two-thirds the distance from that window, it is not considered an obstruction when checking the window for Units of Light Access.

The window at **a** satisfies the requirements for residential buildings: a minimum of eight Units of Light Access, at least six of which are contiguous.

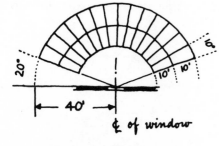

For low-bulk commercial buildings the wedges are within the band between 20 and 40 ft. from the window. Eight wedges (six of them contiguous) must be unobstructed.

For high-bulk commercial and manufacturing buildings the wedges are within the band between 10 and 20 ft. from the window. Eight wedges (all contiguous) must be unobstructed.

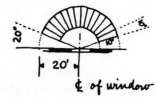

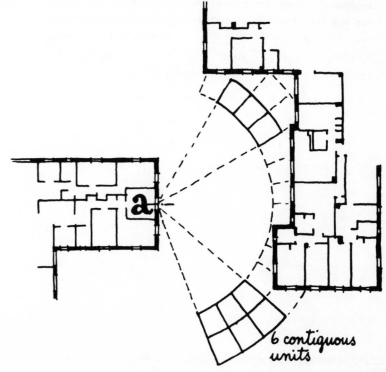

6 contiguous units

SOURCE: Rezoning New York City Edited and Designed by Baker-Funaro New York Chapter, American Institute of Architects

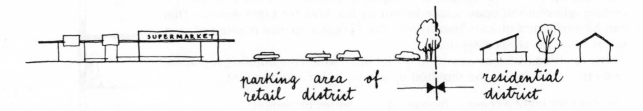

parking area of retail district ⟷ residential district

1. In retail and commercial districts parking areas which adjoin a residential zone must be shielded by walls, shrubs, or trees along the boundary line.

This is applied at the boundary between residential and non-residential districts to prevent this becoming a no-man's-land, undesirable for residences yet so zoned that it cannot be used for anything else. The Zoning Resolution should provide curbs upon business signs, show windows, and entrances to stores adjoining residential districts. Three examples are shown:

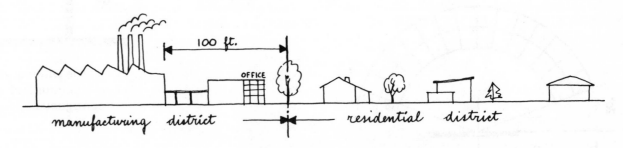

100 ft.

OFFICE

manufacturing district ⟷ residential district

2. In industrial districts adjoining a residential zone a 100 ft. wide strip along the boundary line cannot be used for actual manufacture but must be reserved for less objectionable uses, for example, an administration building or a parking lot.

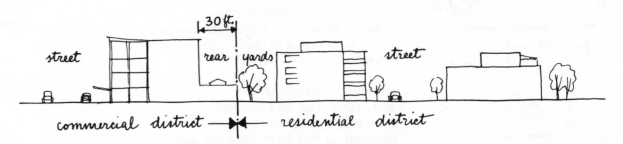

30 ft.

street   rear yards   street

commercial district ⟷ residential district

3. In non-residential lots which are back to back with residential, 30 ft. deep rear yards are prescribed, though a single story rising not more than 23 ft. above curb level may extend to the rear lot line.

SOURCE: *Rezoning New York City Edited and Designed by Baker-Funaro New York Chapter, American Institute of Architects*

CALIFORNIA STANDARDS FOR AMBIENT AIR QUALITY

POLLUTANT	"ADVERSE" LEVEL — Level at which there will be sensory irritation, damage to vegetation, reduction in visibility or similar effects.	"SERIOUS" LEVEL — Level at which there will be alteration of bodily function or which is likely to lead to chronic disease.	"EMERGENCY" LEVEL — Level at which it is likely that acute sickness or death in sensitive groups of persons will occur.
Oxidant		Not applicable	Not applicable
Ozone	"Oxidant Index" 0.15 ppm for one hour by the potassium iodide method (eye irritation, plant damage and visibility reduction)	Footnote 1	Footnote 2
Nitrogen Dioxide		Footnote 3	Footnote 3
Hydrocarbons		Footnote 4	Footnote 4
Photochemical Aerosols		Not applicable	Not applicable
Carcinogens	Not applicable	Footnote 5	Not applicable
Sulfur Dioxide	1 ppm for 1 hour or 0.3 ppm for 8 hours (plant damage)	5 ppm for 1 hour (bronchoconstriction in human subjects)	10 ppm for 1 hour (severe distress in human subjects)
Sulfuric Acid	Footnote 6	Footnote 6	Footnote 7
Carbon Monoxide	Not applicable	30 ppm for 8 hours or 120 ppm for 1 hour (interference with oxygen transport by blood)	Footnote 8
Lead	Not applicable	Footnote 9	Footnote 9
Ethylene	Footnote 10	Not applicable	Not applicable
Particulates	Sufficient to reduce visibility to less than 3 miles when relative humidity is less than 70 percent	Not applicable	Not applicable

1. Ozone, at 1 ppm for eight hours daily for about a year, has produced bronchiolitis and fibrositis in rodents (Stokinger, H. E., Wagner, W. D., and Dobrogorski, O. J. A. M. A. Archives of Industrial Health, 16:514, (1957). Extrapolation of these data to man is difficult. Functional impairment data have been reported by Clamann and Bancroft (Clamann, H. G., and Bancroft, R. W. Advances in Chemistry. No. 21, pp. 352-359, 1959); at 1.25 ppm some effect is observed on residual volume and diffusing capacity. The variability of the tests was not reported. Additional data would be needed before a standard is set.

2. A value of 2.0 ppm of ozone for one hour may produce serious interference with function in healthy persons, and the assumption is made that this might cause acute illness in sensitive persons. (Clamann, H. G. op. cit.)

*3. Five ppm of nitrogen dioxide for eight hours will produce decreased pulmonary function in animals. Slightly more may produce pulmonary fibrosis (Stokinger, personal communication); nitrogen dioxide from air pollution exposures is usually combined with nitric oxide and ozone. More data on human exposures will be needed prior to setting a standard.

4. Hydrocarbons are a group of substances most of which, normally, are toxic only at concentrations in the order of several hundred parts per million. However, a number of hydrocarbons can react photochemically at very low concentrations to produce irritating and toxic substances. Because of the large number of hydrocarbons involved, the complexity of the photochemical reactions, and the reactivity of other compounds such as nitrogen dioxide and ozone, it is not yet possible to establish "serious" and "emergency" levels for hydrocarbons. From the public health standpoint, the concentration of those hydrocarbons which react photochemically should be maintained at or below the level associated with the oxidant index defined in the "adverse" standard.

5. Carcinogens include a few organic compounds such as some polycyclic hydrocarbons, and some metals such as arsenic and chromium. Studies on effects of such substances are currently under way, but there are not sufficient data, at present, to set standards. In the meantime, it is recommended that concentrations of carcinogens in air should be kept as low as possible.

6. A sulfuric acid mist level of 1 mg/M^3 with an average particle size of one micron will produce a respiratory response in man. (Amdur, M. O., Silverman, L., and Drinker, P. Archives of Industrial Hygiene and Occupational Medicine, 6:305, 1952.) It is not possible to generalize from this for all air pollution conditions, because under natural conditions, particle size will vary. Only with large droplets would sensory irritation be produced without other physiological effects.

7. A level of 5 mg/M^3 of sulfuric acid mist for a few minutes produces coughing and irritation in normal individuals (Amdur, M. O., Silverman, L., and Drinker, P. op. cit.). Presumably, it could cause acute illness in sensitive groups of persons in a period of one hour.

8. Given certain assumptions concerning ventilatory rates, acute sickness might result from a carbon monoxide level of 240 ppm for one hour in sensitive groups because of inactivation of ten per cent of the body's hemoglobin. In any event it is clear that when a population exposure limit has been set for carbon monoxide, because of exposures from other sources, community air pollution standards should be based on some fraction of this limit.

9. It is clear that lead levels should be set on the basis of average values for long periods. While data are abundant concerning human response to eight-hours-a-day, five-days-a-week exposures, data are insufficient for the effects of the continuous exposure inherent in community air pollution. While laboratory studies will be pursued with vigor, it becomes very important that local agencies collect data on existing lead levels. Since lead exposures are from multiple sources, community air pollution standards should be based on a portion of the total limit for population exposure.

10. Ethylene causes severe damage to vegetation. Ornamental plants are severely injured by exposures from 0.2 to 0.5 ppm. Tomatoes and fruit are adversely affected at similar levels. Current work is expected to permit a standard to be set within a year.

*Note: In regard to Footnote 3, Dr. Stokinger suggests changes in the first two sentences so that they would read: "Five ppm nitrogen dioxide for eight hours will produce temporarily decreased respiratory function in animals. High levels (150-200 ppm) in short exposures produce fibrotic changes in the lungs of man that may end fatally". However, this change has not yet been approved by the State Board of Public Health.

SOURCE: Air Pollution Control, Field Operations Manual, Public Health Service, U. S. Dept. of Health, Education & Welfare

Some of the well-known odor classification systems are indicated here. They are useful in training inspectors in making associations and analyzing the various component sensations which odors may produce. For field purposes, one system is as good as another. The advantage of all systems is that they yield a usable odor vocabulary.

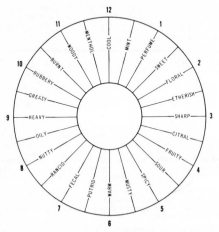

ODOR CHART. This chart attempts to present a complete range of odor terms which can be used to construct phrases of odor description. Each of these terms, moreover, can be numerically fixed from a "clock" chart for map notations, tabulations, or general reporting. Reported by Gruber, and attributed to Dean Foster, Head of the Psychophysical Laboratory at the Joseph E. Seagram Co., Louisville, Kentucky.

HENNING'S ODOR CLASSIFICATION

BASED ON SIX TYPES OF ODOR CLASSIFICATION

1. **Spicy:** Conspicuous in cloves, cinnamon, nutmeg, etc.
2. **Flowery:** Conspicuous in heliotrope, jasmine, etc.
3. **Fruity:** Conspicuous in apple, orange oil, vinegar, etc.
4. **Resinous:** Conspicuous in coniferous oils and turpentine.
5. **Foul:** Conspicuous in hydrogen sulfide and products of decay.
6. **Burnt:** Conspicuous in tarry and scorched substances.

CROCKER-HENDERSON CLASSIFICATION

A CONDENSATION OF THE HENNING ARRANGEMENT

1. Fragrant or sweet.
2. Acid or sour.
3. Burnt or empyreumatic.
4. Caprylic, goaty, or oenanthic.

SOURCE: *Air Pollution Control, Field Operations Manual, Public Health Service, U. S. Dept. of Health, Education & Welfare*

INTENSITY

Intensity is some numerical or verbal indication of the strength of an odor. Intensity may remain constant, vary or fluctuate depending on air/odorant dilution rates. A gradual increase in intensity is readily detected, although persons may have become fatigued by the odor. A sudden increase in odor intensity, however, such as might be encountered by suddenly opening a flask containing ammonia or chlorine in a room has an intensity which may be characterized by an impact. Thus, an intensity has shock value, particularly in relation to pungent or putrid odors.

Some general mathematical relationship exists between quantity of odorant (the stimulus) and odor intensity in any given situation. Equal degrees of subjective odor intensity are stimulated by quantities of odorant which have increased geometrically rather than arithmetically. This phenomenon is described by the well-known Weber-Fechner Psychophysical Law which states that the intensity of the sensation is proportional to the logarithm of the strength of the stimulus, for middling strengths of stimuli. Odorometers and other inanimate odor detection equipment appear to verify this principle both under field and laboratory conditions. According to Gruber, the Scentometer, devised by the Cincinnati Bureau of Air Pollution, provides 5 odorous inlets which permit dilution of 2, 4, 8, 16 and 32 parts total air to one part odorous air on the assumption that a trained observer can detect five levels of odor intensity.

Experimental findings on the discernment of odor intensity are still incomplete. It can be said, however, that the average observer or complainant can be expected to distinguish between three intensities, weak, medium and strong, whereas the expert should be able to distinguish between those five degrees of intensity shown below and at least 16 categories of odor quality in the following typical rating scheme:

The intensity of the odor may be noted as follows:

0. A concentration of an odorant which produces no sensation.
1. Concentration which is just detectable (the threshold dilution).
2. A distinct and definite odor whose unpleasant characteristics are revealed or foreshadowed (the recognition threshold).
3. An odor strong enough to cause a person to attempt to avoid it completely.
4. An odor so strong as to be overpowering and intolerable for any length of time.

This rating system is adapted especially for field work since it is made in terms of the behavior or response of a percipient that can be observed by an inspector. The response here is clearly one of avoidance. The fact that a person desperately attempts to avoid a strong and unpleasant odor clearly indicates the intensity of that odor.

AIR POLLUTION EMISSION TABLE

Type of Pollutant	Effect	Source	Possible Control Measures	Air Pollution Sampling Method
Fallout Particulate Matter	Soiling of property, nuisance	Industry, combustion processes, road mix plants, incinerators, etc.	Cyclones, bag filters, electrostatic precipitators, washers, etc.	Dustfall sampling
Suspended Particulate Matter, Smoke	Soiling of property, visibility reduction, nuisance	Industry, combustion processes, road mix plants, incinerators, etc.	Bag filters, electrostatic precipitators, better combustion	1. High Volume Sampling 2. AISI Smoke Sampling 3. Visibility Determinations
Hydrocarbons	Primary contributors to Los Angeles type smog (eye irritation, rubber cracking, visibility reduction, ozone formation).	Automotive vehicles, oil refineries, fuel handling, solvent handling.	Afterburner and other automotive devices (under development), automotive blowby devices, floating roof covers, vapor recovery systems.	Freezeout method
Oxides of Nitrogen		Automotive vehicles, combustion processes, industry	Automotive devices (under research), controlled combustion	Saltzman method
Oxidant (a measure of Los Angeles smog)		Photochemical reactions in the atmosphere	Controls for hydrocarbons and oxides of nitrogen	1. Potassium iodide method 2. Phenolphthalin method
Carbon Monoxide	Toxic pollutant	Automotive vehicles, industry	Afterburners for industry; automotive exhaust devices (under development)	A modification of the NBS colorimetric detector tube technique
Sulfur Dioxide	Corrosive, odorous plant damage, toxic	Combustion processes, industry, etc.	Absorption towers, control of sulfur content in fuel	West method
Pollen	Allergy, hay fever	Natural—trees, grasses, weeds, etc.	Farming methods, weed control	Collection on slides
Odors	Nuisance	Industry and miscellaneous	Good housekeeping, chemical control, masking, counteractant, etc.	Trained nose

SOURCE: *Environmental Health Planning Guide, Public Health Service, U. S. Dept. of Health, Education, and Welfare—1962*

Classify Waters

Classification is the determination of the manner in which a stream may be used, while standards of quality refer to the physical, chemical and bacteriological characteristics of water. In classifying a stream, there will be a corresponding establishment of standards for each class of water.

Once a stream has been classified, communities along its watershed are normally required to initiate sewage and industrial pollution treatment programs to insure conformity with the classification.

CLASSIFICATION AND STANDARDS OF QUALITY FOR INTERSTATE WATERS
(As Revised and Adapted October 1, 1959)

	CLASS A	CLASS B	CLASS C	CLASS D
	Suitability for Use			
	Suitable for any water use. Character uniformly excellent.	Suitable for bathing and recreation, irrigation and agricultural uses; good fish habitat; good aesthetic value. Acceptable for public water supply with filtration and disinfection.	Suitable for recreational boating, irrigation of crops not used for consumption without cooking; habitat for wildlife and common food and game fishes indigenous to the region; industrial cooling and most industrial process uses.	Suitable for transportation of sewage and industrial wastes without nuisance, and for power navigation and certain industrial uses.
	Standards of Quality			
Dissolved oxygen	Not less than 75% sat.	Not less than 75% sat.	Not less than 5 p.p.m.	Present at all times
Oil and grease	None	No appreciable amount	Not objectionable	Not objectionable
Odor, scum, floating solids, or debris	None	None	None	Not objectionable
Sludge deposits	None	None	None	Not objectionable
Color and turbidity	None	Not objectionable	Not objectionable	Not objectionable
Phenols or other taste producing substances	None	None	None	
Substances potentially toxic	None	None	Not in toxic concentrations or combinations	Not in toxic concentrations or combinations
Free acids or alkalies	None	None	None	Not in objectionable amounts
Radiocativity	Within limits approved by the appropriate State agency with consideration of possible adverse effects in downstream waters from discharge of radioactive wastes; limits in a particular watershed to be resolved when necessary after consulation between States involved.			
Caliform bacteria	Within limits approved by State Department of Health for uses involved	Bacterial content of bathing waters shall meet limits approved by State Department of Health and acceptability will depend on sanitary survey.		

Sea waters used for the taking of market shellfish shall not have a median coliform content in excess of 70 per 100 ml.

NOTE: Waters falling below these descriptions are considered as unsatisfactory and as Class E.

These standards do not apply to conditions brought about by natural causes.

For purpose of distinction as to use, waters used or proposed for public water supply shall be so designated.

NEW ENGLAND INTERSTATE WATER POLLUTION CONTROL COMMISSION

SOURCE: Water Pollution Control, National Association of Counties/Research Foundation, Washington. D. C.

DEFINITION AND CRITERIA

Historic preservation, as defined by the National Trust for Historic Preservation, is a well-rounded program of scientific research and study, protection, restoration, maintenance and the interpretation of sites, buildings and objects significant in American history and culture.

To be of historical and cultural significance, a structure or area should have outstanding historical and cultural significance in the nation or in the state, region, or community in which it exists. Such significance is found in

1. Historic structures or sites in which the broad cultural, political, economic, or social history of the nation, state or community is best exemplified, and from which the visitor may grasp in three-dimensional form one of the larger patterns of the American heritage.

2. Structures or areas that are identified with the lives of historic personages or with important events in the main currents of national, state or local history.

3. Structures or areas that embody the distinguishing characteristics of an architectural type-specimen, inherently valuable for a study of a period-style or method of construction; or a notable work of a master builder, designer or architect whose individual genius influenced his age. Mere antiquity is not sufficient basis for selection of a structure for permanent preservation, but can be a factor if other more significant examples have disappeared or if the building forms part of an especially characteristic section of a given community. Smaller structures, such as the first squared-log cabins or the sod houses of the pioneers, may be as important relatively as the mansions of the past.

4. Structures or sites of archaeological interest that contribute to the understanding of aboriginal man in America.

SUITABILITY

Preference should be given to those structures or sites where there is a preponderance of original material or other physical remains which have retained their integrity. (Integrity is a composite quality derived from original workmanship, original location, and intangible elements of feeling and association.) Repair or restoration of original elements or reconstruction of a building long destroyed demand high professional standards of historical and scientific techniques. Generally speaking, it is better to preserve than repair, better to repair than restore, better to restore than reconstruct.

Property boundaries adequate to protect the essential historical or cultural values of the project should be obtained at the outset if possible.

Other important practical considerations are accessibility to the public; encroachments by business, industry, housing, and traffic; availability of fire and police protection and of essential utilities.

The cost of restoration or reconstruction and of subsequent adequate maintenance and interpretation should not be beyond the means of the sponsors. A well-considered plan should contemplate that the project be fully endowed or potentially self-sustaining.

Since all historic structures significant enough to warrant preservation cannot support themselves as historic museums regularly open to the public, adaptation to other possible uses should be considered. It is essential, however, no matter what the proposed use, that every effort should be made to preserve those elements which account for the significance of a particular structure.

The primary purpose in preserving a structure as a historic museum is public use and enjoyment. Each project should have a place in the national, state or local programs for the preservation of historic sites or buildings and should be coordinated with all similar projects in its area to increase its usefulness as an educational force.

SOURCE: A Report by The Committee on Standards and Surveys National Trust for Historic Preservation Empire State Architect—September-October, 1967

BUILDING CLASSIFICATION ACCORDING TO TYPE OF CONSTRUCTION

Construction Classifications: A classification of buildings into types of construction which is based upon the fire properties of walls, floors, roofs, ceilings and other elements.

Type 1, Fire-resistive Construction: That type of construction in which the walls, partitions, columns, floors, roof, ceilings and other structural members are noncombustible with sufficient fire resistance to withstand the effects of a fire and prevent its spread from one story to another.

*Type 2, Noncombustible Construction: That type of construction in which the walls, partitions, columns, floors, roof, ceilings and other structural members are noncombustible but which does not qualify as Type 1, fire-resistive construction. Type 2 construction is further classified as Type 2a (1-hr. protected) and Type 2b, which does not require protection for certain members.

*Type 3, Exterior Protected Construction: That type of construction in which the exterior walls are of noncombustible construction having a fire resistance rating as specified and which are structurally stable under fire conditions and in which the interior structural members and roof are wholly or partly of combustible construction. Type 3 construction is divided into two subtypes as follows:

Type 3a: Exterior protected construction in which the interior exitways, columns, beams and bearing walls are noncombustible in combination with the floor system, roof construction and nonload bearing partitions of combustible construction.

Type 3b: Exterior protected construction in which the interior structural members are of protected combustible materials, or of heavy timber unprotected construction.

*Type 4, Wood Frame Construction: That type of construction in which the exterior walls, partitions, floors, roof and other structural members are wholly or partly of wood or other combustible materials.

BUILDING CLASSIFICATION ACCORDING TO OCCUPANCY

The classification of buildings according to occupancy, is as follows.

assembly occupancy means the occupancy or use of a building or structure or any portion thereof by a gathering of persons for civic, political, travel, religious, social, or recreational purposes.

business occupancy means the occupancy or use of a building or structure or any portion thereof for the transaction of business, or the rendering or receiving of professional services.

educational occupancy means the occupancy or use of a building or structure or any portion thereof by persons assembled for the purpose of learning or of receiving educational instruction.

high hazard occupancy means the occupancy or use of a building or structure or any portion thereof that involves highly combustible, highly flammable, or explosive material, or which has inherent characteristics that constitute a special fire hazard.

industrial occupancy means the occupancy or use of a building or structure or any portion thereof for assembling, fabricating, finishing, manufacturing, packaging, or processing operations.

institutional occupancy means the occupancy or use of a building or structure or any portion thereof by persons harbored or detained to receive medical, charitable, or other care or treatment, or by persons involuntarily detained.

residential occupancy means the occupancy or use of a building or structure or any portion thereof by persons for whom sleeping accommodations are provided but who are not harbored or detained to receive medical, charitable, or other care or treatment, or are not involuntarily detained.

storage occupancy means the occupancy or use of a building or structure or any portion thereof for the storage of goods, wares, merchandise, raw materials, agricultural or manufactured products, including parking garages, or the sheltering of livestock and other animals, except when classed as a high hazard.

SOURCE: Federal Housing Administration

SOURCE: National Building Code

PURPOSE OF FIRE LIMITS

The purpose of fire limits is the protection of closely built commercial districts of cities against the hazards of fire spreading from building to building, by supplementary restrictions on the construction permitted within such limits. This purpose can be served adequately by a single class of fire limits.

BRIEF STATEMENT OF WHAT FIRE LIMITS SHOULD INCLUDE

The fire limits should include all closely built districts of predominantly business or commercial occupancy, together with such blocks or portions of blocks surrounding these districts on all sides as constitute an exposure to these districts, including areas where a definite trend toward business or commercial development is manifested. The outer belt of blocks or part blocks surrounding the closely built districts ordinarily should be not less than 200 feet wide.

WHAT SHOULD BE INCLUDED IN COMMERCIAL OCCUPANCY

Commercial occupancies should include retail and wholesale mercantile and general business occupancies commonly found in closely-built and developing mercantile districts including banks, business and professional offices, show-rooms, restaurants, theaters, night-clubs, hotels, club buildings having restaurant and hotel accommodations, automobile service and filling stations, repair and storage garages, film exchanges, and shops of small tradesmen and artisans; also newspaper plants and other publishing houses, telephone and telegraph buildings, radio and television studios, freight and express offices and depots and railway and bus stations. Warehouse and storage buildings used for the storage of finished merchandise, goods or wares, except where located together with and forming a part of a manufacturing or industrial plant, shall also be classed as commercial as shall Federal, State or local government owned or leased buildings used for general business or commercial purposes such as business offices, garages or service buildings. Grade floor occupancies shall normally be regarded as governing.

WHAT DISTRICTS SHOULD .BE CONSIDERED CLOSELY BUILT

A block or part block should be considered closely built if at least 50 per cent of the ground area is built upon and 50 per cent or more of the built-on area is devoted to commercial occupancy; except that where the average height of buildings is 2½ stories or more, a block or part block should be considered closely built if the ground area built upon is at least 40 per cent.

HOW LARGE SHOULD A DISTRICT BE TO WARRANT FIRE LIMITS PROTECTION

Any district consisting of two or more adjoining blocks or part blocks comprising an area of 100,000 square feet or more, exclusive of intervening streets, should be considered large enough to warrant fire limits protection.

THE OUTER BELT

The outer belt is included because of its location with respect to the closely built district not primarily because of what it contains. However the construction and occupancy existing in the outer belt may be a factor in determining the proper width of the belt for protection of the closely built district. The outer belt is for the purpose of protecting the closely built district against serious exposure fires starting outside the closely built district.

Full blocks should be taken for the outer belt wherever practicable. The outer belt should ordinarily have a width of at least 200 feet. Where closely built blocks of other than commercial occupancy constitute a serious exposure to the closely built commercial district, the width should be extended to include these areas. In certain cases for small closely built districts or for protection of narrow portions of closely built districts a width of 100 feet may be satisfactory.

Streets and other open spaces not subject to building construction, including rivers, streams, parks, parkways, plazas, railroads and other dedicated rights-of-way, having a width of at least 100 feet, may be appropriately included in the outer belt. Minor extensions of the fire limits to make use of such open spaces are generally desirable.

DEVELOPING COMMERCIAL AREAS

The areas where a definite trend toward commercial development is manifested should be included in anticipation of future growth likely to develop these areas into closely built districts.

A developing commercial area should be included if it consists of two or more adjoining blocks or part blocks comprising an area of 100,000 square feet, exclusive of intervening streets.

A block or part block should be considered as of developing commercial occupancy if at least 25 per cent of the ground area is built upon and 40 per cent or more of the built-on area is devoted to commercial occupancy.

Where appropriately located, developing commercial areas may be counted as part of the outer belt.

ROUNDING OUT THE LIMITS

The general outline of the fire limits should be fairly regular. Blocks or part blocks largely contained within adjacent commercial street frontages or extensions or lying between adjacent component areas should be carefully considered for inclusion on the basis of the general character of the neighborhood and recognized trend of development. In sections where rapid commercial development is manifested, moderate extension of the indicated limits may be warranted. Conversely, certain minor areas known to be of a static or declining nature may be excluded. Consideration should be given to known plans for new construction.

CORRELATION WITH ZONING

Where a land use or zoning ordinance has been adopted, it may be desirable to correlate the fire limits with the provision of the zoning ordinance regarding location of commercial occupancies. Some extension of the fire limits to include areas zoned for commercial occupancies may be appropriate, but it is seldom necessary or desirable to include all such areas within the fire limits.

OERIODIC REVIEW

Periodic review of the extent of the fire limits is desirable so that adjustment of the limits may be made in conformity with changes in the location or extent of commercial occupancies developing into closely built districts.

METHOD OF FIXING THE LIMITS

In the work of actually laying out the fire limits a map showing outlines of blocks and details of building construction is very useful. Up-to-date land use or Sanborn maps usually have sufficient data for the purpose. If tentative limits are drawn from a map, a site survey should be made of the area to check on the adequacy of the proposed limits.

Detailed analysis of individual blocks usually is not necessary as a visual examination of the map or of the area itself will usually permit a reasonably accurate determination of which are closely built and which are of developing commercial occupancy. In questionable cases a more detailed analysis may be made. The material given in the Appendix will be found useful in answering questions which may arise.

SOURCE: Recommended Method of Laying Out Fire Limits, National Board of Fire Underwriters—1956

GOVERNMENTAL PROGRAMS

Section of Act	Purpose of Loan	Amount Insurable	Loan-Value Ratio	Term of Loan	Interest Rate
Section 203(b) 1 2 3 4	Finance proposed or existing 1-4 family housing	Occupant mortgagor: $30,000 1-family $32,500 2- or 3-family $37,500 4-family $12,500 if property meets only Minimum Property Standards for low-cost housing Non-occupant mortgagor: $25,500 1-family $27,600 2- or 3-family $31,800 4-family $10,600 if property meets only Minimum Property Standards for low-cost housing	Occupant mortgagor: Proposed construction or completed more than 1 year: 97% of $15,000 of appraised value + 90% of value above $15,000 but not over $20,000 + 80% above $20,000; limits for 1-family housing for veterans are 100% of $15,000 of appraised value, or sum of such value not in excess of $15,000 and items of prepaid expense, less $200, whichever is less, + 90% of value above $15,000 but not over $20,000 + 85% of value above $20,000. Under construction or completed less than 1 year: 90% of $20,000 of appraised value +80% of value above $20,000; limits for 1-family housing for veterans are 90% of $20,000 of appraised value + 85% of value above $20,000. Non-ocupant mortgagor: 85% of amount computed under any of above formulae.	Occupant or non-occupant mortgager, except operative builder: 30 years, except 35 years, if mortgagor is unacceptable under 30 year term, for housing built under FHA or VA inspection, or ¾ of remaining economic life, whichever is less. Operative builder: 20 years, or ¾ of remaining economic life, whichever is less.	5½%
Section 203(h) 1 2 3	Finance proposed or existing 1-family housing for occupant-mortgagor victim of natural disaster	$12,000 occupant mortgagor	Appraised value	30 years, except 35 years, if mortgagor is unacceptable under a 30 year term, for housing built under FHA or VA inspection, or ¾ of remaining economic life, whichever is less.	5½%
Section 203(i) 1 2 3 5	Finance proposed or existing 1-family non-farm housing or farm housing on 5 or more acres adjacent to highway	$12,500 occupant mortgagor $10,600 operative builder	Occupant mortgagor: Proposed construction or completed more than 1 year: 97% of appraised value. Under construction or completed less than 1 year: 90% of appraised value. Operative builder: 85% of appraised value.	Occupant mortgagor: 30 years, except 35 years, if mortgagor is unacceptable under 30 year term, for housing built under FHA or VA inspection, or ¾ of remaining economic life, whichever is less. Operative builder: 20 years, or ¾ of remaining economic life, whichever is less.	5½%
Section 203(k) 6 7 8	Finance proposed alteration, repair, or improvement of existing 1-4 family housing not within urban renewal areas	$10,000 1-family $20,000 2-family $30,000 3-family $37,500 4-family 9	Amount of loan plus debt on property cannot exceed dollar limitations insurable under Section 203(b).	20 years, or ¾ of remaining economic life, whichever is less.	6%

[1]Certification to mortgagor of FHA appraisal amount required on 1- or 2- family dwellings.
[2]Builder warranty required on proposed construction.
[3]Eligible for open-end advances.
[4]If borrower is 62 years of age or older, down payment, settlement charges, and prepaid expenses may be borrowed from approved corporation or individual.
[5]Down payment, settlement charges, and prepaid expenses may be borrowed from approved corporation or individual.
[6]Housing must be at least 10 years, old, unless loan is primarily to make major structural improvements, or correct faults not known when structure was completed or caused by fire, flood, or other casualty, or construct civil defense shelter.
[7]Loan proceeds may be used to pay municipal assessments or similar charges for water, sewer, sidewalk, curb, or other public improvements.
[8]An insured loan may be made to lessee if term of lease will run more than 10 years beyond maturity of loan.
[9]Limits may be increased up to 45% in high cost construction areas.

SOURCE: Digest of Insurable Loans, Federal Housing Administration, Dept. of Housing and Urban Development, Wash. D. C. 1966

Section of Act	Purpose of Loan	Amount Insurable	Loan-Value Ratio	Term of Loan	Interest Rate
Section 213, Individual Sales 1	Finance individual mortgage on housing released from cooperative project-sales mortgage	Unpaid balance of project mortgage allocable to individual property		30 years, except 35 years, if mortgagor is unacceptable under 30 year term	5½%
Section 220 1 2 3	Finance proposed or rehabilitation of 1-11 family housing in approved urban renewal areas or purchase of existing 1-11 family housing constructed or rehabilitated pursuant to approved urban renewal plan	Occupant mortgagor: $30,000 1-family $32,500 2- or 3-family $37,500 4-family $7,000 per family over 4 mortgagor: Property held for rental purposes: $27,900 1-family $30,200 2- or 3-family $34,800 4-family $6,500 per family over 4 Property held for sale to owner occupant: $25,500 1-family $27,600 2-family	Occupant mortgagor: Proposed construction or completed more than 1 year: 97% of $15,000 of estimated replacement cost + 90% of cost above $15,000 but not over $20,000 + 75% of cost above $20,000 Under construction or completed less than 1 year: 90% of estimated replacement cost + 75% of cost above $20,000 Rehabilitation: Constructed under FHA or VA inspection or completed more than 1 year: 97% of $15,000 of estimated rehabilitation cost + estimated value before rehabilitation + 90% of such sum above $15,000 but not over $20,000 + 75% of such sum above $20,000, or estimated rehabilitation cost + amount required to refinance debt on property, whichever is less Not constructed under FHA or VA inspection or completed less than 1 year: 90% of $20,000 of estimated rehabilitation cost + estimated value before rehabilitation + 75% of such sum above $20,000, or estimated rehabilitation cost + amount required to refinance debt on property, whichever is less Non-occupant mortgagor: Property held for rental purpose: 93% of amount under any of above formulae, but not to exceed estimated rehabilitation cost + amount required to refinance debt on property Property, 1- or 2-family, held for sale to owner occupant: 85% of amount under any of above formulae, but not to exceed estimated rehabilitation cost + amount required to refinance debt on property, or amount available to occupant mortgagor under any of above formulae, subject to at least 15% escrow or refinancing + minimum cash-investment requirements, whichever is less	30 years, except 35 years, if mortgagor is unacceptable under 30 year term for housing built under FHA or VA inspection, or ¾ of remaining economic life, whichever is less	5½%
Section 220(h) Improvement Loans 4	Finance alteration, repair, or improvement of existing 1-11 family structure in approved urban renewal areas 5 6	$10,000 1-family $20,000 2-family $30,000 3-family $37,500 4-family $40,000 5-11 family 7 8	Loan plus debt on property cannot exceed dollar limitations for home mortgages insurable under Section 220	20 years, or ¾ of remaining economic life, whichever is less	6%

[1]Eligible for open-end advances.
[2]Certification to mortgagor of FHA appraisal amount or estimate of replacement cost is required on 1- or 2-family housing.
[3]Builder warranty is required on proposed construction of 1- to 4-family housing.
[4]Cost certification is required if 5-family units or more.
[5]Loan proceeds may be used to pay municipal assessments or similar charges for water, sewer, sidewalk, curb, or other public improvements.
[6]Structure must be at least 10 years old, unless loan is primarily to make major structural improvements, correct faults not known when housing was completed or caused by fire, flood, or other casualty, or construct civil defense shelter.
[7]Limits may be increased up to 45% in high cost construction areas.
[8]Applications for loans to improve 5- to 11-family housing may be processed as home or multifamily improvement loans.
[9]Insured loan may be made to lessee if term of lease is more than 10 years beyond maturity of loan.

SOURCE: Digest of Insurable Loans, Federal Housing Administration, Dept. of Housing and Urban Development, Wash. D. C. 1966

Section of Act	Purpose of Loan	Amount Insurable	Loan-Value Ratio	Term of Loan	Interest Rate

Section 221 (d) (2)
 1
 2
 3
	Finance low-cost 1- to 4-family proposed, existing, or rehabilitated housing for families displaced by urban renewal or other governmental action or 1-family housing for other low- or moderate-income families	Occupant mortgagor:
		 Displaced family:
		 $11,000 1-family
		 $18,000 2-family
		 $27,000 3-family
		 $33,000 4-family
		 Other family:
		 $11,000 1-family
		 Operative builder:
		 $9,350 1-family
		 4
			Displaced family:
			   Proposed construction or completed more than 1 year: appraised value or appraised value + prepaid expenses, minus $200 per unit, whichever is less
			   Construction completed less than 1 year: 90% of appraised value
			   Rehabilitation: appraised value before rehabilitation + estimated cost of rehabilitation or appraised value + prepaid expenses, minus $200 per unit, whichever is less
			 Other low- or moderate-income family:
			   Proposed construction or completed more than 1 year: appraised value or 97% of appraised value + prepaid expenses, whichever is less
			   Construction completed less than 1 year: 90% of appraised value
			   Rehabilitation: appraised value before rehabilitation + estimated rehabilitation cost, appraised value after rehabilitation, or 97% of sum of appraised value + prepaid expenses, whichever is less
			 Operative builder:
			   Proposed construction: 85% of appraised value
			   Rehabilitation: least of 85% of appraised value before rehabilitation, 5 times estimated cost of improvements, or 85% of sum of purchase price of property or appraised value before rehabilitation, whichever is less, + estimated rehabilitation cost
				Displaced family: 30 years, except 35 or 40 years, if mortgagor is unacceptable under 30 year term
				 Other occupant mortgagor:
				   Housing built under FHA or VA inspection: 30 years, except 35 or 40 years if mortgagor is unacceptable under 30 year term
				   Existing construction: 30 years
				 All maturities limited to not more than ¾ of remaining economic life
					5½%

Section 222 1 2 3 5	Finance proposed or existing 1-family housing for mortgagors certified as servicemen by Secretary of Defense or Secretary of Treasury; not available for refinancing existing mortgages executed or assumed by servicemen	Property meeting eligibility criteria of Section 203 (b), $30,000 Property meeting eligibility criteria of Section 203(i), $12,500 Property meeting eligibility criteria of Section 221 (d) (2), $11,000, or up to $15,000 in high cost construction areas	Proposed construction or completed more than 1 year: 97% of $15,000 of appraised value + 90% of value above $15,000 but not over $20,000 + 85% of value above $20,000	30 years, except 35 years, if mortgagor is unacceptable under 30 year term, for housing built under FHA or VA inspection, or ¾ of the remaining economic life, whichever is less	5½%
Section 233, Experimental Housing 1 2 3	Finance proposed or rehabilitation of housing using advanced technology or experimental neighborhood design	Type of construction, mortgage limit, loan ratio, term, interest rate, and fees are governed by eligibility requirements of applicable home mortgage or improvement programs under Sections 203, 213, 220, 221, or 234; under all sections prescribed loan ratios will be applied to estimated replacement cost for proposed construction or for rehabilitation estimated value before rehabilitation plus estimated cost of improvements, using comparable conventional design, material, and construction or advanced technology or experimental property standards, whichever is less			
Section 234(c), Condominium Individual Units 3 5 6 7	Finance detached, semi-detached, row, walkup or elevator type individually owned family unit in project, containing 5 or more units, that is or was insured under any multifamily program, except Section 213, management or sales type	$30,000 occupant mortgagor $25,500 non-occupant mortgagor	Occupant mortgagor: 97% of $15,000 of appraised value + 90% of value above $15,000 but not over $20,000 +75% of value above $20,000 Non-occupant mortgagor: 85% of amount computed under above formula	30 years, except 35 years if owner-occupant mortgagor is unacceptable under 30 year term, or ¾ of remaining economic life, whichever is less	5½%

[1]Certification to mortgagor of FHA appraisal amount required on 1- or 2-family housing.
[2]Builder's warranty required on proposed construction.
[3]Eligible for open-end advances.
[4]Limits may be increased in high cost construction areas up to $15,000, 1-family; $25,000, 2-family; $32,000, 3-family; and $38,000, 4-family.

[5]Certificate to mortgagor of FHA appraisal amount required.
[6]Mortgagor may not own more than 4 insured units.
[7]If mortgagor is 62 years of age or older, down payment, settlement charges, and prepaid expenses may be borrowed from approved corporation or individual.

Section of Act	Purpose of Loan	Amount Insurable	Loan-Value Ratio	Term of Loan	Interest Rate
Section 809 1 2 3	Finance proposed or existing owner-occupied 1-4 family housing for civilian employees at or near research or development installation of Dept. of Defense, NASA, AEC, or contractor thereof on certification by Secretary of Defense, NASA Administrator, or AEC Commissioner	$30,000 1-family $32,500 2- or 3-family $37,500 4-family	Proposed construction of completed more than 1 year: 97% of $15,000 of appraised value + 90% of value above $15,000 but not over $20,000 + 80% of value over $20,000; limits for 1-family housing for veterans are 100% of $15,000 of appraised value or sum of such value not in excess of $15,000 plus items of prepaid expense, less $200, whichever is less, +90% of value above $15,000 but not over $20,000 + 85% of value above $20,000 Under construction or completed less than 1 year: 90% of $20,000 of appraised value + 80% of value over $20,000; limits of 1-family housing for veterns are 90% of $20,000 of appraised value + 85% of value over $20,000	Occupant or non-occupant mortgagor: 30 years, except 35 years, if mortgagor is unacceptable under 30 year term for housing built under FHA or VA inspection of ¾ of remaining economic life, whichever is less	5½%
Section 810 (h) Individual Sales	Finance individual mortgage on detached, semidetached, or row housing released from Section 810 (g) multifamily mortgage for military or essential civilian personnel of Armed Services, NASA, or AEC, or employees of contractors thereof	Determined by proportionate share of unpaid balance of Section 810 (g) multifamily mortgage		Unexpired term of 810 (g) multifamily mortgage or 30 years, whichever is less, or 35 years if mortgagor is ineligible under 30 year term	5½%

[1] Certification to mortgagor of FHA appraisal amount required on 1- or 2-family dwellings.
[2] Builder warranty required on proposed construction.

[3] If borrower is 62 years of age or older, down payment, settlement charges, and prepaid expenses may be borrowed from approved corporation or individual.

Purpose of Loan	Amount Insurable	Loan-Value Ratio	Term of Loan	Interest Rate
Finance purchase of land and development of building sites, including water and sewage systems, streets, etc. 1	$10,000,000	50% of estimated value of land before development plus 90% of estimated cost of development of 75% of estimated value upon completion; whichever is less	7 years, except longer for privately owned water or sewerage systems	5¼%

[1] Cost certification is required.
[2] Limits may be increased up to 45% in high cost construction areas.

Section of Act	Purpose of Loan	Amount Insurable	Loan-Value Ratio	Term of Loan	Interest Rate
Section 207 1	Proposed or rehabilitation of detached, semi-detached, row, walkup, or elevator type rental housing—8 or more units	$20,000,000 private mortgagor $50,000,000 public mortgagor Elevator type: $10,500 No bedroom $15,000 1-bedroom $18,000 2-bedroom $22,500 3-bedroom $25,500 4-bedroom or more All other types: $ 9,000 No bedroom $12,500 1-bedroom $15,000 2-bedroom $18,500 3-bedroom $21,00 4-bedroom or more 2	Proposed construction: 90% of estimated value Rehabilitation: 90% of appraised value after rehabilitation, subject to following limitations: Property to be acquired: 90% of estimated rehabilitation cost + 90% purchase price or appraised value before rehabilitation, whichever is less Property owned: estimated rehabilitation cost + debt on property or 90% of appraised value before rehabilitation, whichever is less Five times estimated rehabilitation cost	Satisfactory to FHA Commissioner (usually 39 years, or ¾ of the remaining economic life, whichever is less)	5¼%
Section 207, Mobile-Home Courts 1	Finance proposed or rehabilitation of mobile-home courts—50 or more spaces	$500,000 $1800 per space 3	75% of estimated value after construction or rehabilitation	15 years	5¼%
Section 213, Management 1	Finance proposed, existing, or rehabilitation of detached, semi-detached, row, walkup, or elevator type housing by a nonprofit cooperative or acquisition from investor sponsor—5 or more units	Same as Section 207, except $25,000,000 public mortgagor 2	Proposed construction: 97% of estimated replacement cost Existing construction: 97% of appraised value Rehabilitation: 97% of estimated value after rehabilitation	40 years, or ¾ of the remaining economic life, whichever is less	5¼%
Section 213, Management Supplementary Loans 1	Finance improvement or repair of existing Section 213, Management, housing; construction of community facilities; or resale of cooperative memberships	Estimated cost of improvements, repairs, and facilities and/or amount needed to finance resales, except supplementary loan plus debt on property plus other loan balances may not exceed orginal mortgage		Remaining term of mortgage	6%
Section 213, Sales	Finance proposed single family detached, semi-detached, or row housing for sale to members of non-profit cooperative—5 or more units	$12,500,000, or sum of separate maximum mortgages on single family housing that meet limits insurable for occupant mortgagors under Section 203(b), whichever is less		35 years, or ¾ of the remaining economic life, whichever is less	5¼%
Section 213, Investor Sponsored 1 2	Finance proposed or rehabilitation of detached, semi-detached, row, walkup, or elevator type housing by corporation intending to sell to non-profit cooperative—5 or more units	Same as Section 213, Management	Proposed construction: 90% of estimated replacement cost Rehabilitation: 90% of appraised value after rehabilitation	40 years, or ¾ of the remaining economic life, whichever is less	5¼%

[1]Cost certification is required.
[2]Limits per family unit may be increased up to 45% in high cost construction areas.
[3]Limit per space may be increased up to 25% in high cost construction areas.

Section of Act	Purpose of Loan	Amount Insurable	Loan-Value Ratios	Term of Loan	Interest Rate
Section 220 [1]	Finance proposed, under construction, or rehabilitation of detached, semi-detached, row, walkup, or elevator type rental housing, which may include non-dwelling facilities, in urban renewal areas—2 or more units [2]	$30,000,000 private mortgagor $50,000,000 public mortgagor Elevator type: $10,500 No bedroom $15,000 1-bedroom $18,000 2-bedroom $22,500 3-bedroom $25,500 4-bedroom or more All other types: $ 9,000 No bedroom $12,500 1-bedroom $15,000 2-bedroom $18,500 3-bedroom $21,000 4-bedroom or more [3]	Proposed construction: 90% of estimated replacement cost Under construction: 90% of estimated value when completed Rehabilitation: 90% of estimated rehabilitation cost + 90% of estimated value before rehabilitation, subject to following limitations: Property to be acquired: 90% of estimated rehabilitation cost + 90% of purchase price or estimated value before rehabilitation, whichever is less Property owned: estimated rehabilitation cost + debt on property of 90% of estimated value before rehabilitation, whichever is less	Satisfactory to FHA Commissioner (usually 40 years, or ¾ of remaining economic life, whichever is less)	5¼%
Section 220 (h) Improvement Loans [1]	Finance alteration, repair, or improvement of existing detached, semi-detached, row, walkup, or elevator type rental housing in urban renewal areas; loan proceeds may be used to pay municipal assessments or similar charges, for water, sewer, sidewalks, curbs, or other public improvements; housing must be at least 10 years old, unless loan is primarily to make structural improvements, correct faults not known when structure was completed or caused by fire, flood, or other casualty, or construct civil defense shelter [2] [4] [5]	$10,000 per family [3]	Loan plus debt on property may not exceed dollar limitation mortgage insurable under Section 220	20 years, or ¾ of remaining economic life, whichever is less [6]	6%

[1]Cost certification is required.
[2]Property must be located in an approved urban renewal or urban redevelopment area or urban area receiving rehabilitation assistance as result or natural disaster.
[3]Limits may be increased up to 45% in high cost construction areas.
[4]If loan is over $40,000, title evidence is required and construction advances may be insured.
[5]Loans in amounts up to $40,000 to improve 5- to 11-family properties may be processed either as home or multifamily housing improvement loans.
[6]Insured loan my be made to lessee if the term of the lease will run more than 10 years beyond the maturity of the loan.

Section of Act	Purpose of Loan	Amount Insurable	Loan-Value Ratio	Term of Loan	Interest Rate
Section 810 (f) [1]	Finance proposed detached, semi-detached, row, walkup, or elevator type rental housing for military or essential civilian personnel of Armed Services, NASA, or AEC or employees of contractors thereof, upon finding of need by FHA—8 or more units	$5,000,000 $ 9,000 No bedroom $12,500 1-bedroom $15,000 2-bedroom $18,500 3-bedroom or more [2]	90% of estimated value	Satisfactory to FHA Commissioner (usually 39 years, or ¾ of the remaining economic life, whichever is less)	5¼%
Section 810 (g) Rental-Eventual Sales		$5,000,000 Sum of unit mortgage amounts computed under Section 203(b), assuming mortgagor to be an owner occupant, subject to escrow of portion of mortgage proceeds		Satisfactory to FHA Commissioner (usually 39 years, or ¾ of the remaining economic life, whichever is less)	5¼%

Section of Act	Purpose of Loan	Amount Insurable	Loan-Value Ratios	Term of loan	Interest Rate

Section 221 (d) (3) (below-market rate)
 	
1
 	
2
 	
3
	Finance proposed or rehabilitation of rental or cooperative detached, semi-detached, row, or walkup housing for low-or moderate-income families or individuals 62 or older or handicapped, with priority in occupancy to those displaced by urban renewal or other governmental action
	Refinance existing housing in urban renewal areas — 5 or more units
		$12,500,00
		$ 8,000 No bedroom
		$11,250 1-bedroom
		$13,500 2-bedroom
		$17,000 3-bedroom
		$19,250 4-bedroom or more
		
		4
			Public, nonprofit, cooperative, builder-seller, or investor-sponsor mortgagor:
			   Proposed construction: estimated replacement cost
			   Rehabilitation: estimated rehabilitation cost + estimated value before rehabilitation, subject to following limitations:
			   Property to be acquired: estimated rehabilitation cost + the lesser of purchase price or estimated value before rehabilitation
			   Property owned: estimated rehabilitation cost + existing debt on property or estimated value before rehabilitation, whichever is less
			   5 times estimated cost of rehabilitation
			   Refinancing: debt on property or appraised value, whichever is less
			Limited-distribution mortgagor:
			   Proposed construction: 90% of estimated replacement cost
			   Rehabilitation: 90% of estimated rehabilitation cost + 90% of estimated value before rehabilitation, subject to following limitations:
			   Property to be acquired: 90% of estimated rehabilitation cost + 90% of purchase price or estimated value before rehabilitation, whichever is less
			   Property owned: estimated rehabilitation cost + debt on property or 90% of estimated value before rehabilitation, whichever is less
			   5 times estimated cost of rehabilitation
			   Refinancing: debt on property or 90% of appraised value, whichever is less
			Builder-seller or investor-sponsor mortgagor subject to 10% escrow
				Satisfactory to FHA Commissioner (usually 40 years, or ¾ of remaining economic life, whichever is less)	5¼% which is reduced at final endosement of mortgage of insurance to 3% or rate determined by the Secretary of the Treasury, whichever is lower

Section 221 (d) (3) (market rate program) requirements same as below-market rate, except ½% insurance premium and no reduction in interest rate at time of final endorsement — 5 or more units

3

Section of Act	Purpose of Loan	Amount Insurable	Loan-Value Ratios	Term of loan	Interest Rate

Section 211 (d) (4)
 	
1
 	
2
	Finance proposed or rehabilitation of detached, semi-deached, row, walkup, or elevator type rental housing for low- or moderate-income families or persons 62 or older or handicapped, with priority in occupancy to those displaced by urban renewal or other governmental action — 5 or more units	$12,500,000
		Elevator type:
		 $ 9,500 No bedroom
		 $13,500 1-bedroom
		 $16,000 2-bedroom
		 $20,000 3-bedroom
		 $22,750 4-bedroom or more
		All other types:
		 $ 8,000 No bedroom
		 $11,250 1-bedroom
		 $13,500 2-bedroom
		 $17,000 3-bedroom
		 $19,250 4-bedroom or
		
		4
			Private profit-motivated mortgagor:
			   Proposed construction: 90% of estimated replacement cost
			   Rehabilitation: 90% of estimated rehabilitation cost + 90% of estimated value before rehabilitation, subject to following limitations:
			   Property to be acquired: 90% of estimated rehabilitation cost + 90% of purchase price or estimated value before rehabilitation, whichever is less
			   Property owned: estimated rehabilitation cost + debt on property or 90% of estimated value before rehabilitation, whichever is less
			   5 times estimated cost of rehabilitation
				Satisfactory to FHA Commissioner (usually 40 years, or ¾ of remaining economic life, whichever is less)	5¼%

¹Cost certification required.

²Property must be located in community certified by Secretary, Department of Housing and Urban Development.

³Data on Rent Supplement Program.

⁴Limits per family unit may be increased up to 45% in high cost construction areas.

Section of Act	Purpose of Loan	MAXIMUM LIMITS		Term of Loan	Interest Rate
		Amount Insurable	Loan-Value Ratio		
Section 231, Housing for Elderly Persons 1	Finance proposed or rehabilitation of detached, semi-detached, row, walk-up, or elevator type rental housing designed for occupancy by elderly or handicapped individuals — 8 or more units 2	$12,500,000 private mortgagor $50,000,000 public mortgagor Elevator type: $ 9,500 No bedroom $13,500 1-bedroom $16,000 2-bedroom $20,000 3-bedroom $22,750 4-bedroom or more All other types: $ 8,000 No bedroom $11,250 1-bedroom $13,500 2-bedroom $17,000 3-bedroom $19,250 4-bedroom or more 3	Nonprofit mortgagor: Proposed construction: estimated replacement cost Rehabilitation: estimated value after rehabilitation, subject to following limitations: Property to be acquired: estimated rehabilitation cost + actual purchase price or estimated value before rehabilitation, whichever is less Property owned: estimated rehabilitation cost + debt on property or estimated value before rehabilitation, whichever is less 5 times estimated cost of rehabilitation Profit mortgagor: Proposed construction: 90% of estimated replacement cost Rehabilitation: 90% of estimated value after rehabilitation, subject to following limitations: Property to be acquired: 90% of estimated rehabilitation cost + 90% of purchase price or 90% of estimated value before rehabilitation, whichever is less Property owned: 100% of estimated rehabilitation cost + debt on property or 90% of estimated value before rehabilitation, whichever is less 5 times estimated cost of rehabilitation	Satisfactory to Commissioner (usually 40 years, or ¾ of remaining economic life, whichever is less)	5¼%
Section 232, Nursing Homes 1	Finance proposed or rehabilitation of facilities, accommodating 20 or more patients, for care and treatment of convalescents or other individuals who are not acutely ill and not in need of hospital care but require skilled nursing care and related medical services	$12,500,000	Proposed construction: 90% of estimated value Rehabilitation: 90% of estimated value after rehabilitation, subject to following limitations: Property to be acquired: 90% of estimated rehabilitation cost + 90% of purchase price of 90% of estimated value before rehabilitation, whichever is less Property owned: estimated rehabilitation cost + debt on property or 90% of estimated value before rehabilitation, whichever is less 5 times estimated cost of rehabilitation	Satisfactory to FHA Commissioner (usually 20 years, or ¾ of remaining economic life, whichever is less)	5¼%
Section 233, Experimental Housing 1	Finance proposed or rehabilitation of rental housing, using advanced technology or experimental property standards for neighborhood design	Type of construction, mortgage limit, loan ratio, term, interest rate, and fees are governed by eligibility requirements of applicable mortgage or improvement loan insurance programs under Sections 207, 220, 221, 231, 232, or 234; under all Sections prescribed loan ratios will be applied to estimated replacement cost for proposed construction or for rehabilitation appraised value before rehabilitation plus estimated cost of improvements, using comparable conventional design, materials, and construction or advanced technology or experimental property standards, whichever is less 3			
Section 234(d) Condominium 1	Finance proposed or rehabilitation of detached, semi-detached, row, walk-up, or elevator type housing by sponsor intending to sell individual units as condominiums — 5 or more units	$20,000,000 private mortgagor $25,000,000 public mortgagor Elevator type: $10,500 No bedroom $15,000 1-bedroom $18,000 2-bedroom $22,500 3-bedroom $25,500 4-bedroom or more All other types: $ 9,000 No bedroom $12,500 1-bedroom $15,000 2-bedroom $18,500 3-bedroom $21,000 4-bedroom or more 3	Proposed construction: 90% of replacement cost or sum of unit mortgage amounts computed under Section 234(c) assuming mortgagor to be owner occupant, whichever is less Rehabilitation: 90% of estimated rehabilitation cost + 90% of estimated value before rehabilitation or sum of unit mortgage amounts computed under Section 234(c) assuming mortgagor to be an owner occupant, subject to following limitations: Property to be acquired: 90% of estimated rehabilitation cost + 90% of purchase price or estimated value before rehabilitation, whichever is less Property owned: estimated rehabilitation cost + debt on property or 90% of estimated value before rehabilitation, whichever is less 5 times estimated cost of rehabilitation	Blanket mortgage: Satisfactory to Commissioner (usually 39 years, or ¾ of remaining economic life, whichever is less) Owner-occupant mortgagor: 30 years, except 35 years if unacceptable under lesser term, or ¾ of remaining economic life, whichever is less	5¼%

¹Cost certification is required.
³Limits per family unit may be increased up to 45% in high cost construction areas.

²Data covering Rent Supplement Program.

The Housing and Urban Development Act of 1965 includes authorization for the Secretary, Department of Housing and Urban Development, to make payments to owners of certain multifamily housing rental projects to supplement the rentals eligible tenants can afford to pay. Rental payments under the Rent Supplement Program are contingent upon the appropriation of funds for this purpose.

Eligible projects:

Basic program—Section 221(d)(3) (market-interest rate) covers proposed or rehabilitation of multifamily housing project with private non-profit, limited-distribution, or cooperative housing corporation mortgagor for which the mortgage was insured after August 10, 1965.

Experimental programs—Section 221(d)(3) (below market-interest rate) covers proposed or rehabilitation of project with private nonprofit, limited-distribution, or cooperative housing corporation mortgagor for which a commitment to insure was issued after August 10, 1965.

Section 231 covers proposed or rehabilitation of project with private nonprofit mortgagor for which commitment to insure was issued after August 10, 1965.

Eligible tenants:

To be eligible for rent supplement payments a tenant must be an individual or family that has been determined to have assets and income below the established maximums and must be one of the following: an individual or family displaced by governmental action, 62 years of age or older or whose spouse is 62 or older, physically handicapped, occupying substandard housing, or occupant of housing affected by a natural disaster. (Tenants other than those eligible for rent supplement payments may occupy units in the project.)

Amount of payment:

The amount of the rent supplement payable for an individual or family is the difference between the rental for the dwelling unit and one-fourth of the tenant income, except that the payment may not be more than seventy per cent or less than five per cent of the unit rental.

Income and asset controls:

The Department of Housing and Urban Development will impose controls to prevent payments on behalf of tenants whose income or assets exceed permissable limits after occupancy.

■ADVANCES FOR PUBLIC WORKS PLANNING

PURPOSES: Provides interest-free advances to assist planning for individual local public works and for area-wide and long-range projects which will help communities deal with their total needs.

SPECIFIC USES: All types of public works, except public housing, are eligible. Examples include water and sewer systems, school buildings, recreational projects, public buildings, irrigation projects, health facilities, bridges, and a variety of other public works.

TERMS: The advance is repayable to HUD promptly upon start of construction of the planned public work.

WHO MAY APPLY: States, municipalities and other public agencies.

SPECIFIC REQUIREMENTS: An applicant must show that it intends to start construction within a reasonable period of time considering the nature of the project and that financing of such construction is feasible. The public work must conform to a state, local, or regional plan, as appropriate, approved by a competent state, local, or regional authority.

RELATED PROGRAMS: Grants for basic water and sewer facilities, urban planning assistance, public facility loans, and grants for advance acquisition of land.

■GRANTS FOR ADVANCE ACQUISITION OF LAND

PURPOSES: To encourage communities to acquire, in a planned and orderly fashion, land for future construction of public works and facilities.

TERMS: Grants may not exceed the interest charges on a loan incurred to finance the acquisition of land for a period of not more than 5 years.

WHO MAY APPLY: Local public bodies and agencies.

SPECIFIC REQUIREMENTS: The facility for which the land is to be used must be started within a reasonable period of time, not exceeding 5 years after the grant is approved. Construction of the facility must contribute to the comprehensively planned development of the area.

RELATED PROGRAMS: Grants for basic sewer and water facilities, advances for public works planning, urban planning assistance, and public facility loans.

■GRANTS FOR BASIC SEWER AND WATER FACILITIES

PURPOSES: This program is designed to assist and encourage the communities of the nation to construct adequate basic water and sewer facilities to promote their efficient and orderly growth and development.

SPECIFIC USES: Provides grants to local public bodies and agencies to finance up to 50 percent of the cost of improving or constructing basic water and sewer facilities. Where there is no existing system, the project must be so designed that it can be linked with other independent water and sewer facilities in the future.

TERMS: Terms will be determined shortly.

WHO MAY APPLY: Local public bodies and agencies.

SPECIFIC REQUIREMENTS: A grant may be made for any project if it is determined that the project is necessary to provide adequate water or sewer facilities for the people to be served, and that the project is

1. designed so that an adequate capacity will be available to serve the reasonably foreseeable growth needs of the area,

2. consistent with a program for a unified or officially coordinated area-wide water or sewer facilities system as part of the comprehensively planned development of the area, and

3. necessary to orderly community development.

No grant shall be made for any sewer facilities unless the Secretary of Health, Education, and Welfare certifies to the Secretary of the Department of Housing and Urban Development that any waste material carried by such facilities will be adequately treated before it is discharged into any public waterway so as to meet applicable Federal, State, interstate, or local water quality standards.

RELATED PROGRAMS: Public facility loans program, public works planning advances, urban planning grant program and grants for advance land acquisition.

SOURCE: Programs of Dept. of Housing and Urban Development, Washington, D. C., May—1966

■URBAN RENEWAL

PURPOSE: To assist cities undertaking local programs for the elimination and prevention of slums and blight, whether residential or nonresidential, and the elimination of the factors that create slums and blight. Urban renewal is a long-range effort to achieve better communities through planned redevelopment of deteriorated and deteriorating areas by means of a partnership among local governments, private enterprise, citizens, and the Federal Government.

SPECIFIC USES: Community-wide renewal programs which identify needs and resources and establish schedules and priorities for accomplishing the work to be done; plan and carry out urban renewal projects for the rehabilitation and redevelopment of blighted area; and undertake programs of concentrated code enforcement and demolition of buildings that are substandard and constitute a hazard to public health and welfare.

TERMS: Activities and projects are financed with Federal advances and loans, Federal grants, and local contributions. Federal grants generally pay up to two-thirds of net project cost, but may be as much as three-fourths in some instances. Local contributions may include cash or noncash grants in aid. Also available are special rehabilitation loans and grants, and housing assistance programs for low income, elderly, and handicapped individuals and families who reside in project areas.

WHO MAY APPLY: Local public agencies authorized by State law to undertake projects with Federal assistance. LPA's may be separate public agency, local housing authority, or a department of the city government.

SPECIFIC REQUIREMENTS: Community must certify that it cannot carry out its urban renewal plans with local resources alone; must adopt and have certified by the Department of Housing and Urban Development a Workable Program for Community Improvement; and must have a feasible plan for the relocation of families and individuals displaced as a result of governmental action into decent, safe, and sanitary housing at prices or rentals within their means. A renewal project must conform to a general plan for the development of the community as a whole.

■URBAN PLANNING ASSISTANCE PROGRAM

PURPOSES: To foster good community, metropolitan area, regional and statewide planning.

SPECIFIC USES: Preparation of comprehensive development plans, including planning for the provision of public facilities; transportation facilities, and long-range fiscal plans. Programming and scheduling of capital improvements.

TERMS: Federal grants of two-thirds of the cost of the work; local contribution of one-third. In some instances, Federal grants may amount to as much as three-fourths.

WHO MAY APPLY: Cities and other municipalities with less than 50,000 population, counties, and Indian reservations, through their State Planning Agencies.

Official State, metropolitan, and regional planning agencies. Metropolitan organizations of public officials. Cities and counties in redevelopment areas, without regard to size. Official governmental planning agencies for Federally impacted areas. Localities which have suffered a major disaster and areas which have suffered a decline in employment as a result of decline in Federal purchases may apply directly to the Department of Housing and Urban Development.

■PUBLIC FACILITY LOANS

PURPOSES: This program provides long-term loans for the construction of needed public facilities such as sewer or water facilities.

SPECIFIC USES: A variety of public works may be financed under this program. When aid is available from other Federal agencies, such as for airports, highways, hospitals and sewage treatment facilities, HUD assists only with those parts of the project not covered by other Federal programs.

TERMS: Term of loan may be up to 40 years. It will be governed by the applicant's ability to pay and by the estimated useful life of the proposed facility. The interest rate for fiscal year 1966 to be determined.

WHO MAY APPLY: Local units of government or State instrumentalities. Private non-rofit corporations for sewer and water facilities needed to serve a small municipality if there is no existing public body able to construct and operate the facilities.

SPECIFIC REQUIREMENTS: The population of the applicant community must be under 50,000, with two exceptions. In those communities near a research or development installation of the National Aeronautics and Space Agency, the population requirement does not apply. In the case of communities located in redevelopment areas so designated under the Public Works and Economic Development Act of 1965, the population limit is 150,000.

RELATED PROGRAMS: Grants for basic water and sewer facilities, public works planning advances, urban planning assistance and grants for advance acquisition of land.

■URBAN MASS TRANSPORTATION GRANTS

PURPOSES: To help localities provide and improve urban mass transportation facilities and equipment; encourage planning and establishment of areawide urban transportation systems; and aid financing of such systems.

Federal grants may be made for up to two-thirds of the cost of facilities and equipment that cannot reasonably be financed by revenues. Local grants are required for the other one-third.

Federal loans for a maximum period of 40 years may be made for the entire cost of capital improvements, where financing is not available privately on reasonable terms.

WHO MAY APPLY: Qualified State or local public bodies or agencies, including those of one or more States, or one or more municipalities or other political subdivisions of a single State.

SPECIAL REQUIREMENTS: All projects must be needed for carrying out a program for a unified or officially coordinated transit system as part of the comprehensively planned development of the urban area. However, until July 1, 1967, loans and grants may be made on an emergency basis with less strict planning requirements, but grants are limited to one-half rather than two-thirds of net project cost. The full grant would be available upon completion of the full planning requirements within three years.

RELATED PROGRAMS: Mass Transportation Demonstration Program: Federal grants up to two-thirds of the cost of projects to test and demonstrate new ideas and new methods for improving mass transportation systems and service.

Urban Planning Assistance: Federal grants help finance comprehensive planning for urban areas, including mass transportation planning.

Public Works Planning Advances: Interest-free advances for engineering surveys, designs and plans for specific public works, including public transportation facilities.

■ OPEN SPACE LAND AND URBAN BEAUTIFICATION GRANTS

PURPOSES: To assist communities in acquiring and developing land for open-space uses and in carrying out urban beautification programs.

SPECIFIC USES: Provide parks and other recreation, conservation, and scenic areas or preserve historic places. Urban beautification and improvement includes such activities as street landscaping, park improvements, tree planting, and upgrading of malls and squares. Relocation payments are provided for individuals, families, and businesses displaced by land acquisition.

TERMS: Federal assistance has been increased from 20 and 30 percent to a single level of 50 percent to help public agencies acquire and preserve urban lands having value for park, recreation, scenic, or historic purposes. Where necessary to provide open space in built-up urban areas, grants can cover up to 50 percent of the cost of acquiring and clearing developed land. Fifty percent assistance is also available to assist in developing lands acquired under the open-space land program.

A grant for urban beautification can be up to 50 percent of the expenditures for urban beautification. However, grants of up to 90 percent are authorized to carry out projects of special value for demonstrating new and improved methods and materials for urban beautification.

WHO MAY APPLY: State and local public bodies.

SPECIFIC REQUIREMENTS: Assisted open-space activities must be part of an area-wide open-space acquisition and development program which, in turn is consistent with area-wide comprehensive planning. Developed lands in built-up areas are eligible only if open-space needs cannot be met with existing undeveloped or predominantly undeveloped land. Beautification activities must have significant, long-term benefits to the community and must be part of a local beautification program. Such programs must (1) represent significant and effective efforts, involving all available public and private resources for urban beautification and improvement, and (2) be important to the comprehensively planned development of the locality.

RELATED PROGRAMS: Urban renewal; urban planning assistance; outdoor recreation and parks programs of Department of Interior; neighborhood facilities program of HUD; small watershed Program of Department of Agriculture; landscaping activities under Federal highway program; FHA Land Development Program.

■ REHABILATION AIDS AND PROGRAMS

OBJECTIVE: To effect rehabilitation and renewal of housing, buildings and communities by repairing, remodeling and restoring rather than be clearance and demolition.

Major grant, loan and mortgage insurance programs are:

Direct grants of up to $1500, to enable low income homeowners in urban renewal areas and areas of concentrated code enforcement to bring their homes up to required standards.

Direct loans with maximum interest rate of 3 percent and maximum terms of 20 years to property owners for rehabilitation of residential or business structures in urban renewal areas and areas of concentrated code enforcement. Structures are to be brought up to local code requirements or standards set by an urban renewal plan.

FHA insurance of loans made by private lenders for repairs of existing housing, with special provisions for major repairs of housing in urban renewal areas and areas of concentrated code enforcement. The special loans can be up to $10,000 (45% higher in high cost areas) per dwelling unit. Interest rate is 6 percent plus 1/2 percent mortgage insurance premium and terms can be up to 20 years.

FHA mortgage insurance for low-cost rehabilitated housing for sale or rent to moderate income families, including the elderly and those displaced by government action. Mortgage amount can be up to 100 percent of the value of rehabilitated structures; interest rate at 5 1/4 percent plus 1/2 percent mortgage insurance premiums; terms to 30 years.

FHA insured below-market interest rate loans for rehabilitated rental and cooperative housing for low and moderate income families. Mortgage amount can be up to 100 percent of value for nonprofit sponsors, at maximum interest rate of 3 percent. Terms are usually the lesser of 40 years or 3/4 of the remaining economic life of the structure.

Local housing authorities under 1965 legislation are enabled to purchase, lease and rehabilitate existing housing which can be rented to low-income families.

The Department can make grants to cities for 2/3 of the cost of planning and carrying out programs of concentrated code enforcement in deteriorated or deteriorating areas. This program is not limited to urban renewal areas. Grants can also be made for planning rehabilitation projects and for city-wide surveys or rehabilitation needs.

■ **GRANTS FOR NEIGHBORHOOD FACILITIES**

PURPOSES: To provide neighborhood facilities needed for programs carrying out health, recreation, social or similar necessary community services in the area.

SPECIFIC USES: Finances specific projects, such as neighborhood or community centers, youth centers, health stations and other public buildings to provide health or recreational or similar social services.

TERMS: Grants can cover up to two-thirds of the project cost, or 75 percent in redevelopment areas designated under the Public Works and Economic Development Act of 1965, or any act supplemental to it.

WHO MAY APPLY: A local public body or agency. (In some circumstances, projects may be undertaken by a local public body or agency through a nonprofit organization.)

SPECIFIC REQUIREMENTS: Emphasis will be placed on projects which are so located as to be available for use by a significant portion of the area's low- or moderate- income residents, and on those which will support a community action program under the Economic Opportunity Act.

■ **COLLEGE HOUSING**

PURPOSES: To help colleges and hospitals expand their facilities to absorb the increasing influx of students.

SPECIFIC USES: The loans must be used for the construction of college residence halls, faculty and married student housing, dining facilities, college unions and housing for student nurses and interns.

TERMS: Loans may be repaid over periods as long as 50 years, at an interest rate of 3 percent.

WHO MAY APPLY: Public or private nonprofit colleges and universities, if they offer at least a two-year program acceptable for full credit toward a bachelor's degree. Public or private nonprofit hospitals, if approved by the appropriate State authority to operate a nursing school beyond the high school level, or approved for internship and residencies by the American Medical Association or American Osteopathic Association.

SPECIFIC REQUIREMENTS: Each institution develops its own plans, subject to local zoning and building codes. Engineering plans are reviewed by HUD. Competitive bidding is required.

■ **LOW-RENT PUBLIC HOUSING**

PURPOSES: The low-rent public housing program was established by Congress in the Housing Act of 1937 to aid communities to provide decent housing for low-income families who cannot afford standard private housing. Subsequent Federal housing Act have made special provision for low-income elderly families and individuals, the handicapped, and those displaced by urban renewal and other governmental action. Forty-nine States now have enabling legislation under which local public housing programs can be initiated. Of major importance are new provisions in the Housing Act of 1965 which expands and gives greater flexibility to the program.

NEW PROVISIONS: The 1965 Act provides for 60,000 public housing units a year—240,000 in four years. Of these, an estimated 35,000 a year will be the traditional new construction. However, the new provisions permit an estimated 15,000 units a year to be bought from existing housing and rehabilitated if necessary. And an estimated 10,000 units a year will be leased from existing housing for short term use in meeting particular needs. Such housing will be particularly suited to large families.

Increase in unit costs: The 1965 Act increases per room construction and equipment ceiling costs from $2,000 to $2,400 per room in regular housing, and from $3,000 to $3,500 per room for elderly units. In Alaska ceiling cost would increase from $3,000 to $3,500 per room for regular, and $3,500 to $4,000 per room for elderly units.

Purchase of units by tenants: The 1965 Act permits a local housing authority to sell a detached or semi-detached dwelling to a tenant.

Reallocation of units: The 1965 Act provides that any units not under construction by an authority within five years of the date they were reserved may be reallocated to another authority. These units could be placed in any State without limitation.

Parity of treatment for the handicapped: The 1965 Act gives the handicapped the same special treatment as the elderly, including higher room cost limits.

■ SENIOR CITIZENS HOUSING PROGRAMS

PURPOSES: To provide good housing for elderly and handicapped persons of low- and moderate-income at prices they can afford.

Low-rent public housing built, owned and operated by local housing authorities. Federal financial assistance to these authorities includes temporary loans to build the projects and annual contributions to amortize bond issues sold on the private market by the authorities for permanent financing. The annual contributions are used to secure these bonds as well as to retire the temporary notes and the capital cost of the housing within 40 years. Existing private housing can be leased or purchased by the local authorities under new provisions in the 1965 Housing Act and assisted by annual contributions.

Direct loan program for the moderate income elderly and handicapped whereby 100 percent loans are made by the HUD to nonprofit sponsors at a 3 percent maximum interest rate for 50 years. This housing is for older people with incomes too high for public housing, but too low for the private housing market. Church groups, labor unions, fraternal and civic clubs, etc. are eligible for these loans.

Mortgage insurance for housing for older people in a wider income range. FHA insures private lenders against losses on loans to nonprofit or profit-motivated sponsors which include church groups, labor unions, fraternal and civil clubs, etc. The maximum interest rate is 5 1/4 percent plus 1/2 percent mortgage insurance premium for 40 years. Mortgage amounts may be up to 100 percent of replacement cost for nonprofit and up to 90 percent for profit motivated projects. These projects may include more facilities and services than direct loan projects.

Rent supplements for the low-income elderly is a major new program included in the 1965 Housing Act. It provides Federal payments by the Secretary, HUD, to certain new or rehabilitated housing to enable elderly with incomes no higher than those permitted for tenants of public housing to obtain decent housing. Rent supplements on behalf of eligible tenants cannot exceed the amount by which the fair market rental for the unit occupied exceeds one-fourth of the tenant's income. In certain circumstances rent supplements can be made to owners of housing financed under FHA's programs for low-income families and for the elderly, and the HUD direct loan program.

■ RELOCATION

PURPOSES: To assist in the relocation of individuals, families, businesses and non-profit organizations displaced by the urban renewal, urban mass transportation, open-space, community facilities, and public housing programs.

TERMS: For Individuals and Families: Federal payment is made for moving expenses, including storage costs, and loss of property up to $200. Families and elderly persons not able to secure low-rent public housing or housing under the Federal rent supplement program are also entitled to a relocation adjustment payment for a limited period of time.

For Businesses and Nonprofit Organizations: Each organization is entitled to receive moving expenses, including storage costs, and reimbursement for property loss incurred in the move, up to $3,000; if moving expenses exceed $3,000, reimbursement for actual moving expenses may be made up to a maximum of $25,000. These payments, up to $25,000, are covered by a Federal relocation grant. Payments for moving expenses in excess of $25,000 may be made (except in the case of displacement by public housing) if the locality shares the cost of the excess with the Federal Government. A small business displacement payment of $2,500 is made to a small business with annual net earnings of less than $10,000, providing its gross annual receipts are in excess of $1,500.

The Small Business Administration is authorized to make loans of up to 20 years to assist displaced small business concerns in reestablishing or to insure the owner or lessor of property leased to an eligible displaced small business concern against any loss which might result from the failure of the business concern to abide by the terms of the lease.

For Individuals, Families, Businesses and Nonprofit Organizations: Relocation payment can include, in addition, certain settlement costs incurred in conveying property, such as recording fees and transfer taxes, if reimbursement for these costs is not otherwise made.

WHO MAY APPLY: Any individual, family, business, or nonprofit association displaced or about to be displaced by one of the programs.

BASIC DATA

Map Scales are commonly expressed either **mathematically,** as 1 inch 200 feet or 1: 2,400, or

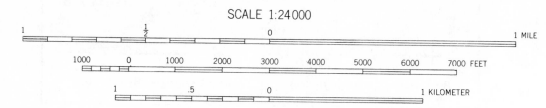

SCALE 1:24000

Graphically, by a bar scale shown upon the map itself.

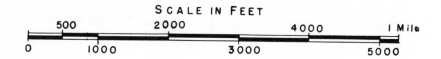

Base maps prepared by federal agencies are generally available in standardize scales. The various scales can be divided into five general groups.

SCALE A—STATE AND DISTRICT MAPS
1:10,000,000 or 1 inch = 160 miles (approximate)
1: 2,500,000 or 1 inch = 40 miles (approximate)
1:    500,000 or 1 inch = 8 miles (approximate)
1:    250,000 or 1 inch = 4 miles (approximate).

SCALE B—REGIONAL AND COUNTY MAPS
1:125,000 or 1 inch = 2 miles (approximate)
1: 62,500 or 1 inch = 1 mile (approximate)
1: 31,680 or 1 inch = ½ mile

SCALE C—DETAIL SECTION AND STUDY MAPS
1:24,000 or 1 inch = 2,000 feet
1:12,000 or 1 inch = 1,000 feet

SCALE D—CITY MAPS AND PLANS
1 inch = 800 feet
1 inch = 400 feet

SCALE E—MAPS FOR ACCURATE DESIGNING AND COST ESTIMATING
1 inch = 200 feet
1 inch = 100 feet

RATE YEARS	5%	5¼%	5½%	5¾%	6%	6¼%	6½%	7%	7¼%
2	43.88	43.99	44.10	44.21	44.33	44.44	44.55	44.66	44.78
4	23.03	23.15	23.26	23.38	23.49	23.60	23.72	23.83	23.95
6	16.11	16.23	16.34	16.46	16.58	16.70	16.81	16.92	17.04
8	12.66	12.78	12.60	13.03	13.15	13.27	13.39	13.51	13.63
10	10.61	10.73	10.86	10.98	11.11	11.23	11.36	11.48	11.61
12	9.25	9.38	9.51	9.63	9.76	9.89	10.02	10.15	10.28
14	8.29	8.42	8.55	8.68	8.82	8.95	9.09	9.22	9.36
16	7.58	7.71	7.85	7.98	8.12	8.26	8.40	8.54	8.68
18	7.04	7.17	7.31	7.45	7.59	7.73	7.87	8.01	8.15
20	6.60	6.74	6.88	7.03	7.17	7.31	7.46	7.60	7.75
22	6.26	6.40	6.54	6.69	6.84	6.98	7.13	7.27	7.42
24	5.97	6.12	6.27	6.41	6.56	6.72	6.87	7.02	7.17
26	5.74	5.89	6.04	6.19	6.34	6.60	6.65	6.80	6.96
28	5.54	5.69	5.84	6.00	6.16	6.40	6.48	6.64	6.82
30	5.37	5.53	5.68	5.84	6.00	6.16	6.33	6.49	6.65
35	5.05	5.21	5.38	5.54	5.71	5.88	6.05	6.22	6.39
40	4.83	4.99	5.16	5.33	5.51	5.68	5.86	6.03	6.20

A TRANSPARENT NOMOGRAPH FOR MEASURING THE AREA OF POLYGONAL FIGURES

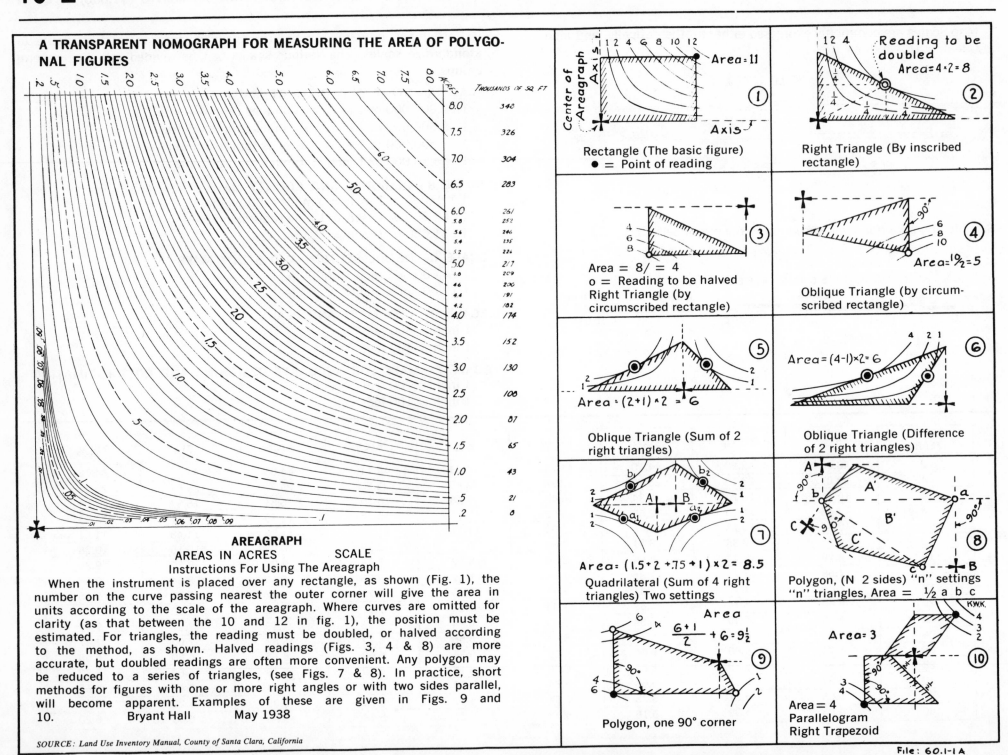

AREAGRAPH

AREAS IN ACRES   SCALE

Instructions For Using The Areagraph

When the instrument is placed over any rectangle, as shown (Fig. 1), the number on the curve passing nearest the outer corner will give the area in units according to the scale of the areagraph. Where curves are omitted for clarity (as that between the 10 and 12 in fig. 1), the position must be estimated. For triangles, the reading must be doubled, or halved according to the method, as shown. Halved readings (Figs. 3, 4 & 8) are more accurate, but doubled readings are often more convenient. Any polygon may be reduced to a series of triangles, (see Figs. 7 & 8). In practice, short methods for figures with one or more right angles or with two sides parallel, will become apparent. Examples of these are given in Figs. 9 and 10.   Bryant Hall   May 1938

SOURCE: Land Use Inventory Manual, County of Santa Clara, California

① Rectangle (The basic figure)   ● = Point of reading

② Right Triangle (By inscribed rectangle)

③ Area = 8/ = 4   o = Reading to be halved   Right Triangle (by circumscribed rectangle)

④ Oblique Triangle (by circumscribed rectangle)

⑤ Oblique Triangle (Sum of 2 right triangles)

⑥ Oblique Triangle (Difference of 2 right triangles)

⑦ Quadrilateral (Sum of 4 right triangles) Two settings

⑧ Polygon, (N 2 sides) "n" settings "n" triangles, Area = ½ a b c

⑨ Polygon, one 90° corner

⑩ Area = 4 Parallelogram Right Trapezoid

File: 60.1-1A

1. Grade
2. Basement sash areaway
3. Siding
4. Building paper
5. Sheathing (diagonal)
6. Board and batten siding
7. Fascia
8. Rough window opening
9. Window header
10. Rafters
11. Collar beams
12. Ridge board
13. Chimney cap
14. Chimney flue
15. Flashing
16. Ceiling joists
17. Furring strips
18. Roof sheathing
19. Roof shingles
20. Gutter
21. Shutters
22. Wall studs
23. Entrance, frame and door
24. Downspout
25. Brick veneer
26. Concrete stoop
27. Interior doors and trim
28. Concrete block basement wall
29. Drain tile
30. Wall footing
31. Basement stair treads and risers
32. Gravel base
33. First floor joists
34. Heating unit
35. Beam
36. Concrete floor
37. Basement column
38. Plaster
39. Concrete basement wall
40. Waterproofing
41. Building paper
42. Sub-floor (diagonal)
43. Finish floor
44. Baseboard
45. Plaster or drywall
46. Insulation
47. Second floor joists
48. Bridging
49. Partition studs
50. Plaster base, gypsum lath
51. Double hung window
52. Insulation
53. Header joist

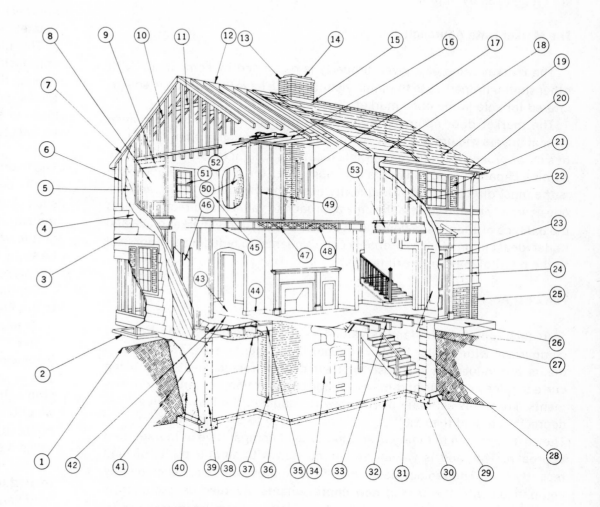

SOURCE: Boeckh Building Valuation Manual, Boeckh Division, the American Appraisal Co., Milwaukee, Wis. 1967

THE THREE APPROACHES TO VALUE

In appraising the market value of real property three basic approaches are recognized by appraisers:

The Market Data Approach

The market value of a given property is estimated by comparison with other similar properties in the same vicinity which have recently been sold or offered for sale in the open market.

The market data approach applies the principle of substitution since typical buyers will not purchase a property at a price higher than the prices of similar properties with comparable locations, characteristics, and future earning capabilities. Of all appraisal approaches the market data approach is the most direct, the most frequently used, the best understood, and the one generally preferred. It is the only approach to value that directly reflects the balance of supply and demand in actual trading in the market place and under ideal circumstances probably comes nearest to reducing an appraisal to the point of lease approximation.

The Cost Approach

In this approach the land is valued as if unimproved, on the basis of comparison with similar tracts of vacant land recently sold. The improvements are valued on the basis of their cost of replacement new, using current prices of labor and materials for construction of similar improvements. From this estimate of cost new is deducted the loss in value from depreciation, and the resulting amount is added to the land value.
The cost approach in reality is another type of comparative or market data approach. The land is valued by comparison with similar tracts of land recently sold. The replacement cost of the improvements is developed by comparison with the cost of new improvements. Accrued depreciation is measured by comparison with known depreciation of similar improvements

The cost approach often develops the highest indication of value because the appraiser may not have recognized all the depreciation that has accured to the property. Occasionally the cost approach develops a low indication of value because the estimate of depreciation is too high.

SUMMARY OF COST APPROACH

The cost approach has the distinct advantage of universal application to all types of real property. It is the principal and sometimes the sole approach for special purpose properties which rarely sell on the open market.

This manual provides reliable information for the preparation of a cost approach to all types of property. It sets forth proper procedures for making the inspection and recording the data, and contains numerous cost tables giving the unit-in-place, square-foot, and component costs for all kinds of structures. It also includes suggested depreciation schedules for various types of construction.

The Income Approach

The income approach is used in the valuation of investment properties such as stores, apartments, shopping centers, commercial buildings certain industrial buildings, and other real estate which is bought and sold primarily on the basis of the income produced. The value of such properties tends to be set by the quantity, quality, and durability of the net income generated by the property.

Capitalization of anticipated net income indicates the investment required to produce that income. Extreme care must be used both in estimating net income and in selecting the proper rate of capitalization.

One of the first steps is to secure a statement of the historical record of income and expenses for the past three to five years. An average of income and expenses is satisfactory if both income and expenses are relatively stable. If the historical record shows an upward or downward trend, more weight should be given to the latest years. Past income and expense information is used solely for an indication of the future as any prospective buyer would be purchasing future income.

The income approach, like the market data and cost approaches, is closely related to the market. The anticipated income, the operating expenses, the land value, the proper capitalization rate—all are developed and checked for reasonableness by comparisons with similar rental properties and investments.

SOURCE: Boeckh Building Valuation Manual, Boeckh Division, the American Appraisal Co., Milwaukee, Wis. 1967

DEPTH TABLES

The following are tables for apportioning the value of front lots that are longer or shorter than 25 x 100 feet. These rules are helpful guides, but actual value in each instance much depends on the use to which such lots or parts of lots can be profitably put, their marketability for such use, and the usual factors of value. The tables are not strictly applicable to rear or inside land when the frontage is in different ownership.

HOFFMAN RULE

The first recognized rule for appraising lots of varying depths is credited to Judge Murray Hoffman in 1866 and is generally known as the Hoffman Rule. In his opinion the front half (50 feet deep) of a 100-foot deep lot is worth two-thirds its whole value. It was assumed, therefore, that the first 25 feet was worth two-thirds of 50 feet, 12½ feet two-thirds of 25 feet, and so on.

4-3-2-1 RULE

This method gives the front 25 feet 40% of a full lot value, the next 25 feet 30% of the full value, the next 25 feet 20% and the last 25 feet 10% of a full lot value.

HOFFMAN-NEILL RULE

The following table revising and elaborating on the Hoffman Rule was published in the Evening Mail by its real estate editor, the late Henry Harmon Neill.

Standard appraisal methods:
The Hoffman Neill rule: "Two thirds of the value of a rectangular lot is in the front half."

Values of lot depth in percentage of 100 foot depth							
Depth	0/0	Depth	0/0	Depth	0/0	Depth	0/0
5	.17	55	.70.7	110	106.0	220	159.0
10	.26	60	.74.4	120	111.7	240	167.5
15	.33	65	.77.9	130	116.9	260	175.3
20	.39	70	.81.5	140	122.3	280	183.6
25	.44	75	.84.8	150	127.3	300	191.0
30	.49	80	.88.0	160	132.1	320	198.3
35	.54	85	.91.3	170	137.0	340	205.5
40	.58	90	.94.3	180	141.5	360	212.3
45	.62	95	.97.3	190	146.0	380	219.0
50	.66	100	1.00.0	200	150.0	400	225.0

SOURCE: The Manual of the Real Estate Board of New York, Inc.

Corner Lot Rules

Corner lots are usually considered as worth from 20% to 70% more than inside lots. The corner lot as worth the sum of an inside lot on both streets. Following is a table showing the percentage of side street lot value to be added to avenue lot value to find corner value and showing the degree of corner influence for every 10 feet from the corner, as given by John A. Zangerle in "Principles of Real Estate Appraising."

Feet	Zangerle Curve	Feet	Zangerle Curve
10	25%	60	68%
20	40	80	70
30	51	90	71
40	58	100	72
50	63		

Ratio of Main St. to Side St. Value	Central Retail Districts Frontage on High Valued Street									Semi-Business Wholesale Suburban Retail	Residential†
	20'	30'	40'	50'	60'	70'	80'	90'	100'		
(1)	(2)	(3)	(4)	(5)	(6)	(7)	(8)	(9)	(10)	(11)	(12)
	%	%	%	%	%	%	%	%	%	%	%
10 to 10	125	98	85	74	65	60	54	47	43	50.0	10.0
10 to 9	108	85	75	64	57	51	47	41	36	43.6	9.1
10 to 8	92	74	65	55	50	44	41	35	31	38.2	8.3
10 to 7	79	63	55	47	43	37	35	30	27	33.3	7.6
10 to 6	68	53	47	40	36	31	29	26	23	28.9	7.0
10 to 5	57	45	39	33	29	27	23	22	19	25.0	6.5
10 to 4	48	37	33	27	25	22	20	18	16	21.2	6.1
10 to 3	40	31	26	23	20	18	16	15	13	18.5	5.8
10 to 2	33	25	22	19	17	14	13	12	11	16.4	5.6
10 to 1	25	20	17	15	13	12	10	9	8	15.0	—

* These rules are widely used throughout the Southwest. They are an outgrowth of an early corner rule devised by W. A. Somers, and first used in St. Paul in 1896, Camden, N.J., uses a similar rule. The table was compiled from percentages used by J. B. Stoner of San Antonio.

† In semi-business, wholesale, suburban retail and residential properties in a uniform percentage of base value is added for corner influence regardless of the frontage of the corner parcel on the high valued street.

Description of Rural Land. In the older portions of the United States, nearly all of the original land grants were of irregular shape, many of the boundaries following stream and ridge lines. Also, in the process of subdivision the units were taken without much regard for regularity, and it was thought sufficient if lands were specified as bounded by natural or artificial features of the terrain and if the names of adjacent property owners were given. Thus a description of a tract as recorded in a deed reads:

Bounded on the north by Bog Brook, bounded on the northeast by the irregular line formed by the southwesterly border of Cedar Swamp of land now or formerly belonging to Benjamin Clark, bounded on the east by a stone wall and land now or formerly belonging to Ezra Pennell, bounded on the south and southeast by the turnpike road from Brunswick to Bath, and bounded on the west by the irregular line formed by the easterly fringe of trees of the wood lot now or formerly belonging to Moses Puringt

1. By Metes and Bounds. As the country developed and land became more valuable, and as many boundaries such as those listed in the preceding description ceased to exist, land litigations became numerous. It then became the general practice to determine the lengths and directions of the boundaries of land by measurements with the link chain and surveyor's compass, and to fix the locations of corners permanently by monuments. The lengths were ordinarily given in rods or chains, and the directions were expressed as bearings usually referred to the magnetic meridian. Surveys of this character are now usually made with the transit and tape, distances being recorded in feet or chains, and directions being given in true bearings computed from angular measurements. In describing a tract surveyed in this manner the lengths and bearings of the several courses are given in order, and the objects marking the corners are described; if any boundary follows some prominent feature of the terrain, the fact is stated; and the calculated area of the tract is given. When the bearings and lengths of the sides are thus given, the tract is said to be described by **metes and bounds.**

2. By Subdivisions of Public Land. The type of description employed for lands which have been divided in accordance with the rectangular system of the Bureau of Land Management. The records and plats of the United States surveys are a part of the permanent public records and are accessible to anyone desiring to consult them. In conveying by deed a United States subdivision or fraction thereof, no doubt can at any time exist as to the tract involved if it is described by stating its sectional subdivision, section number, township, range, and name of the principal meridian on which the initial point is located. Following is an example of the legal description of a 40-acre tract comprising a full quarter-quarter section:

The north-east quarter of the south-west quarter of section ten (10), Township four (4) South, Range six (6) East, of the Initial Point of the Mount Diablo Meridian, containing forty (40) acres, more or less, according to the United States Survey.

3. By Coordinates. In some states, the locations of land corners are legally described by their coordinates with respect to the state-wide plane-coordinate system.

Description of Urban Land. The manner of legally describing the boundaries of a tract of land within the corporate limits of a city depends upon conditions attached to the survey by which the boundaries of the tract were first established, as indicated by the following classification:

1. By Lot and Block. If the boundaries of the tract coincide exactly with a lot which is a part of a subdivision or addition for which there is recorded an official map, the tract may be legally described by a statement giving the lot and block numbers and the name and date of filing of the official map. Most city property is described in this way. Following is a description of this character occurring in a deed:

Lot 15 in Block 5 as said lots and blocks are delineated and so designated upon that certain map entitled **Map of Thousand Oaks, Alameda County, California,** filed August 23, 1909, in Liber 25 of Maps, page 2, in the office of the County Recorder of the said County of Alameda.

2. By Metes, Bounds, and Lots. If the boundaries of a given tract within a subdivision for which there is a recorded map do not conform exactly to boundaries shown on the official map, the tract is described by metes and bounds, with the point of beginning referred to a corner shown on the official map. Also, the numbers of lots of which the tract is composed are given. Following is an example of a description of this kind:

Beginning at the intersection of the Northern line of Escondido Avenue, with the Eastern boundary line of Lot 16, hereinafter referred to; running thence Northerly along said Eastern boundary line of Lot 16, and the Eastern boundary line of Lot 17, eighty-nine (89) feet; thence at right angles Westerly, fifty-one (51) feet; thence South 12°6' East, seventy-five (75) feet to the Northern line of Escondido Avenue; thence Easterly along said line of Escondido Avenue, fifty-three and $^{13}/_{100}$ (53.13) feet, more or less, to the point of beginning.

Being a portion of Lots 16 and 17, in Block 5, as said lots and blocks are delineated and so designated upon that certain map entitled **Map of Thousand Oaks, Alameda County, California,** filed August 23, 1909, in Liber 25 of Maps, page 2, in the office of the County Recorder of the said County of Alameda.

3. By Metes and Bounds to City Monuments. Some of the larger and older cities of the United States have, by precise surveys, established a system of reference monuments and have determined the coordinates of these monuments with respect to an arbitrarily selected initial point. If the tract cannot be defined by descriptions such as the preceding, the point of beginning may be definitely fixed by stating its direction and distance from an official reference monument and by describing the monument that marks the corner. The boundaries of the tract may then be described by metes and bounds.

The location of corners may also be defined by rectangular coordinates referred to the origin or initial point of the city system and/or the state system.

If the tract is within an area not so monumented, the point of beginning of the boundary description may be referred by direction and distance to the intersection of the center lines of streets. It is not good practice to refer to the intersection of sidewalk or curb lines, for these are apt to be changed from time to time. In sections of the country within the rectangular system of United States surveys, the point of beginning of a boundary description may properly be referred to section lines and corners.

SOURCE: Davis, Foote, Kelly, Surveying: Theory and Practice, McGraw-Hill Book Co. NY 5th Edition 1966

A topographic map shows by the use of suitable symbols (1) the configuration of the earth's surface, called the **relief,** which includes such features as hills and valleys; (2) other natural features such as trees and streams; and (3) the physical changes wrought upon the earth's surface by the works of man, such as houses, roads, canals, and cultivation. The distinguishing characteristic of a topographic map, as compared with other maps, is the representation of the terrestrial relief.

Topographic maps are used in many ways. They are a necessary aid in the design of any engineering project which required a consideration of land forms, elevations, or gradients, and they are used to supply the general information necessary to the studies of geologists, economists, and others interested in the broader aspects of the development of natural resources.

The preparation of general topographic maps is largely in the hands of governmental organizations. The principal example is the topographic map of the United States being constructed by the U.S. Geological Survey. This map is published in quadrangle sheets, which usually include territory 15' in latitude by 15' in longitude at a scale of 1:62,500 although they range from 7½' by 7½' at a scale of 1:24,000 to 4° by 12° at a scale of 1:1,000,000. A portion of a typical map the scale of which is 1:62,500 is shown. Altogether there are more than 30 Federal agencies engaged in surveying and mapping. The central source of information regarding all Federal maps and aerial photographs is the Map Information Office, U. S. Geological Survey, Washington, D. C. Likewise, many maps are available from state, county, and city agencies.

Land Survey. Land Surveying may consist of one or more of the following operations:

1. Rerunning old land lines to determine their length and direction.
2. Reestablishing obliterated land lines from recorded lengths and directions. This will require research into tax maps, building department files, subdivision maps, etc., to secure the required information.
3. Subdividing lands into parcels of predetermined shape and size.
4. Setting monuments to preserve the location of land lines.
5. Locating the position of such monuments with respect to permanent landmarks.
6. Calculating areas, distances and angles or directions.
7. Portraying the data of the survey on a land map.
8. Writing descriptions for deeds.

SOURCE: Davis, Foote, Kelly, Surveying: Theory and Practice, McGraw-Hill Book Co. NY 5th Edition 1966

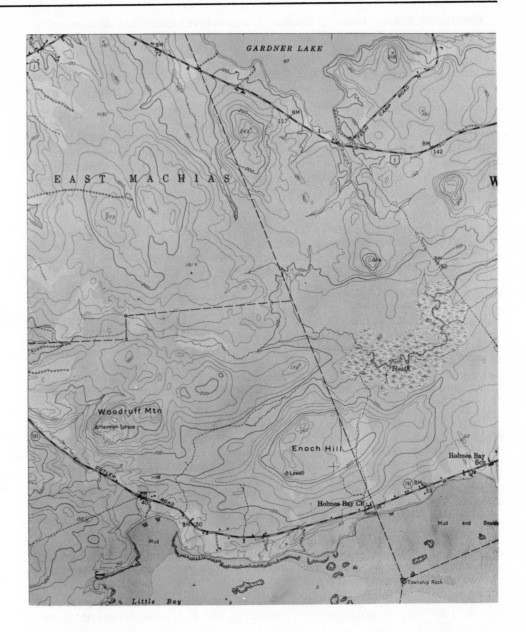

Typical contour map of U. S. Geological Survey. Scale approximately 1 in. = 1 mile (representative fraction 1/62,500). Contour interval 10 ft.

City Survey. The term city survey, has come to mean an extensive coordinated survey of the area in and near a city for the purposes of fixing reference monuments, locating property lines and improvements, and determining the configuration and physical features of the land. Such a survey is of value for a wide variety of purposes, particularly for planning city improvements. Briefly, the work consists in:

1. Establishing horizontal and vertical control, as described for topographic surveying. The primary horizontal control is usually by triangulation, supplemented as desired by precise traversing. Secondary horizontal control is by traversing of appropriate precision. Primary vertical control is by precise leveling.

2. Making a topographic survey and topographic map. Usually the scale of the topographic map is 1 in. = 200 ft. The map is divided into sheets which cover usually 5,000 ft. of longitude and 4,000 ft. of latitude. Points are plotted by rectangular plane coordinates.

3. Monumenting a system of selected points at suitable locations such as street corners, for reference in subsequent surveys. These monuments are referred to the plane-coordinate system and to the city datum.

4. Making a property map. The survey for the map consists in (a) collecting recorded information regarding property, (b) determining the location on the ground of street intersections, angle points, and curve points, (c) monumenting the points so located, and (d) traversing to determine the coordinates of the monuments. Usually the scale of the property map is 1 in. = 50 ft. The map is divided into sheets which cover usually 1,250 ft. of longitude and 1,000 ft. of latitude, thus bearing a convenient relation to the sheets of the topographic map. The property map shows the length and bearing of all street lines and boundaries of public property, coordinates of governing points, control, monuments, important structures, natural features of the terrain, etc., all with appropriate legends and notes

5. Making a wall map which shows essentially the same information as the topographic map but which is drawn to a smaller scale; the scale should be not less than 1 in. = 2,000 ft. The wall map is reproduced in the usual colors—culture in black, drainage in blue, wooded areas in green, and contours in brown.

6. Making an underground map. Usually the scale and the size of the map sheets are the same as those for the property map. The underground map shows street and casement lines, monuments, surface structures and natural features affecting underground construction, and underground structures and utilities (with dimensions), all with appropriate legends and notes

Construction Survey. Construction surveys consist of the following operations:

1. Topographic survey of site, to be used in preparation of plans for the structure.

2. Establishment on ground of a system of stakes, or other markers, both in plan and in elevation, from which measurement of earthwork and structures can be conveniently taken by construction forces.

3. The giving of line and grade as needed.

4. The making of measurements necessary to verify the location of completed parts of structure and to determine volume of completed work, as a basis for payment to the contractor.

Route Survey. Route surveying is the operation necessary for the location and construction of lines of transportation and communication, such as highways, railroads, canals, transmission lines, pipe lines, etc. The preliminary work usually consists of a topographic survey. The location and construction surveys may further consist of the following:

1. Establishing the center line by setting stakes at intervals.
2. Running levels to determine the profile of the ground along the center line.
3. Plotting such profile, and fixing grades.
4. Taking cross sections.
5. Calculating volumes of earthwork.
6. Measuring drainage areas.
7. Laying out structures, such as culverts and bridges.
8. Locating right-of-way boundaries.

SOURCE: *Davis, Foote, Kelly, Surveying: Theory and Practice, McGraw-Hill Book Co. NY 5th Edition 1966*

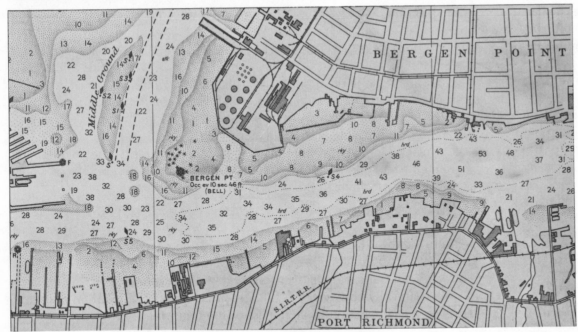

Typical hydrographic map of U.S. Coast and Geodetic Survey. Representative fraction, 1/80,000.

1.9 Hydrographic surveying refers to surveying bodies of water for purposes of navigation, water supply, or subaqueous construction. The operations of hydrographic surveying consist broadly in:

1. Making a topographic survey of shores and banks.
2. Taking soundings to determine the depth of water and the character of the bottom.
3. Locating such soundings by angular and linear measurements.
4. Plotting the hydrographic map showing the topography of the shores and banks, the depths of soundings, and other desirable details.
5. Observing the fluctuation of the ocean tide or of the change in level of lakes and rivers.
6. Measuring the discharge of streams.

In a sense, the surveys for drainage and for irrigation are hydrographic in character, but the principal work is essentially either topographic or route surveying.

a. Hydrographic Maps. A hydrographic map is similar to the ordinary topographic map but has its own particular symbols. These may be found in almost any book on topographic drawing or in the manual issued by the U.S. Coast and Geodetic Survey. The amount and kind of information shown on a hydrographic map vary with the use of the map. A harbor map should show enough shore-line topography to locate and plan wharves, docks, warehouses, roads, and streets along the water front. A navigation chart should show only shore details which are useful aids to navigation, such as church spires, smokestacks, towers, and similar landmarks. Maps of rivers should show both low-water and high-water marks and all topography within the zone between these marks. A hydrographic map should contain the following information:

1. Datum used for elevations.
2. High-water and low-water lines.
3. Soundings, usually in feet and tenths, with the decimal point occupying the exact plotted location of the point.
4. Lines of equal depth interpolated from soundings. On navigation charts for offshore areas, the lines of equal depth are usually shown in fathoms (1 fathom equals 6 ft.); for harbors, the lines of equal depth are shown in feet.
5. Conventional signs for land features as on topographic maps.
6. Lighthouses, navigation lights, buoys, etc., either shown by conventional signs or lettered on the map.

The illustration is a portion of a typical hydrographic map of the U.S. and Geodetic Survey. Soundings are shown in feet, referred to mean low water. Elevations of contours and high points on land are likewise shown in feet.

SOURCE: Davis, Foote, Kelly, Surveying: Theory and Practice, McGraw-Hill Book Co. NY 5th Edition 1966

A soil survey includes finding out which properties of soils are important, organizing the knowledge about the relations of soil properties and soil use, classifying soils into defined and described units, locating and plotting the boundaries of the units on maps, and preparing and publishing the maps and reports.

The soil survey report consists of a map that shows the distribution of soils in the area descriptions of the soils, some suggestions as to their use and management and general information about the area.

Reports usually are prepared on the soils of one county, although a single report may cover several small countries or only parts of countries.

Soil surveys are made cooperatively by the Soil Conservation Service of the Department of Agriculture, the agricultural experiment stations, and other Stations, and other State and Federal Agencies. Plans for the work in any area are developed jointly, and the reports are reviewed jointly before publication.

Soil maps have many uses, but generally they are made for one main purpose—to identify the soil as a basis for applying the results of research and experience to individual fields or parts of fields. Results from an experiment on a given soil can be applied directly to other areas of the same kind of soil with confidence. Two areas of the same kind of soil are no more identical than two oak trees, but they are so similar that (with comparable past management) they should respond to the same practices in a similar manner.

The soil map shows the distribution of specific kinds of soil and identifies them through the map legend. The legend is a list of the symbols used to identify the kinds of soil on the map.

The most common soil units shown on maps are the phases of soil types, but other kinds of units may be shown.

Soils are classified and named, just as plants and animals are. Soils are identified by such characteristics as the kinds and numbers of horizons, or layers, that have developed in them, the texture (the relative amounts of stones, gravel, sand, silt, and clay), the kind of minerals present and their amounts, and the presence of salts and alkali help distinguish the horizons.

Most of the characteristics that identify soils can be determined in the field.

The type is the smallest unit in the natural classification of soils. One or a few types constitute a soil series. These are the common classification units seen on soil maps and survey reports.

A soil series is a group of soils that have horizons that are essentially the same in the properties used to identify soils, with the exception of the

SOURCE: *The Use of Soil Maps, Soils—Yearbook of Agriculture—1957, U. S. Dept. of Agriculture*

Soil and capability map. The symbols refer to types of soil, steepness, and degree of erosion. Example: 2B1 refers to the kind of soil, the number 2 to the type of soil, B to steepness of slope, and 1 to degree of erosion. The Roman numerals, such as II, refer to the capability class in the areas that are suitable for cultivation. Capability class symbols are not shown on areas that are generally better suited for range or woodland than for cultivation. Heavy lines on map indicate the boundaries of a capability unit.

texture of the surface soil and the kinds of layers that lie below what is considered the true soil.

The names of soil series are taken from the towns or localities near the place where the soils were first defined.

The soil type, a subdivision of the soil series, is based on the texture of the surface soil. Stones, gravel, sand, silt, and clay have been defined as having the following diameters. Gravel, between 0.08 inch and 3 inches; sand, between 0.08 and 0.002 **inch**, silt, between 0.002 and 0.00003 inch, and clay, less than 0.00003 inch.

The full name of soil type includes the name of the soil series and the textural class of the surface soil equivalent to the plow layer, that is, the upper 6 or 7 inches. Thus, if the surface of an area of the Fayette series is a silt loam, the name of the soil type is "Fayette silt loam."

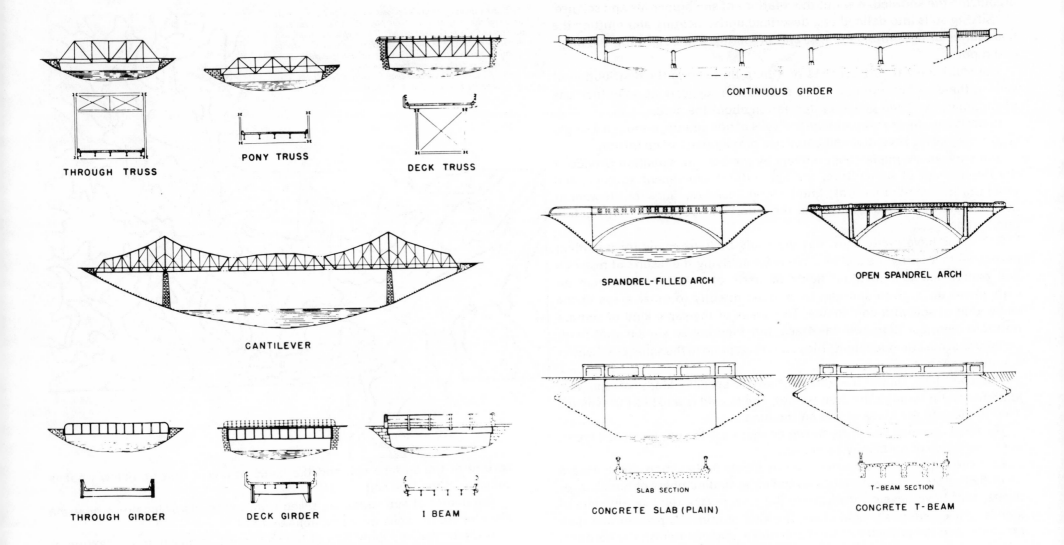

THROUGH TRUSS

PONY TRUSS

DECK TRUSS

CONTINUOUS GIRDER

CANTILEVER

SPANDREL-FILLED ARCH

OPEN SPANDREL ARCH

THROUGH GIRDER

DECK GIRDER

I BEAM

SLAB SECTION

CONCRETE SLAB (PLAIN)

T-BEAM SECTION

CONCRETE T-BEAM

SOURCE: Guide for a Road Inventory-Manual of Instructions U. S. Dept. of Transportation, Federal Highway Administration Bureau of Public Roads, April 1967

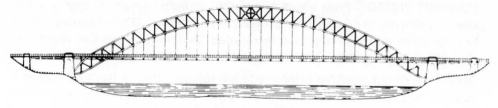

THROUGH-ARCH TRUSS

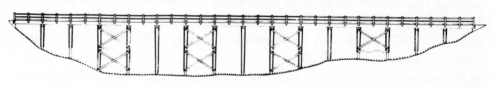

TIMBER TRESTLE

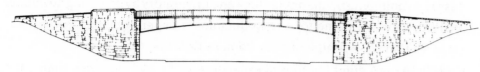

RIGID FRAME-STEEL

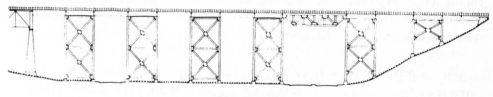

STEEL VIADUCT

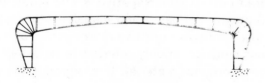

RIGID FRAME
(STEEL GIRDER ELEMENT)

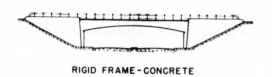

RIGID FRAME-CONCRETE

SUSPENSION

AUTOPOSITIVE—A trade name for a direct contact positive intermediate translucent print on paper or film. Autopositives are made same size from positive translucent material or from opaque material by reflex printing. When working from a negative, the resulting print is an AUTONEGATIVE.

BLACK & WHITE PRINT—A trade name for a direct positive contact Diazo reproduction print. See DIAZO.

BLACK & WHITE TRANSPARENCY—A trade name for a translucent Diazo direct positive print (Sepia Intermediate). See DIAZO and SEPIA INTERMEDIATE.

BLUE LINE PRINT (Wet)—An opaque contact positive print having a blue line on a white background; made same size from translucent negative material. This type of Blue Line Print is superior to the Diazo type of print in permanency and durability, yet can be processed with speed and economy on either paper or cloth.

BLUE PRINT—An opaque contact print having white lines on a blue background. A Blue Print is made same size from positive translucent originals or intermediate material. This original Blue Print is still noted for its durability and strength plus speed and economy in production. It is available on paper and cloth.

BROWN LINE PRINT (Van Dyke Positive)—A translucent contact positive print having brown lines on a white background; this print is made on a high quality rag content paper stock and is readily used as an intermediate for printing. Made same size from translucent negative material, Brown Lines can be ordered enlarged or reduced from positive material if the proper intermediate negative is ordered reduced or enlarged.

C. B.—A trade name for a reproducible on paper or cloth.

CAMERA CONTRAST NEGATIVE—Made photographically. Depending on the copy photographed and the use intended, this translucent negative is available on paper, transloid or film. The positive material to be copied, opaque or translucent, can be photographed the same size, reduced or enlarged. The camera contrast process gives a reverse reading image which is one of the finest means available for direct contact printing particularly when film is used.

CAMERA CONTRAST POSITIVE—Made photographically, basically this translucent positive has all the qualities of the Camera Contrast Negative and can be made same size, reduced or enlarged from negative material.

CONTACT PHOTO—Print which has a photographic emulsion and is made same size by direct contact with translucent negatives. Offered in a variety of finishes from matte to hi-glossy ferrotyped, this opaque positive reproduction depends in quality upon the type of negative used.

DIAZO—A direct positive print made same size directly from translucent positive originals or intermediate material. Diazo Prints are available on opaque stock, translucent paper (Sepia Intermediates), cloth and film and are often preferred because they are quickly made and make excellent check prints. The image reproduced on Diazo Prints is available in a variety of colors, but black line on white paper is most widely used. Sepia Diazo prints are reproduced by two methods, an ammonia vapor development and a semi-dry (moist) developer. A variety of colors are available in both processes; in ammonia by changing stock and in semi-dry by changing developer.

DUPRO—A trade name for a reproducible on paper or cloth.

FILM NEGATIVE—A high quality Camera Contrast Negative.

GIANTSTAT—A giant Photoprint exceeding 18" x 24", enlarged from a film negative. As Photoprints are limited to 18" x 24" in one piece, prints exceeding maximum Photoprint size, which may not be joined, utilize this process. A Camera Contrast Film Negative is first made, usually 8" x 10", and the positive Giantstat on opaque or translucent stock is projected from it.

REPRODUCIBLE (On Cloth)—A positive reproduction on translucent reproducible waterproof cloth commonly referred to as a See Bee. Made from virtually any type of original material, this reproduction uses an extreme contrast translucent negative as an intermediate. It is available same size, reduced or enlarged and erases easily. Sections of the image can be blocked out or eliminated during the negative step before processing the final print. Available on a blue or white cloth

REPRODUCIBLE (On Vellum)—A positive reproduction on translucent waterproof vellum often referred to as a Vellum or Paper See Bee. These reproducibles are made essentially the same way as the Reproducibles on Cloth and in both cases the type of negative intermediate used is determined by the type and condition of the material to be reproduced and the final size of the Reproducible required. Reproducibles on Vellum have a very black image and make exceptionally fine 'second originals'.

SOURCE: Versatility in Reproduction Printing, Hudson Blue and Photo Print Co., Inc., New York—1959

LITHOGRAPHY—A type of printing. Defined under PHOTO OFFSET.

LITHOPRINT—A positive ink reproduction made by transferring an image from prepared gelatine onto a suitable material, translucent or opaque. Lithoprints can be obtained same size, reduced or enlarged from the material being reproduced.

MICROFILM—A reduced film negative used in copying original material to a smaller size for convenient storage. FLO-FILM, a trade name, is the 35mm microfilming of any length original in one continuous un-interrupted image.

MULTILITH PRINTS—Quantity reproductions made on a Multilith (trade name) press.

OZALID PRINT—A trade name for a DIAZO direct positive print made same size on an ammonia vapor machine.

PHOTO ENLARGEMENT—A photographic blow-up or enlargement made from a film negative by projection. Usually positive and opaque, these prints come in a variety of weights and finishes and can be mounted on cardboard or cloth for display or permanency.

PHOTO OFFSET PRINTS—As the name implies, the material to be reproduced is photographed, negatives are stripped onto flats, exposed to sensitized plates and run on a press. The image, positive and right reading, is transferred to a rubber blanket which actually makes the ink impression on the stock. This form of reproduction is highly recommended for 'quality in quantity'. Virtually any type of original material can be reproduced by the Photo Offset Process on a variety of stock including papers of various weights, colors and finishes, translucent vellum and cloth. Photo Offset prints, which utilize a camera process, can be had same size, reduced or enlarged

PHOTOPRINT—A photographic print on paper, sometimes referred to as a PHOTOSTAT.

PHOTOPRINT NEGATIVES—Right reading negatives on paper, which can be made same size, reduced or enlarged in one piece up to 18″ x 24″. These negatives are available in a variety of weights and finishes and are economical reproductions from opaque material. A black background with white lines.

PHOTOPRINT POSITIVES—Right reading paper positives which are available in the same weights and finishes as the Photoprint Negatives, from which they are usually made. They may be made larger by joining. A black image on a white background.

PHOTOSTAT PRINT—A trade name for a Photoprint on paper.

SEE BEE—A reproducible on waterproof cloth or vellum. Further information is available under REPRODUCIBLE (On Cloth) and REPRODUCIBLE (On Vellum).

SEPIA INTERMEDIATE—A same size contact DIAZO positive print having a sepia image. Frequently used as a 'second original', these transparencies can be made reverse reading for sharper contact reproductions.

VAN DYKE PRINT—A trade name for a translucent contact brown print. See BROWN LINE PRINT (Van Dyke Positive) and VAN DYKE NEGATIVE.

VAN DYKE NEGATIVE—Translucent negatives having a white image on a deep brown background on high quality, strong and durable rag content paper. Van Dyke Negatives are used instead of original tracings for reproductions, i.e., Brown Line Prints and Blue Line Prints. When made by contact from translucent positive material, these prints are the same size and are available reverse reading for sharper contact reproductions.

VIEW FILM—Contact reproductions on a clear transparent film base with line images available in a variety of colors. This Diazo type film is popular principally because it can be made direct from fairly clean positive translucent material. The availability of View Film as a direct positive in color makes it very advantageous for color overlays, presentations and visual instruction.

WHITE PRINT—A direct positive same size contact print made by the Diazo Process.

XEROGRAPHY—A trade name for a reproduction process.

ZINC-O-STAT—The same as PHOTO OFFSET PRINTS.

	Inch	Link	Foot	Vara (Calif.)	Vara (Texas)	Yard	Meter	Rod, Pole, or Perch	Chain	Furlong	Kilo-meter	Mile (Statute)
Inch	1	0.12626	0.08333	0.03030	0.03	0.02778	0.02540	0.00505	0.00126			
Link	7.92	1	0.66	0.24	0.2376	0.22	0.20117	0.04	0.01	0.001		
Foot	12	1.51515	1	0.36364	0.36	0.33333	0.30480	0.06061	0.01515	0.00152		
Vara (Calif.)	33	4.16667	2.75	1	0.99	0.91667	0.8382	0.16667	0.04167	0.00417		
Vara (Texas)	33.333	4.20875	2.77778	1.01010	1	0.92583	0.84667	0.16835	0.04209	0.0042		
Yard	36	4.54545	3	1.09091	1.08	1	0.9144	0.18182	0.04545	0.00455		
Meter	39.37	4.97096	3.28083	1.19303	1.1811	1.09361	1	0.19884	0.04971	0.00497	0.001	
Rod, Pole, or Perch	198	25	16.5	6	5.94	5.5	5.02921	1	0.25	0.025	0.00503	0.00313
Chain	792	100	66	24	23.76	22	20.11684	4	1	0.1	0.02012	0.0125
Furlong	7920	1000	660	240	237.6	220	201.168	40	10	1	0.20117	0.125
Kilometer	39370	4970.96	3280.83	1193.03	1181.1	1093.61	1000	198.838	49.7096	4.97096	1	0.62137
Mile (Statute)	63360	8000	5280	1920	1900.8	1760	1609.35	320	80	8	1.60935	1

SOURCE: *Boeckh Building Valuation Manual, Boeckh Division, the American Appraisal Co., Milwaukee, Wis. 1967*

	Square Inch	Square Link	Square Foot	Square Vara (Calif.)	Square Vara (Texas)	Square Yard	Square Meter	Sq. Rod, Pole, or Perch	Square Chain	Rood	Acre	Square Kilometer	Square Mile (Statute)
Square Inch	1	0.01594	0.00694										
Square Link	62.7264	1	0.4356	0.0576	0.05645	0.0484	0.04047	0.0016					
Square Foot	144	2.29568	1	0.13223	0.1296	0.11111	0.0929	0.00367					
Square Vara (Calif.)	1089	17.3611	7.5625	1	0.9801	0.84028	0.70258	0.02778	0.00174				
Square Vara (Texas)	1111.11	17.7136	7.71605	1.0203	1	0.85734	0.71685	0.02834	0.00177				
Square Yard	1296	20.6612	9	1.19008	1.1664	1	0.83613	0.03306	0.00207				
Square Meter	1549.80	24.7104	10.7639	1.42332	1.395	1.19599	1	0.03954	0.00247				
Sq. Rod, Pole, or Perch		625	272.25	36	35.2836	30.25	25.2930	1	0.0625	0.025	0.00625		
Square Chain		10000	4356	576	564.538	484	404.687	16	1	0.4	0.1		
Rood		25000	10890	1440	1411.34	1210	1011.72	40	2.5	1	0.25	0.00101	
Acre		100000	43560	5760	5645.38	4840	4046.87	160	10	4	1	0.00405	0.00156
Square Kilometer							1000000	39536.7	2471.044	988.418	247.104	1	0.3861
Square Mile (Statute)								102400	6400	2560	640	2.59	1

SOURCE: Boeckh Building Valuation Manual, Boeckh Division, the American Appraisal Co., Milwaukee, Wis. 1967

LINEAL MEASURE, METRIC SYSTEM

Millimeter = 0.001 Meter
Centimeter = 0.01 Meter
Decimeter = 0.1 Meter
Meter = 39.3685 Inches
Kilometer = 1000 Meters

ARPENT

The Arpent is a unit of measure common to parts of Canada, mainly Quebec, where land was originally granted under seigniorial tenure. Surveys currently made in these areas now use the English units, but the Arpent may be encountered.

This unit is also in use in parts of the State of Louisiana.

The basis of the Arpent is the "Old French Foot" having the following equivalents:

French Foot = 12.789 English Inches
= 1.06575 English Feet

English
Foot = 12 English (U.S.) Inches
= 0.938306 French Feet

Square
French Foot = 1.135823 Square English Feet

Lineal Arpent = 180 French Feet
= 191.835 English Feet
= 10 Old French Perches

Square Arpent = 36800.667 Square English Feet
= 4088.89 Square English Yards
= 32400 Square French Feet
= 0.845 U.S. Acre

The Old French Perch is equivalent to 18 French Feet or 19.1835 English Feet.

AREA MEASURE, METRIC SYSTEM

Square Centimeter = 0.0001 Square Meter
Square Decimeter = 0.01 Square Meter
Are = 100 Square Meters
Hectare = 10,000 Square Meters
= 2.471 Acres
Square Kilometer = 247.1 Acres
= 0.386 Square Mile

VARA

The Vara is a unit of measurement originally used by the Spanish and is still in common use throughout Central and South America.

The exact length of the Vara ranges varies from 32.9931 to 34.1208 inches with each country using a variation within this range. It is a unit of measure.

Within the United States, two areas still make use of this measurement unit.

California

Vara is equal to 33 inches.

Many lots in San Francisco and other areas were laid out on the basis of multiples of 50 Varas (137'6").

Texas

Vara is equal to 33.33333 inches.

Early deeds used "Leagues" and "Labors" having the following values:

League = 4428.4 Acres
= 5000 Varas Square
= 25,000,000 Square Varas

Labor = 177.1 Acres
= 1000 Varas Square
= 1,000,000 Square Varas

Conversion of these two variations of the Vara in standard United States units can be found in the conversion tables.

SECTIONS 1, 2, 3, 4, 5, 6, 7, 18, 19, 30, 31 ARE OFTEN FRACTIONAL

LAND MEASURE

1 mile	=	5,280	feet
	=	1,760	yards
	=	320	rods
	=	80	chains
1 chain	=	66	feet
	=	100	links
	=	4	rods
1 rod	=	25	links
	=	16.5	feet
	=	1	perch
	=	1	pole
1 link	=	7.92	inches

1 township	=	36	sections
1 full section	=	640	acres
1 sq. mile	=	640	acres
	=	1	full section
1 acre	=	43,560	sq. feet
	=	4,840	sq. yards
	=	160	sq. rods
	=	10	sq. chains
1 sq. chain	=	10,000	sq. links
1 sq. rod	=	30.25	sq. yards
1 sq. yard	=	9	sq. feet
1 sq. foot	=	144	sq. inches

SOURCE: *Boeckh Building Valuation Manual, Boeckh Division, the American Appraisal Company, Milwaukee, Wis. 1967*

COMPUTER WORKFLOW

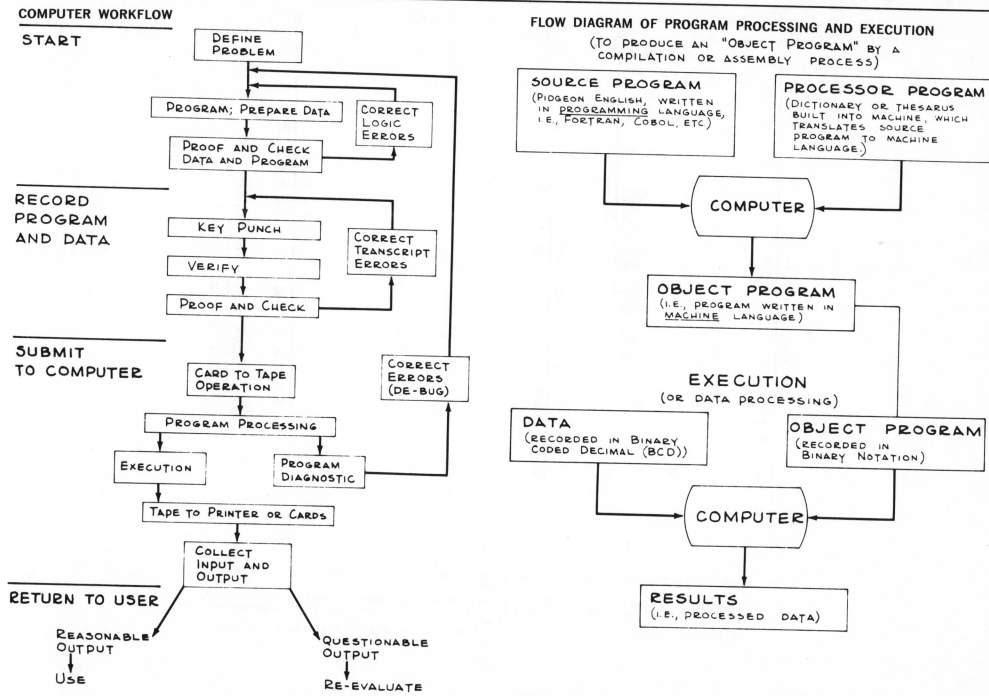

START

DEFINE PROBLEM

PROGRAM; PREPARE DATA

CORRECT LOGIC ERRORS

PROOF AND CHECK DATA AND PROGRAM

RECORD PROGRAM AND DATA

KEY PUNCH

VERIFY

CORRECT TRANSCRIPT ERRORS

PROOF AND CHECK

SUBMIT TO COMPUTER

CARD TO TAPE OPERATION

CORRECT ERRORS (DE-BUG)

PROGRAM PROCESSING

EXECUTION

PROGRAM DIAGNOSTIC

TAPE TO PRINTER OR CARDS

COLLECT INPUT AND OUTPUT

RETURN TO USER

REASONABLE OUTPUT

USE

QUESTIONABLE OUTPUT

RE-EVALUATE

FLOW DIAGRAM OF PROGRAM PROCESSING AND EXECUTION

(TO PRODUCE AN "OBJECT PROGRAM" BY A COMPILATION OR ASSEMBLY PROCESS)

SOURCE PROGRAM
(PIDGEON ENGLISH, WRITTEN IN PROGRAMMING LANGUAGE, I.E., FORTRAN, COBOL, ETC.)

PROCESSOR PROGRAM
(DICTIONARY OR THESARUS BUILT INTO MACHINE, WHICH TRANSLATES SOURCE PROGRAM TO MACHINE LANGUAGE.)

COMPUTER

OBJECT PROGRAM
(I.E., PROGRAM WRITTEN IN MACHINE LANGUAGE)

EXECUTION
(OR DATA PROCESSING)

DATA
(RECORDED IN BINARY CODED DECIMAL (BCD))

OBJECT PROGRAM
(RECORDED IN BINARY NOTATION)

COMPUTER

RESULTS
(I.E., PROCESSED DATA)

SOURCE: Using Computer Graphics in Community Renewal, Urban Renewal Service, Urban Renewal Administration, Housing and Home Finance Agency, Wash., D. C.—1963

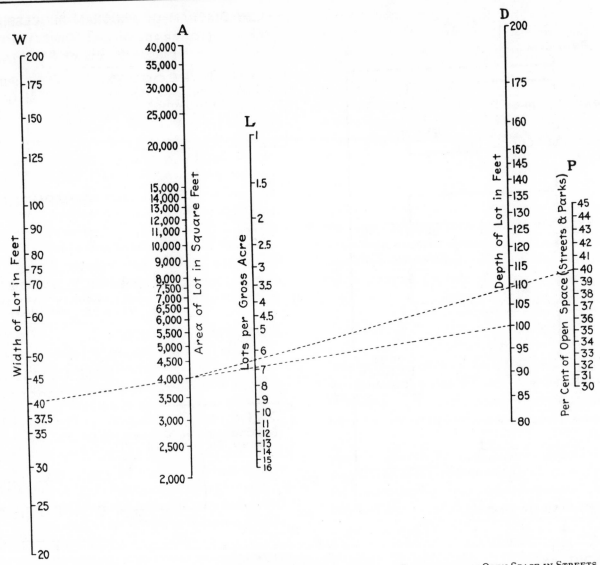

DIAGRAM FOR DETERMINING LOTS PER GROSS ACRE FOR VARYING LOT SIZES AND PERCENTAGES OF OPEN SPACE IN STREETS AND PARKS

Method of using diagram: Start with values on W and D scales; lay straight-edge between them and read area of lot on A scale; choose value on P scale; lay straight-edge between this value and determined value on A scale; read required answer on L scale.

In example shown, W = 40 feet and D = 100 feet; hence A = 4,000 square feet. With P = 40 per cent, L = 6.5 lots per gross acre.

SOURCE: NY Regional Survey of New York and Its Environs—1929

Land value is a local product. It arises from demand in the market where the property is located and bears only coincidental relation to the value of similar land in other localities. The valuation of land must therefore be based on analysis of its local market.

For valuation, land can be classified into five broad categories based on its potential use: natural resource, agricultural, residential, commercial, or industrial. Although the following basic valuation principles apply to each category, the forces which create value in the individual markets cause variations.

BASIC PRINCIPLES

Land, whether vacant or improved, is valued as if available for development to its highest and best use; that most likely legal use which will yield the highest present worth. That use must be acceptable to the market and it must conform to existing zoning and land use ordinances. Occasionally land value is reduced by the cost of demolition of an existing building which cannot generate a return sufficient to support the land.

Four methods are available to determine the value of land:

COMPARISON METHOD

This method is preferred whenever sufficient data exists to permit its use. Because comparison of the properties available for sale is the measure which investors use in choosing properties for purchase, this method of valuation most closely reflects the market. It therefore provides the most accurate measure of land value.

No two pieces of land are alike though they may be similar in many respects. Consequently, adjustments to sale prices are required to indicate the value of a specific parcel: adjustment for date of purchase, for location, for all the ways in which the sale property differs from the land being valued.

RESIDUAL METHOD

In heavily built-up areas where sales of vacant land cannot be found, an indication of land value can be developed by capitalizing net income which be produced by a proper new building improvement on the site, after deduction of the expenses required for the building.

To select a hypothetical improvement, highest and best use of the land must be determined, often obvious from the development of surrounding land. Whatever the improvement selected, it must be used with care, as variations in the capitalization rate or changes in the projected improvement may cause wide variation in the value indicated.

ALLOCATION METHOD

When the only sales available are those of improved property, a measure of land value can be gained by allocating from the total selling price that portion reasonably attributable to the building. The remainder is assumed to be land value. The building value can be estimated from study of sales of similar properties in other locations where land values also can be determined.

Allocation between land and building is sometimes derived from application of the reported ratio between assessed value and market value. The fairness of a value obtained in this way depends upon the skill and proficiency of the assessor.

DEVELOPMENT METHOD

Land with a potential use for residential or industrial subdivision is often valued by the development method. Since many estimates are required, the method should be used only when sales of comparable acreage are not available or as a check of the results indicated by the comparison method.

To indicate present value, the development method requires estimates of the selling price of the lots; of the costs required for the development, financing, carrying, and sales; of the period necessary to sell the developed lots; and of the amount by which the net sale price must be discounted.

This method has validity only if a ready and present market exists for the developed lots. To achieve reasonable results a thorough and comprehensive investigation of all variables is required.

SUMMARY

The comparison method of valuation is applicable to all classes of land, whether residential, agricultural, commercial, or industrial. If based on sufficient factual data properly processed, the comparison method provides the most accurate measure of land value. The residual, allocation, and development methods are helpful as alternates when market sales do not exist, or as checks on the comparison method.

SOURCE: Boeckh Building Valuation Manual, Boeckh Division, the American Appraisal Co., Milwaukee, Wis. 1967

INDEX